Great Science Adventures

The World of Space

by
Dinah Zike
and
Susan Simpson

See where learning takes you.

www.greatscienceadventures.com

Great Science Adventures is a comprehensive project which is projected to include the titles below. Please check our website, www.greatscienceadventures.com, for updates and product availability.

Great Life Science Studies:

The World of Plants
The World of Insects and Arachnids
The World of the Human Body
The World of Vertebrates
The World of Biomes
The World of Health

Great Physical Science Studies:

The World of Tools and Technology
The World of Matter and Energy
The World of Light and Sound
The World of Electricity and Magnets

Great Earth Science Studies:

The World of Space
The World of Atmosphere and Weather
The World of Lithosphere / Earth
The World of Hydrosphere / Fresh Water
The World of Hydrosphere / Oceans
The World of Rocks and Minerals

Common Sense Press
8786 Highway 21
Melrose, FL 32666
(352) 475–5757
www.greatscienceadventures.com

Printed in the United States of America
Rev 03/04
ISBN 1-929683-07-3

The authors and the publisher have made every reasonable effort to ensure that the experiments and activities in this book are safe when performed according to the book's instructions. We assume no responsibility for any damage sustained or caused while performing the activities or experiments in *Great Science Adventures*. We further recommend that students undertake these activities and experiments under the supervision of a teacher, parent, and/or guardian.

Table of Contents

Introduction

Great Science Adventures is a unique, highly effective program that is easy to use for teachers as well as students. This book contains 24 lessons. The concepts to be taught are clearly listed at the top of each lesson. Activities, questions, clear directions, and pictures are included to help facilitate learning. Each lesson will take one to three days to complete.

This program utilizes highly effective methods of learning. Students not only gain knowledge of basic science concepts, but also learn how to apply them.

Specially designed *3D Graphic Organizers* are included for use with the lessons. These organizers review the science concepts while adding to your students' understanding and retention of the subject matter.

This *Great Science Adventures* book is divided into four parts:

1) Following this *Introduction* you will find the *How to Use This Program* section. It contains all the information you need to make the program successful. The *How to Use This Program* section also contains instructions for Dinah Zike's *3D Graphic Organizers*. Please take the time to learn the terms and instructions for these learning manipulatives.

2) In the *Teacher's Section,* the numbered lessons include a list of the science concepts to be taught, simple to complex vocabulary words, and activities that reinforce the science concepts. Each activity includes a list of materials needed, directions, pictures, questions, written assignments, and other helpful information for the teacher.

   The *Teacher's Section* also includes enrichment activities, entitled *Experiences, Investigations, and Research.* Alternative assessment suggestions are found at the end of the *Teacher's Section.*

3) The *Lots of Science Library Books* are next. These books are numbered to correlate with the lessons. Each *Lots of Science Library Book* will cover all the concepts included in its corresponding lesson. You may read the *LSLB* books to your students, ask them to read the books on their own, or make the books available as research materials. Covers for the books are found at the beginning of the *LSLB* section. (Common Sense Press grants permission for you to photocopy the *Lots of Science Library Books* pages and covers for your students.)

4) *Graphics Pages,* also listed by lesson numbers, provide pictures and graphics that can be used with the activities. They can be duplicated and used on student–made manipulatives, or students may draw their own illustrations. The *Investigative Loop* at the front of this section may be photocopied, as well. (Common Sense Press grants permission for you to photocopy the *Graphics Pages* for your students.)

How to Use This Program

This program can be used in a single–level classroom, multilevel classroom, homeschool, co–op group, or science club. Everything you need for a complete space study is included in this book. Intermediate students will need access to basic reference materials.

Take the time to read the entire *How to Use this Program* section and become familiar with the sections of this book described in the *Introduction.*

Begin a lesson by reading the *Teacher Pages* for that lesson. Choose the vocabulary words for each student and the activities to complete. Collect the materials you need for these activities.

Introduce each lesson with its corresponding *Lots of Science Library Book* by reading it aloud or asking a student to read it. (The *Lots of Science Library Books* are located after the *Teacher's Section* in this book.)

Discuss the concepts presented in the *Lots of Science Library Book,* focusing on the ones listed in your *Teacher's Section.*

Follow the directions for the activities you have chosen.

How to Use the Multilevel Approach

The lessons in this book include basic content appropriate for grades K–8 at different mastery levels. For example, throughout the teaching process, a first grader will be exposed to a lot of information but would not be expected to retain all of it. In the same lesson, a sixth–grade student will learn all the steps of the process, be able to communicate them in writing, and be able to apply that information to different situations.

In the *Lots of Science Library Books,* the words written in larger type are for all students. The words in smaller type are for upper level students and include more scientific details about the basic content, as well as interesting facts for older learners.

In the activity sections, icons are used to designate the levels of specific writing assignments.

This icon ✎ indicates the Beginning level, which includes the nonreading or early reading student. This level applies mainly to kindergarten and first grade students.

This icon ✎✎ is used for the Primary level. It includes the reading student who is still working to be a fluent reader. This level is designed primarily for second and third graders.

This icon ✎✎✎ denotes the Intermediate level, or fluent reader. This level of activities will usually apply to fourth through eighth grade students.

If you are working with a student in seventh or eighth grade, we recommend using the assignments for the Intermediate level, plus at least one *Experiences, Investigations, and Research* activity per lesson.

No matter what grade level your students are working on, use a level of written work that is appropriate for their reading and writing abilities. It is good for students to review data they already know, learn new data and concepts, and be exposed to advanced information and processes.

Vocabulary Words

Each lesson lists vocabulary words that are used in the content of the lesson. Some of these words will be "too easy" for your students, some will be "too hard," and others will be "just right." The "too easy" words will be used automatically during independent writing assignments. Words that are "too hard" can be used during discussion times. Words that are "just right" can be studied by definition, usage, and spelling. Encourage your students to use these words in their own writing and speaking.

You can encourage beginning students to use their vocabulary words as you reinforce reading instruction and enhance discussions about the topic, and as words to be copied in cooperative, or teacher guided, writing.

Primary and Intermediate students can make a Vocabulary Book for new words. Instructions for making a Vocabulary Book are found on page 3. The Vocabulary Book will contain the word definitions and sentences composed by the student for each word. Students should also be expected to use their vocabulary words in discussions and independent writing assignments. A vocabulary word with an asterisk (*) next to it is designated for Intermediate students only.

Using 3D Graphic Organizers

The *3D Graphic Organizers* provide a format for students of all levels to conceptualize, analyze, review, and apply the concepts of the lesson. The *3D Graphic Organizers* take complicated information and break it down into visual parts so students can better understand the concepts. Most *3D Graphic Organizers* involve writing about the subject matter. Although the content for the levels will generally be the same, assignments and expectations for the levels will vary.

Beginning students may dictate or copy one or two "clue" words about the topic. These students will use the written clues to verbally communicate the science concept. The teacher should provide various ways for the students to restate the concept. This will reinforce the science concept and encourage the students in their reading and higher order thinking skills.

Primary students may write or copy one or two "clue" words and a sentence about the topic. The teacher should encourage students to use vocabulary words when writing these sentences. As students read their sentences and discuss them, they will reinforce the science concept, increasing their fluency in reading, and higher order thinking skills.

Intermediate students may write several sentences or a paragraph about the topic. These students are also encouraged to use reference materials to expand their knowledge of the subject. As tasks are completed, students enhance their abilities to locate information, read for content, compose sentences and paragraphs, and increase vocabulary. Encourage these students to use the vocabulary words in a context that indicates understanding of the words' meanings.

Illustrations for the *3D Graphic Organizers* are found on the *Graphics Pages* and are labeled by the lesson number and a letter, such as 5–A. Your students may use these graphics to draw their own pictures, or cut out and glue them directly on their work.

Several of the *3D Graphic Organizers* will be used over a series of lessons. For this reason, you will need a storage system for each student's *3D Graphic Organizers.* A pocket folder or a reclosable plastic bag works well. See page 1 for more information on storing materials.

Investigative Loop™

The *Investigative Loop* is used throughout *Great Science Adventures* to ensure that your labs are effective and practical. Labs give students a context for the application of their science lessons, so that they begin to take ownership of the concepts, increasing understanding as well as retention.

The *Investigative Loop* can be used in any lab. The steps are easy to follow, user friendly, and flexible.

Each *Investigative Loop* begins with a **Question or Concept.** If the lab is designed to answer a question, use a question in this phase. For example, the question could be: "How do Saturn and Earth compare in density?" Since the activity for this lab will show the density of two different objects, a question is the best way to begin this *Investigative Loop*.

If the lab is designed to demonstrate a concept, use a concept statement in this phase, such as: "The Moon reflects the light of the Sun." The lab will demonstrate that fact to the students.

After the **Question or Concept** is formulated, the next phase of the *Investigative Loop* is Research and/or Predictions. Research gives students a foundation for the lab. Having researched the question or concept, students enter the lab with a basis for understanding what they observe. Predictions are best used when the first phase is a question. Predictions can be in the form of a statement, a diagram, or a sequence of events.

The **Procedure** for the lab follows. This is an explanation of how to set up the lab and any tasks involved in it. A list of materials for the lab may be included in this section or may precede the entire *Investigative Loop.*

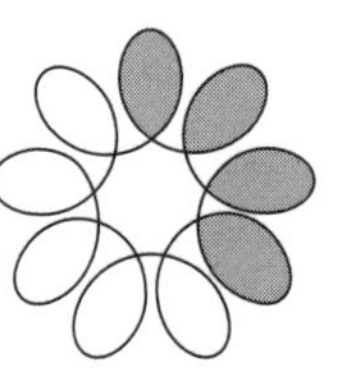

Whether the lab is designed to answer a question or demonstrate a concept, the students' **Observations** are of prime importance. Tell the students what they are to focus upon in their observations. The Observation phase will continue until the lab ends.

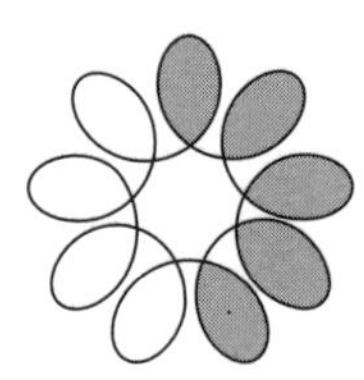

Once observations are made, students must **Record the Data**. Data may be recorded through diagrams or illustrations. Recording quantitative or qualitative observations of the lab is another important activity in this phase. Records may be kept daily for an extended lab or at the beginning and end for a short lab.

Conclusions and/or Applications are completed when the lab ends. Usually the data records will be reviewed before a conclusion can be drawn about the lab. Encourage the students to defend their conclusions by using the data records. Applications are made by using the conclusions to generalize to other situations or by stating how to use the information in daily life.

Next, **Communicate the Conclusions**. This phase is an opportunity for students to be creative. Conclusions can be communicated through a graph, story, report, video, mock radio show, etc. Students may also participate in a group presentation.

Questions that are asked as the activity proceeds are called **Spark Questions.** Questions that the lab sparks in the minds of the students are important to discuss when the lab ends. The lab itself will answer many of these questions, while others may lead to a new *Investigative Loop*. Assign someone to keep a list of all Spark Questions.

One lab naturally leads to another. This begins a new *Investigative Loop*. The phase called **New Loop** is a brainstorming time for narrowing the lab down to a new question or concept. When the new lab has been decided upon, the *Investigative Loop* begins again with a new Question or Concept.

Take the time to teach your students to make qualitative and quantitative observations. Qualitative observations involve recording the color, texture, shape, smell, size (such as small, medium, large), or any words that describe the qualities of an object. Quantitative observations involve using a standard unit of measurement to determine the length, width, weight, mass, or volume of an object.

All students will make a Lab Book, in the form of a Large Question and Answer Book, to record information about the *Investigative Loops*. Instructions are found on page 2. Your students will make a new Lab Book as needed to glue side–by–side to the previous one. Instructions can be found in the *Teacher's Section.*

Predictions, data, and conclusions about the *Investigative Loops* are written under the tabs of the Lab Book.

When you begin an *Investigative Loop*, ask your students to glue or draw the graphic of the experiment on the tab of the Lab Book. Each *Investigative Loop* is labeled with the lesson number and another number. These numbers are also found on the corresponding graphics.

During an *Investigative Loop*, beginning students should be encouraged to discuss their answers to all experiment questions. By discussing the topic, the students will not only learn the science concepts and procedures, but will be able to organize their thinking in a manner that will enhance their writing skills. This discussion time is very important for beginning students and should not be rushed.

After the discussion, work with the students to construct a sentence about the topic. Let them copy the sentence. Students can also write "clue" words to help them remember key points about the experiment and discuss it at a later time.

Primary students should be encouraged to verbalize their answers. By discussing the topic, students will learn the science concepts and procedures and learn to organize their thinking, increasing their ability to use higher–level thinking skills. After the discussion, students can complete the assignment using simple phrases or sentences. Encourage students to share the information they have learned with others, such as parents or friends. This will reinforce the content and skills covered in the lesson.

Even though Intermediate students can write the answers to the lab assignments, the discussion process is very important and should not be skipped. By discussing the experiments, students review the science concepts and procedures as well as organize their thinking for the writing assignments. This allows them to think and write at higher levels. These students should be encouraged to use their vocabulary words in their lab writing assignments.

Design Your Own Experiment

After an *Investigative Loop* is completed, intermediate students have the option to design their own experiments based on that lab. The following procedure should be used for those experiments.

Select a Topic based upon an experience in an *Investigative Loop*, science content, an observation, a high-interest topic, a controversial topic, or a current event.

Discuss the Topic as a class, in student groups, and with knowledgeable professionals.

Read and Research the Topic using the library, the Internet, and hands-on investigations and observations, when possible.

Select a Question that can be investigated and answered using easily obtained reference materials, specimens, and/or chemicals, and make sure that the question selected lends itself to scientific inquiry. Ask specific, focused questions instead of broad, unanswerable questions. Questions might ask "how" something responds, forms, influences, or behaves, or how it is similar or different to something else.

Predict the answer to your question, and be prepared to accept the fact that your prediction might be incorrect or only partially correct. Examine and record all evidence gathered during testing that both confirms and contradicts your prediction.

Design a Testing Procedure that gathers information that can be used to answer your question. Make sure your procedure results in empirical, or measurable, evidence. Don't forget to do the following:

> Determine where and how the tests will take place – in a natural (field work) or controlled (lab) setting.
>
> Collect and use tools to gather information and enhance observations. Make accurate measurements. Use calculators and computers when appropriate.
>
> Plan how to document the test procedure and how to communicate and display resulting data.
>
> Identify variables, or things that might prevent the experiment from being "fair." Before beginning, determine which variables have no effect, a slight effect, or a major effect on your experiment. Create a method for controlling these variables.

Conduct the Experiment carefully and record your findings.

Analyze the Question Again. Determine if the evidence obtained and the scientific explanations of the evidence are reasonable based upon what is known, what you have learned, and what scientists and specialists have reported.

Communicate Findings so that others can duplicate the experiment. Include all pertinent research, measurements, observations, controls, variables, graphs, tables, charts, and diagrams. Discuss observations and results with relevant people.

Reanalyze the Problem and if needed, redefine the problem and retest. Or, try to apply what was learned to similar problems and situations.

Ongoing Project: Timeline Book

One of the activities in Lesson 1 is to make an Accordion Book for the Timeline Book. This will be an ongoing project for your students. In each *Lots of Science Library Book,* there is information on Space events. In the Graphics Pages there are identical pictures of these events. Your students will use a copy of these graphics to cut out and glue to the appropriate page in the Timeline Book. After the picture is glued in place, ask your students to draw a line from the picture to the correct time on the line. Encourage students to complete independent research on other events for the Timeline Book.

Ongoing Projects: Problem Solving and Inquiry Scenarios

In the Graphic Pages, following the *Investigative Loop,* you will find the Problem Solving and Inquiry Scenarios. Photocopy this page for your students. Allow the students to work on one or more of these scenarios while completing this study of space. Although designed for intermediate students, the Problem Solving and Inquiry Scenarios are beneficial for all students' participation, if possible.

Experiences, Investigations, and Research

At the end of each lesson in the *Teacher's Section* is a category of activities entitled *Experiences, Investigations, and Research.* These activities expand upon concepts taught in the lesson, provide a foundation for further study of the content, or integrate the study with other disciplines. The following icons are used to identify the type of each activity.

Space

Hands On

Computer

Writing

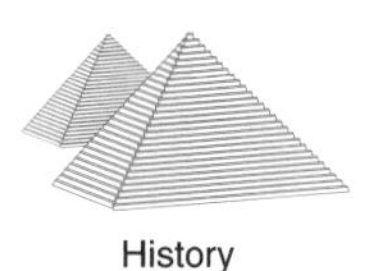
History

Literature

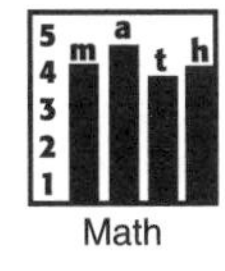

Math

Research

Cumulative Project

At the end of the program we recommend that students compile a Cumulative Project using the activities they have completed during their course of study. It may include the Investigative Loops, Lab Record Cards, and the *3D Graphic Organizers* on display.

Please do not overlook the Cumulative Project, as it provides immeasurable benefits for your students. Students will review all the content as they create the project. Each student will organize the material in his or her own unique way, thus providing an opportunity for authentic assessment and reinforcing the context in which it was learned. This project creates a format where students can make sense of the whole study in a way that cannot be accomplished otherwise.

These 3D Graphic Organizers are used throughout Great Science Adventures.

Fast Food and Fast Folds

"If making the manipulatives takes up too much of your instructional time, they are not worth doing. They have to be made quickly, and they can be, if the students know exactly what is expected of them. Hamburgers, Hot Dogs, Tacos, Mountains, Valleys, and Shutter–Folds can be produced by students, who in turn use these folds to make organizers and manipulatives."– Dinah Zike

Every fold has two parts. The outside edge formed by a fold is called the **"Mountain."** The inside of this edge is the **"Valley."**

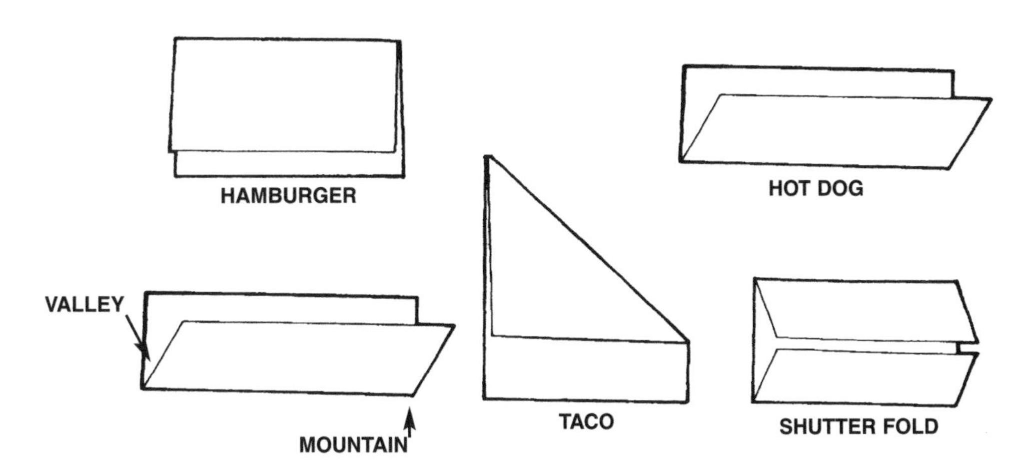

Storage – Book Bags

One–gallon reclosable plastic bags are ideal for storing ongoing projects and books that students are writing and researching.

Use strips of clear, 2" tape to secure 1" x 1" pieces of index card to the front and back of one of the top corners of a bag, under the closure. Punch a hole through the index cards. Use a giant notebook ring to keep several of the "Book Bags" together.

Label the bags by writing on them with a permanent marker.

Alternatively, the bags can be stored in a notebook if you place the 2" clear tape along the side of the storage bag and punch 3 holes in the tape.

Half Book

Fold a sheet of paper in half like a Hamburger.

Large Question and Answer Book

1. Fold a sheet of paper in half like a Hamburger. Fold it in half again like a Hamburger. Make a cut up the Valley of the inside fold, forming two tabs.

2. A larger book can be made by gluing Large Question and Answer Books "side–by–side."

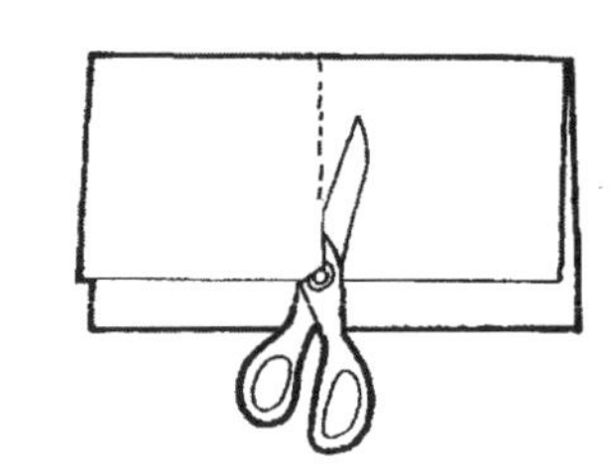

Small Question and Answer Book

1. Fold a sheet of paper in half like a Hot Dog.

2. Fold this long rectangle in half like a Hamburger.

3. Fold both ends back to touch the Mountain top.

4. On the side forming two valleys and one Mountain top, make vertical cuts through one thickness of paper, forming tabs for questions and answers. These four tabs can also be cut in half, making eight tabs.

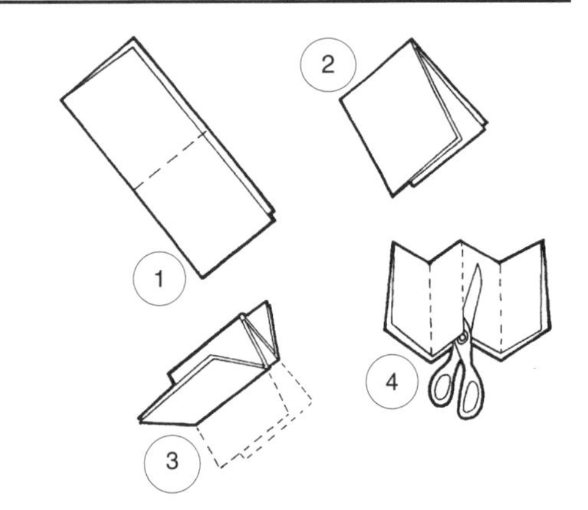

3 Tab Book

1. Fold a sheet of paper in half like a Hamburger or Hot Dog. Fold it into thirds. Cut the inside folds to form three tabs.

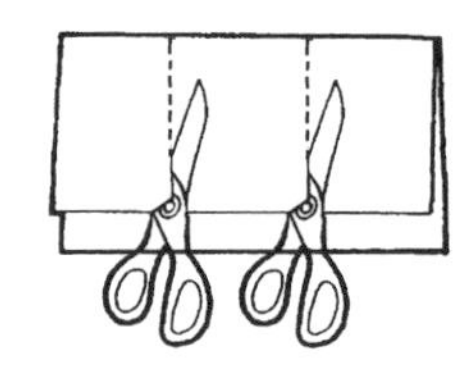

Pocket Book

1. Fold a sheet of paper in half like a Hamburger.

2. Open the folded paper and fold one of the long sides up two and a half inches to form a pocket. Refold along the Hamburger fold so that the newly formed pockets are on the inside.

3. Glue the outer edges of the two–and–a–half–inch fold with a small amount of glue.

4. Make a multi–paged booklet by gluing several Pocket Books "side–by–side."

5. Glue a construction paper cover around the multi–paged pocket booklet.

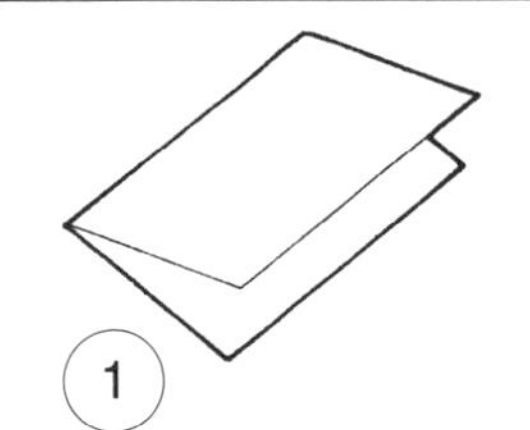

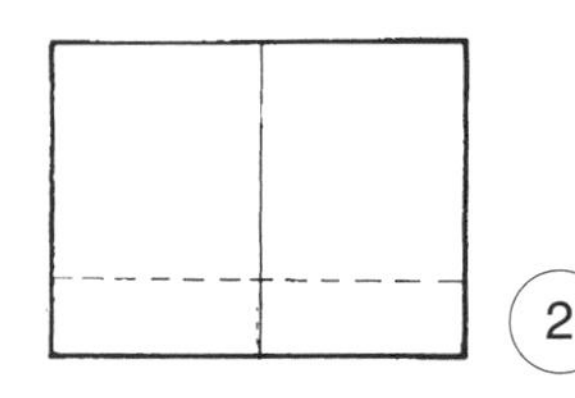

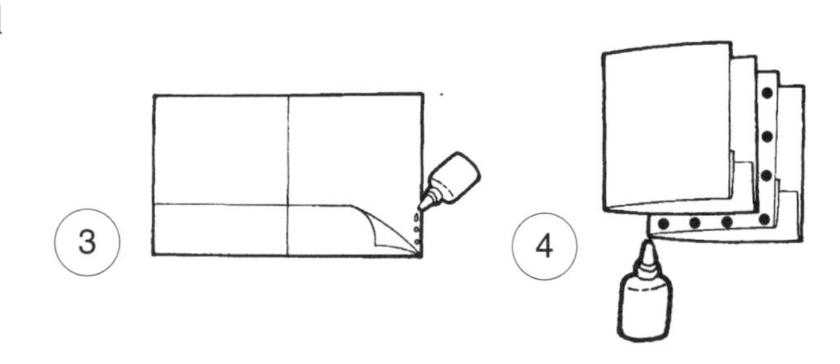

Side–by–Side

Some books can easily grow into larger books by gluing them side–by–side. Make two or more of these books. Be sure the books are closed, then glue the back cover of one book to the front cover of the next book. Continue in this manner, making the book as large as needed. Glue a cover over the whole book.

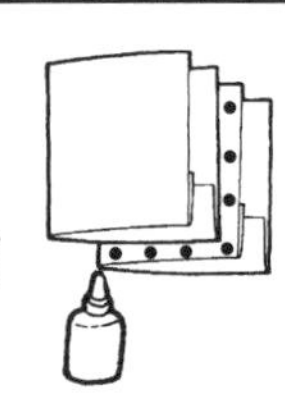

Vocabulary Book

1. Take two sheets of paper and fold each sheet like a Hot Dog.

2. Fold each Hot Dog in half like a Hamburger. Fold each Hamburger in half two more times and crease well. Unfold the sheets of paper, which are now divided into sixteenths.

3. On one side only, cut the folds up to the Mountain top, forming eight tabs. Repeat this process on the second sheet of paper.

4. Take a sheet of construction paper and fold like a Hot Dog. Glue the back of one vocabulary sheet to one of the inside sections of the construction paper. Glue the second vocabulary sheet to the other side of the construction paper fold.

5. Vocabulary Books can be made larger by gluing them "side–by–side."

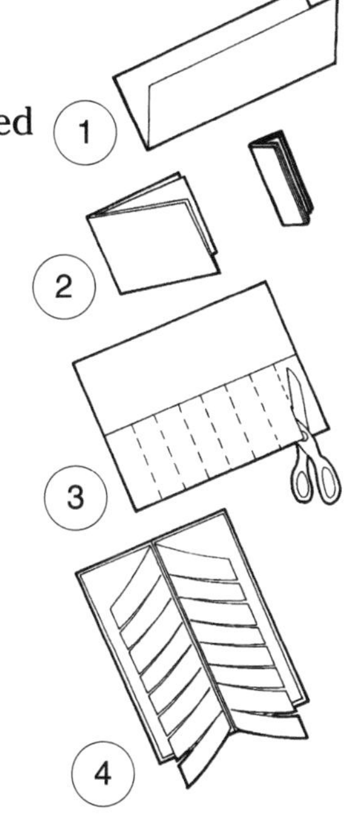

Pyramid Project

1. Fold a sheet of paper into a Taco. Cut off the excess tab formed by the fold.

2. Open the folded taco and refold it the opposite way, forming another taco and an X fold pattern.

3. Cut up one of the folds to the center of the X and stop. This forms two triangular–shaped flaps.

4. Glue one of the flaps under the other flap, forming a pyramid.

5. Set the Pyramid up on one end or glue two or more together to make a diorama.

Layered Look Book

1. Stack two sheets of paper and place the back sheet one inch higher than the front sheet.

2. Bring the bottom of both sheets upward and align the edges so that all of the layers or tabs are the same distance apart.

3. When all tabs are an equal distance apart, fold the papers and crease well.

4. Open the papers and glue them together along the Valley/center fold.

4 Door Book

1. Fold a sheet of paper into a Shutter Fold.
2. Fold it into a Hamburger.
3. Open the Hamburger and cut the Valley folds on the Shutters only, creating four tabs.

   Refold it into a Hamburger, with the fold at the top. Decorate the top sheet as the cover.

Bound Book

1. Take two sheets of paper and fold each like a Hamburger.
2. Mark both folds 1" from the outer edges.
3. On one of the folded sheets, "cut up" from the top and bottom edge to the marked spot on both sides.
4. On the second folded sheet, start at one of the marked spots and "cut out" the fold between the two marks. Do not cut into the fold too deeply; just shave it off.
5. Take the "cut up" sheet and roll it. Place it through the "cut out" sheet and then open it up. Fold the bound pages in half to form a book.

Variation...

To make a larger book, use additional sheets of paper, marking each sheet as explained in #3. Use an equal number of sheets for the "cut up" and "cut out." Place them one on top of the other and follow the directions in #4 and #5.

Trifold Book

1. Fold a sheet of paper into thirds.
2. Use this book as is, or cut into shapes. If the trifold is cut, leave plenty of fold on both sides of the designed shape, so the book will open and close in three sections.

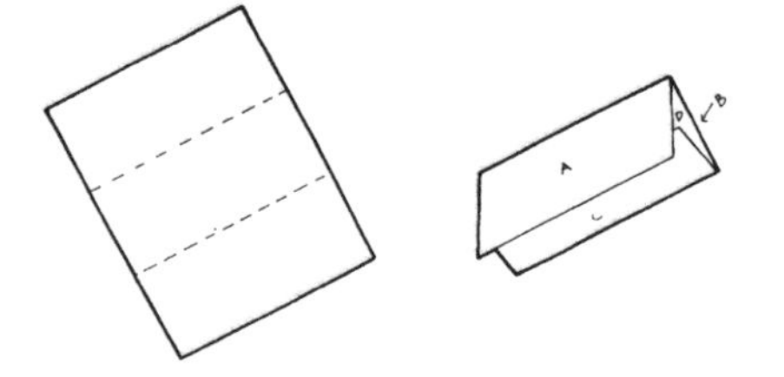

Accordion Book

1. Fold each section of paper into a Hot Dog; however, fold one side 1/2 inch shorter than the other side. This will form a tab that is 1/2 inch long. Fold this tab back away from the shorter piece of paper. Do not fold this tab over the short side, fold it the opposite way.
2. Glue together to form an accordion by gluing a straight edge of one section into the Valley of another section.

Note: Stand the sections on end and form an accordion with them before gluing. (See illustration.)

10 Top Tab Book

1. Fold one sheet of paper into a Hot Dog. Fold it into a Hot Dog again. Open the paper.

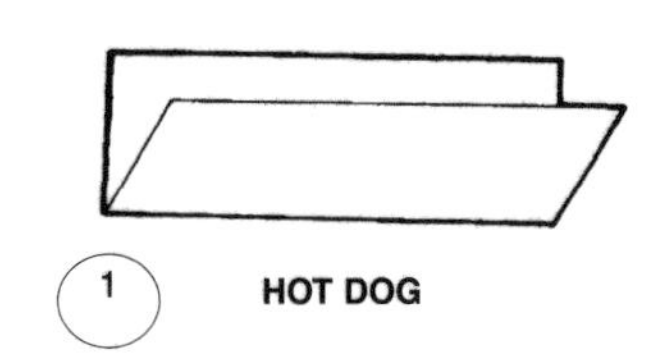

2. Lay the paper horizontally. Fold 1/3 of the paper to the left.

3. Fold the double thickness on the right side in half. Fold the single thickness on the left side backward on the fold line. See illustration.

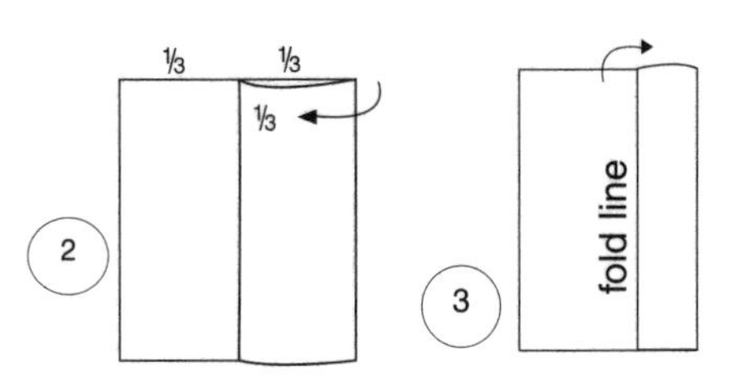

4. Fold the five thicknesses in half again. Open the paper. This is your pattern for the 10 Top Tab Book. There is a 2" section on the left for the Sun and 1" sections for each planet.

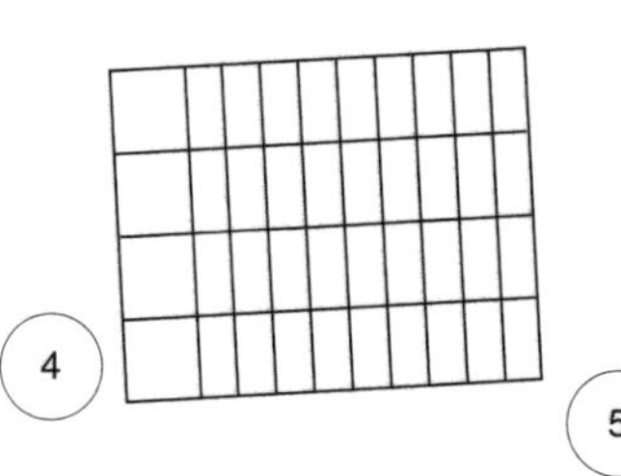

5. You will now begin stacking the paper for the 10 Top Tab Book. Begin the stack with one sheet of paper.

6. Hold the pattern vertically and place another sheet of paper under the pattern. (The pattern was made in steps 1-4.) Cut the bottom right–hand section out of both sheets. Put the underneath sheet on the stack that you started in step 5.

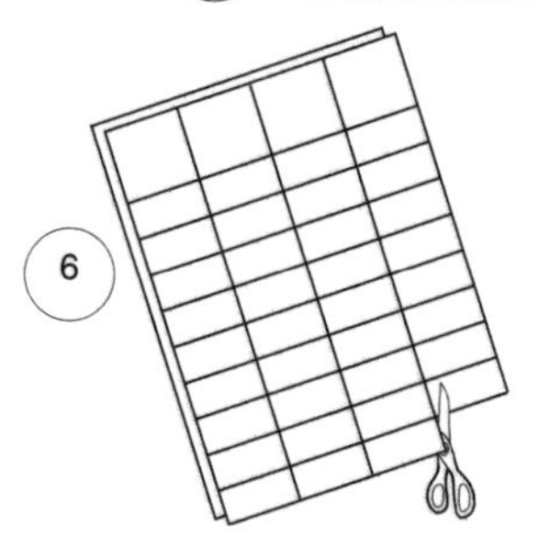

7. Take a second sheet of paper and place it under the pattern. Cut the first and second right–hand sections out of both sheets. Place the underneath sheet on the stack.

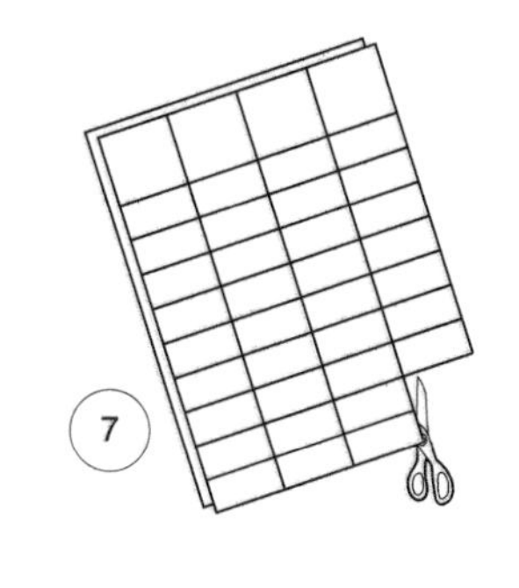

8. Take a third sheet of paper and place it under the pattern. Cut the first, second, and third right–hand sections out of both sheets. Place the underneath sheet on the stack.

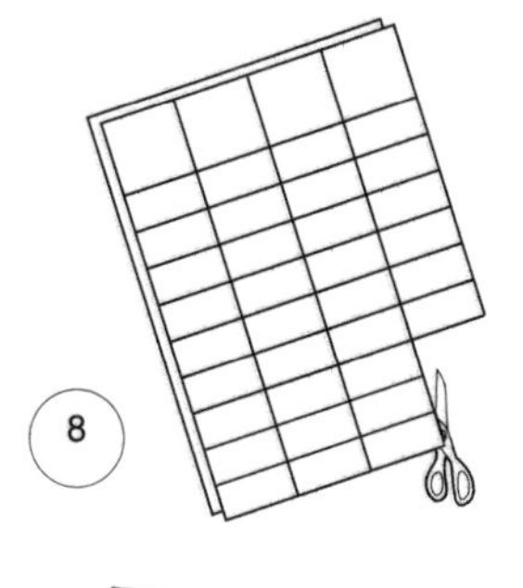

9. Continue this process with the next 5 sheets of paper. Cut the last sheet of paper all the way across the top. This makes a cover for the 10 Top Tab Book.

10. Stack the 11 sheets of paper together and staple or glue them on the left side.

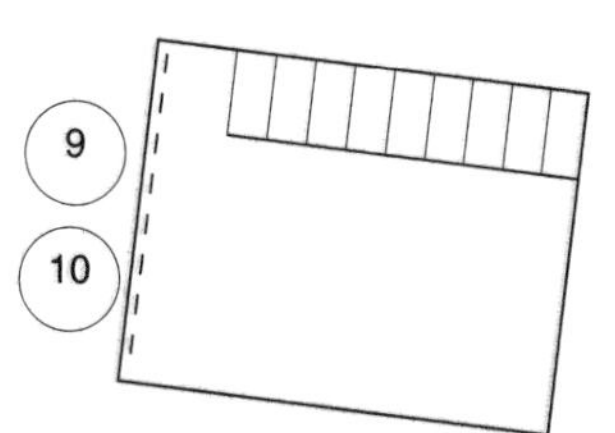

Pop-Up Book

Dinah's Rule for Pop-Up Books: Always cut on a fold; never glue on a fold.

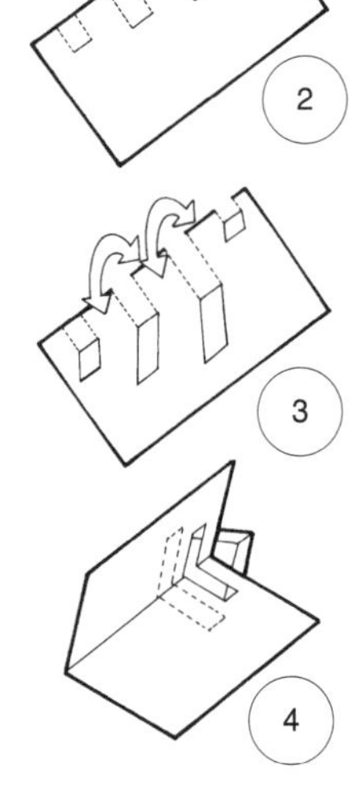

1. Fold a sheet of paper (8.5" x 11") in half like a Hamburger.
2. Beginning at the fold, or mountain top, cut one or more tabs.
3. Fold the tabs back and forth several times until a good fold line is formed.
4. Partially open the hamburger fold and push the tabs through to the inside.
5. Using one small dot of glue, glue figures for the Pop-Up Book to the front of each tab. Allow the glue to dry before going on to the next step.
6. To make a cover for the book, fold a sheet of construction paper in half like a hamburger.
7. Place glue around the outside edges of the Pop-Up Book and firmly press inside the construction paper hamburger.

Patch Word Quilt Square

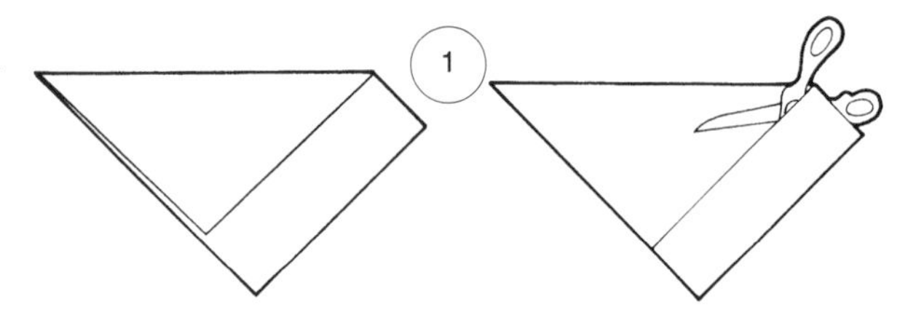

1. Fold a sheet of paper (8 1/2"x11") into a Taco, forming a square. Cut off the excess paper strip formed by the fold.
2. Open the folded Taco and refold it the opposite way, forming another Taco and an X fold pattern.
3. Hold the Taco flat, so that it looks like a mountain with the long side of the triangle forming the base of the mountain, and the top the peak.

   Cut up the center of the mountain from the base toward the peak. Stop one inch from the peak.
   Refold the Taco along the other fold of the X pattern, and cut up the center of the mountain from the base toward the peak again. Stop one inch from the peak.

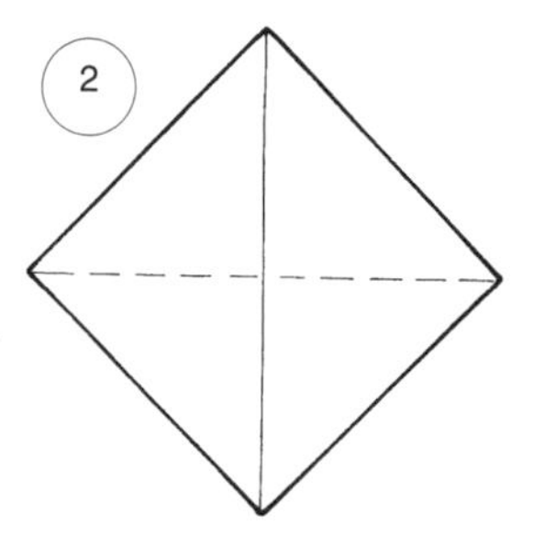

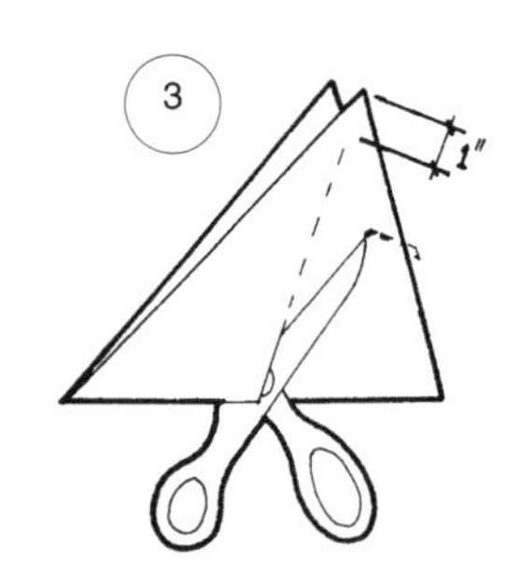

4. The cuts will form an X in the middle of the square.
5. Place a small amount of glue around the outer edges of the square, then glue it onto a slightly larger construction paper square.
   Fold the four triangular tabs back and forth to form windows. This hides whatever is glued or written underneath on the construction paper.

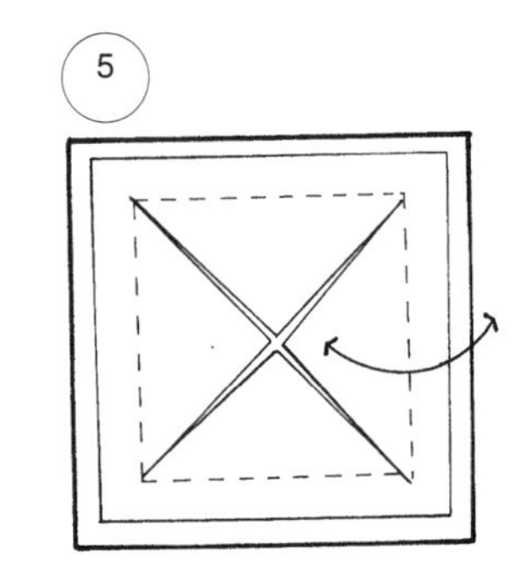

The *Lots of Science Library Book* Shelf

Make a bookshelf for the *Lots of Science Library Books* using an appropriate sized box or by following the instructions below.

1. Begin with an 11" x 12" piece of poster board or cardboard. Mark lines 3" from the edge of each side. Fold up on each folded line.
   Cut on the dotted lines as indicated in illustration 1. Refold on the line.

2. Glue the tabs under the top and bottom sections of the shelf. See illustration 2.
   Cover your shelf with attractive paper.

3. If you are photocopying your *Lots of Science Library Books*, consider using green paper for the covers and the same green paper to cover your bookshelf.

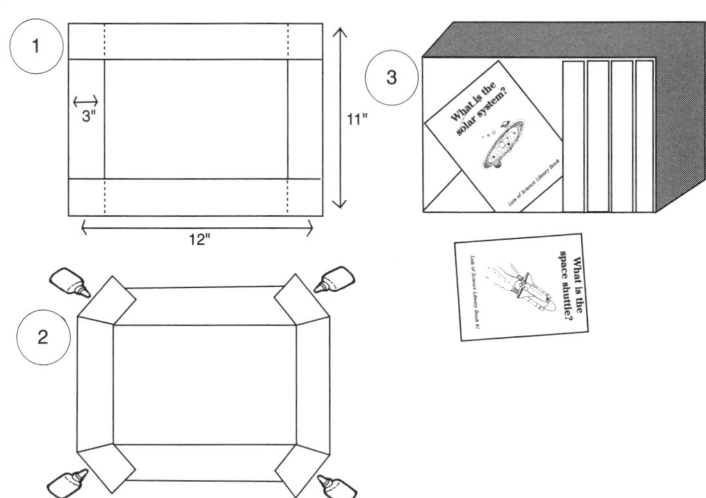

Notes

Teacher's Section

Poems used in this study were taken from *Space* by Dinah Zike and used by permission. For information on ordering *Space,* call 1-210-698-0123 or visit www.dinah.com.

Website addresses used as resources in this book are accurate and relevant at the time of publication. Due to the changing nature of the Internet, we encourage teachers to preview the websites prior to assigning them to students.

The authors and the publisher have made every reasonable effort to ensure that the experiments and activities in this book are safe when performed according to the book's instructions. We recommend that students undertake these activities and experiments under the supervision of a teacher, parent, and/or guardian.

Notes

Space Concept Map

Lessons 1-6

Numbers Refer to Lesson Numbers

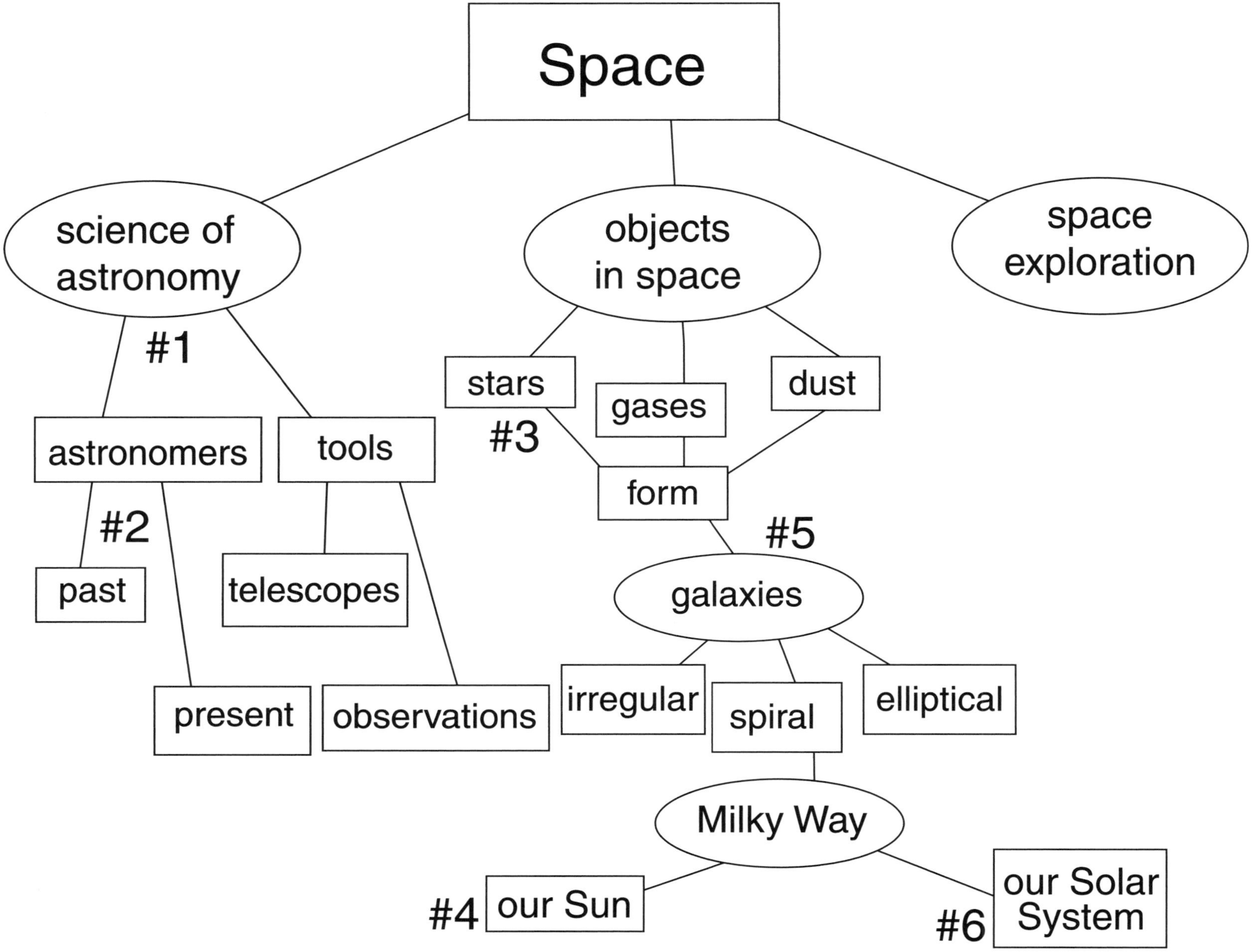

Space
science of astronomy
objects in space
space exploration
#1
astronomers
tools
#2
past
present
telescopes
observations
stars
gases
dust
#3
form
#5
galaxies
irregular
spiral
elliptical
Milky Way
#4
our Sun
#6
our Solar System

What is astronomy?

Space Concepts:

- Ancient people used the moon and stars as a guide to know when to sow and harvest crops, how to navigate in the seas, and how to record the passing of time.
- A building used to observe stars and other heavenly bodies is an observatory.
- "Astronomy" comes from the Greek word *astron,* meaning "star," and *nemein,* meaning to "name."
- A constellation is a group of stars visible from Earth that form a picture or a pattern.

Vocabulary: space star *astronomy *constellation

Read: *Lots of Science Library Book #1.*

Activities:

Investigative Loop – Find North without a Compass Lab 1-1

Teacher's Note: This activity needs to be scheduled at noon, or 1 p.m. Daylight Saving Time.
Focus Skill: applying information
Activity Materials: newspaper yardstick or long dowel modeling clay rocks compass
Paper Handouts: 8.5" x 11" sheet of paper a copy of Lab Graphic 1–1
Graphic Organizer: Make a Large Question and Answer Book. Glue Lab Graphic 1–1 on the left tab. This is the students' Lab Book. It will be used in this and future lessons.
Concept: At certain times of the day, shadows indicate the direction north.
Research: Read *Lots of Science Library Book #1* and review the Concept.
Procedure: Find an open area outdoors, away from shade. Lay newspapers on the ground and weight the edges down with rocks. Form the modeling clay into a base and place it in the middle of the newspaper. Stick the yardstick in the clay base.
Observations: Look at the shadow of the yardstick on the newspaper.
Record the Data: Trace the yardstick's shadow with a marker. If you live in the Northern Hemisphere, the direction the line points is north. If you live in the Southern Hemisphere, the line points south.
Conclusions: Check the direction with the compass. What does this tell you about shadows at this time of day?
Communicate the Conclusions: Under the left tab in the Lab Book:

✎ Draw a picture of the activity. Draw a compass showing the direction the shadow is pointing.
✎✎ Complete ✎. Describe the activity.
✎✎✎ Complete ✎✎. Explain why the shadow points in the direction it does.

Spark Questions: Discuss questions sparked from the lab.
New Loop: Choose a question to investigate further.
✎✎✎ **Design Your Own Experiment:** Select a topic based upon the experiences in these *Investigative Loops*. See page viii for more details.

Investigative Loop – The Big Dipper Lab 1–2

Focus Skill: comparing
Paper Handouts: a copy of Lab Graphic 1–2 Lab Book
Graphic Organizer: Glue Lab Graphic 1–2 on the right tab of the Lab Book.
Concept: The Big Dipper is observed in the night sky.
Research: Read *Lots of Science Library Book #2* and review the Concept.
Procedure: On a clear night, look in the northern sky and find the Big Dipper.
Observations: Observe the position of the Big Dipper.
Record the Data: Compare it with the diagram in the Lab Book. Circle the one that best represents the Observations.
Conclusions: Draw conclusions about the Big Dipper's location in the sky.
Communicate the Conclusions: Under the tab:
✎ Draw the night sky showing the Big Dipper.
✎✎ Complete ✎. Describe the Big Dipper in the night sky.
✎✎✎ Complete ✎✎. Explain how the position of the Big Dipper will change throughout the year.

Lab 1-1 Lab 1-2

Spark Questions: Discuss questions sparked by this lab.
New Loop: Choose a question to investigate further.
✎✎✎ **Design Your Own Experiment:** Select a topic based upon the experiences in the *Investigative Loop*. See page viii for more details.

Space Timeline

Paper Handouts: 6 sheets of 12" x 18" construction paper
a copy of Graphics 1A–R
Graphic Organizer: Make an Accordion Book out of the 6 sheets of paper. This is the Space Timeline Book. Glue Graphic 1A across the middle of the first page of the Space Timeline Book. Glue Graphic 1B to the second page of the book. Continue with Graphics 1C–L. Glue Graphics 1M–R to the correct pages of the Space Timeline Book.
✎ Copy/dictate the name of the person or event under the graphic.
✎✎ Copy the name of the person or event under the graphic.
✎✎✎ Describe another detail about the person or event under the graphic.

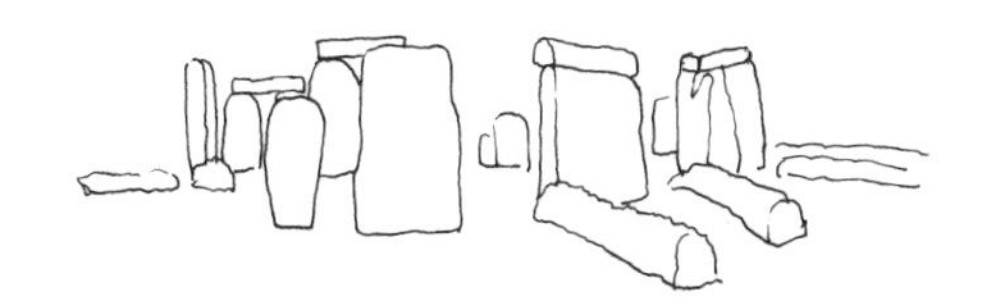

Experiences, Investigations, and Research

Select one or more of the following activities for individual or group enrichment projects. Allow your students to determine the format in which they would like to report, share, or graphically present what they have discovered. This should be a creative investigation that utilizes your students' strengths.

1. Use a stopwatch or clock with a second hand. Without looking at a clock, guess how long a minute is. What helped you determine the time?

2. Using an almanac, find information on stars, moons, and tides for this month. When would this information be helpful?

3. Read *A Wrinkle in Time* by Madeleine L'Engle. ✎✎✎

4. Read *Carry On, Mr. Bowditch* by Jean Lee Latham. ✎✎✎

5. http://www.almanac.com/cgi–bin/heaven.pl?mooninput=current

6. To view the night sky in your area:
   Go to www.census.gov
   Click on your state.
   Click on your county.
   Click on "more data for this area."
   This will give you the longitude and latitude of your area.
   Go to http://www.fourmilab.ch/yoursky.
   Enter your longitude and latitude.

7. http://www.earthsky.com/Features/skywatching

Notes

Who were the first astronomers?

Space Concepts:

- Scientists who study stars and planets are called astronomers.
- In 150 A.D., a Greek astronomer named Ptolemy believed Earth stood still and the Sun, stars, and planets circled around it.
- In 350 B.C., the Greek philosopher Aristotle argued that Earth was round, not flat.
- In 1543, Nicolaus Copernicus (1473–1543), a Polish monk and astronomer, claimed that Earth and all known planets circled around a still Sun.
- Galileo Galilei (1564–1642) proved Copernicus' theory by observing the planets with the first telescope.
- Johannes Kepler (1571–1630), a German mathematician, proposed three laws of planetary motion.
- Isaac Newton (1642–1727), an English scientist, invented the reflecting telescope, which used mirrors instead of lenses.

Vocabulary: sun planet telescope *astronomer

Read: *Lots of Science Library Book #2.*

Lab 2-1

Activities:

Investigative Loop – Round Earth Lab 2–1

Focus Skill: compare and contrast
Activity Materials: colored paper toothpick flat eraser large ball
Paper Handouts: 8.5" x 11" sheet of paper Lab Book a copy of Lab Graphic 2–1
Graphic Organizer: Make a Large Question and Answer Book. Glue it side–by–side to the Lab Book. See page 2 for instructions. Glue Lab Graphic 2–1 on the left tab.
Concept: The curvature of the earth can be observed at the horizon.
Research: Read *Lots of Science Library Book #2* and review the Concept.
Procedure: Cut a small triangle from the colored paper to make a flag. Tape the flag onto the toothpick and stick the toothpick into the flat eraser to make a ship. Place the ship on the table and gradually move it to the edge of the table, then over the edge. Now, hold the large ball at the same level as the table top and do the same with the ship on the ball.
Observations: Watch the ship sail over each edge. Compare and contrast the ship's disappearance on each surface.
Record the Data: On the top section under the tab, draw the ship going over the edge of the table and draw it going over the ball.

Conclusions: Describe how the ship looked when it went over the table. Describe how the ship looked when it went over the ball. How were the two alike? How did they differ? **Possible answer: The ship disappears immediately over the table and gradually over the ball.**

Communicate the Conclusions: On the bottom section, under the tab:

✎ Color the drawings while orally comparing and contrasting the ship's disappearances.

✎✎ Explain why the ship looks different when it goes over the ball than over the table.

✎✎✎ Complete ✎✎. Explain how this lab demonstrates Earth.

Spark Questions: Discuss questions sparked by this lab.

New Loop: Choose a question to investigate further.

✎✎✎ **Design Your Own Experiment:** Select a topic based upon the experiences in the *Investigative Loop*. See page viii for more details.

Night–Friendly Flashlight

When you go stargazing, you will need a flashlight. To help your eyes adjust to the dark, make a night–friendly flashlight. Your eyes adjust more easily and quickly to red light than white light.

Focus Skill: following oral directions

Activity Materials: flashlight red cellophane tape

Activity: Read the following directions aloud. Read one step and ask your students to complete it. Repeat with each step.

1. Put the flashlight head down on the red cellophane.
2. On the cellophane, draw a circle about 1 inch bigger than the flashlight head.
3. Cut out the red cellophane.
4. Hold the cellophane on the flashlight head, with the extra inch overlapping it.
5. Tape the cellophane to the side of the flashlight head.

Timeline

Paper Handouts: Space Timeline Book a copy of Graphics 2A–E

Graphic Organizer: Glue Graphics 2A–E to the correct pages in the Space Timeline Book.

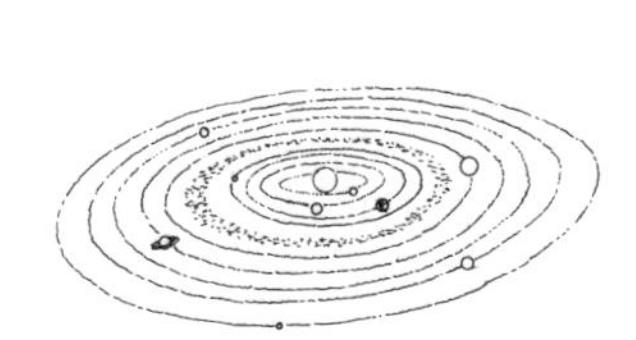

Experiences, Investigations, and Research

Select one or more of the following activities for individual or group enrichment projects. Allow your students to determine the format in which they would like to report, share, or graphically present what they have discovered. This should be a creative investigation that utilizes your students' strengths.

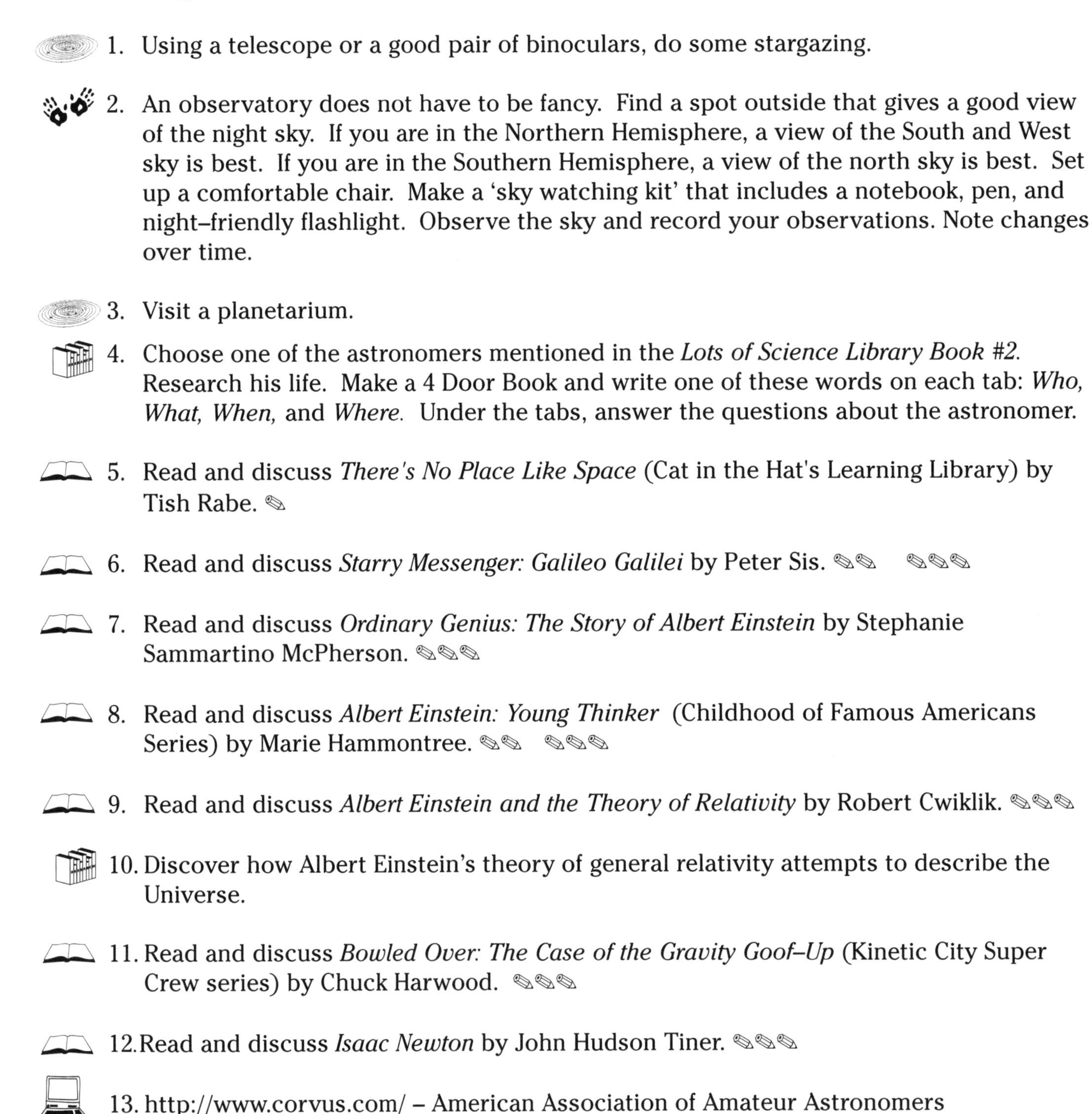

1. Using a telescope or a good pair of binoculars, do some stargazing.

2. An observatory does not have to be fancy. Find a spot outside that gives a good view of the night sky. If you are in the Northern Hemisphere, a view of the South and West sky is best. If you are in the Southern Hemisphere, a view of the north sky is best. Set up a comfortable chair. Make a 'sky watching kit' that includes a notebook, pen, and night–friendly flashlight. Observe the sky and record your observations. Note changes over time.

3. Visit a planetarium.

4. Choose one of the astronomers mentioned in the *Lots of Science Library Book #2.* Research his life. Make a 4 Door Book and write one of these words on each tab: *Who, What, When,* and *Where.* Under the tabs, answer the questions about the astronomer.

5. Read and discuss *There's No Place Like Space* (Cat in the Hat's Learning Library) by Tish Rabe. ✎

6. Read and discuss *Starry Messenger: Galileo Galilei* by Peter Sis. ✎✎ ✎✎✎

7. Read and discuss *Ordinary Genius: The Story of Albert Einstein* by Stephanie Sammartino McPherson. ✎✎✎

8. Read and discuss *Albert Einstein: Young Thinker* (Childhood of Famous Americans Series) by Marie Hammontree. ✎✎ ✎✎✎

9. Read and discuss *Albert Einstein and the Theory of Relativity* by Robert Cwiklik. ✎✎✎

10. Discover how Albert Einstein's theory of general relativity attempts to describe the Universe.

11. Read and discuss *Bowled Over: The Case of the Gravity Goof–Up* (Kinetic City Super Crew series) by Chuck Harwood. ✎✎✎

12. Read and discuss *Isaac Newton* by John Hudson Tiner. ✎✎✎

13. http://www.corvus.com/ – American Association of Amateur Astronomers

Notes

What are stars?

Space Concepts:

- Stars experience life stages: birth, childhood, adolescence, maturity, middle age, old age, and death.
- Stars are born in giant clouds of dust and gases, mostly hydrogen and helium. Gravity pulls the giant clouds together to form a spinning cloud. The spinning causes the hydrogen atoms to collide and heat up. As heat increases, the core of the new star is formed and starts to burn, or shine.
- A star's color can be used to determine its surface temperature.
- The Sun is our closest star.

Vocabulary: gas hydrogen spin collide *temperature *supernova

Read: *Lots of Science Library Book #3.*

Activities:

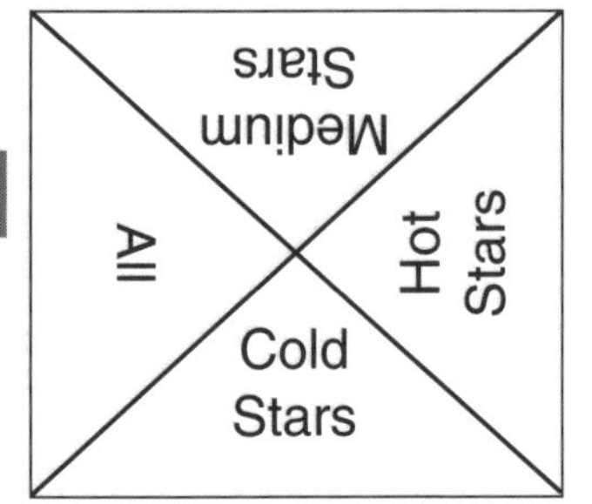

Hot Stars – Graphic Organizer

Focus Skill: memorizing information
Paper Handouts: 8.5" x 11" sheet of paper; black construction paper; a copy of Graphic 3A
Activity Materials: white pen or white–out pen; colored markers

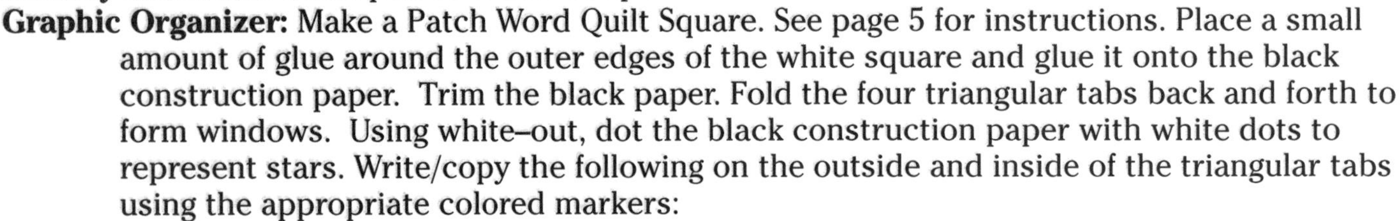

Graphic Organizer: Make a Patch Word Quilt Square. See page 5 for instructions. Place a small amount of glue around the outer edges of the white square and glue it onto the black construction paper. Trim the black paper. Fold the four triangular tabs back and forth to form windows. Using white–out, dot the black construction paper with white dots to represent stars. Write/copy the following on the outside and inside of the triangular tabs using the appropriate colored markers:

Tab 1: use orange and red markers:
outside tab: "Cold stars" inside tab: "Orange and red"

Tab 2: use blue marker:
outside tab: "Hot stars" inside tab: "Blue and white"

Tab 3: use yellow markers.
outside tab: "Medium stars" inside tab: "White and yellow"

Tab 4: use orange, red, blue, and yellow markers.
outside tab: "All" inside tab: "producing heat and light."

Glue Graphic 3A on the back of the Patch Word Quilt Square. Memorize the poem.

Cold stars
Orange and red,
Hot stars
Blue and white,
Medium stars
White and yellow,
All producing
Heat and light.
Dinah Zike

Investigative Loop – The North Star, or Polaris Lab 3–1

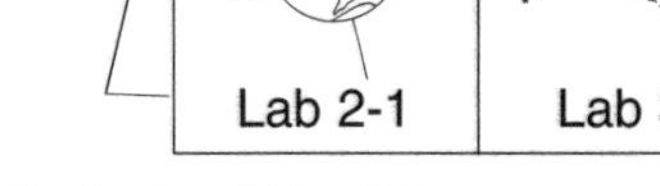

Focus Skill: diagramming
Paper Handouts: a copy of Lab Graphic 3–1 Lab Book
Graphic Organizer: Glue Lab Graphic 3–1 on the right tab.
Concept: Locate the North Star, or Polaris, in the night sky.
Research: Review Graphic 3–1 to find the North Star's location.
Procedure: Use Lab Graphics 3–1 and 1–2 to locate the North Star, or Polaris. The Big Dipper is a group of seven stars that illustrate a pan with a curved handle. Mentally draw a line along the two stars forming the side of the pan away from the handle.
Observations: Imagine this line with an arrow point moving away from the pan and into space. Follow the arrow until it runs into a very bright star. That is the North Star, or Polaris.
Record the Data: Diagram The Big Dipper and the North Star on the top section under the tab.
Conclusions: The North Star is used for navigational purposes. How could you find the North Star, if you needed to.
Communicate the Conclusions: On the bottom section under the tab:

✎ Draw the Big Dipper and the North Star.
✎✎ Complete ✎. Describe how to locate the North Star.
✎✎✎ Complete ✎✎. Research the North Star and explain why it is so widely used for navigation.

Spark Questions: Discuss questions sparked by this lab.
New Loop: Choose one question to investigate further or make an *Investigative Loop* using this concept:
By facing the North Star, you can locate east, west, and south. Turn to face the North Star. North will be in front of you, south will be behind you, east to your right, and west to your left.

✎✎✎ **Design Your Own Experiment:** Select a topic based upon the experiences in the *Investigative Loop*. See page viii for more details.

Experiences, Investigations, and Research

Select one or more of the following activities for individual or group enrichment projects. Allow your students to determine the format in which they would like to report, share, or graphically present what they have discovered. This should be a creative investigation that utilizes your students' strengths.

1. Use Lab Graphic 3-1 as a guide to mark the stars with straight pins on dark felt or fabric. Sew buttons on as stars.

2. Research the names of the stars that make up the Big Dipper. Label them on your sewing project or on a sketch of the Big Dipper.

3. Read *Sally Ride: Shooting for the Stars* by Jane Hurwitz and Sue Hurwitz. ✎✎ ✎✎✎

4. http://www.casonline.org/ (Calumet Astronomical Society)

What is the Sun?

Space Concepts:

- The Sun is the center of our solar system.
- The Sun is a star. Like all stars, it gives off heat and light.
- It is not solid, but a huge ball of gases that is made of a core, photosphere, chromosphere, and corona.
- The Sun's diameter is about 865,000 miles (1,392,000 km).

Teacher's Note: An alternative assessment suggestion for this lesson is found on pages 82–84. If Graphic Pages are being consumed, photocopy the assessment graphics that are needed first.

Vocabulary:
heat light energy core sunspots *photosphere *chromosphere *corona *magnetic

corona
photosphere
core
chromosphere

Read: *Lots of Science Library Book #4.*

Activities:

Parts of the Sun – Graphic Organizer

Focus Skill: defining components

Paper Handouts: ✎ a copy of Graphic 4A–C ✎✎ ✎✎✎ a copy of Graphic 4A–B
9" x 12" sheet of yellow construction paper

Graphic Organizer: Make a Half Book from the yellow construction paper, turn it so the fold is on the left, and put it aside. Pinch and cut the dotted lines on Graphic 4A to make four tabs. Fold the tabs back and forth to create windows. Put glue on the back of Graphic 4A, being sure not to glue the openings made by the tabs. Glue Graphic 4A onto the cover of the Half Book. Do not glue the tabs shut. Glue Graphic 4B or copy the poem "The Sun: Inside and Out" inside the Half Book.

✎ Cut Graphic 4C into four words, and glue the correct words on each tab: *core, photosphere, chromosphere, corona.* Review the parts of the Sun.

✎✎ Write/copy the parts of the Sun under each tab. Write clue words about each part inside the Half Book.

✎✎✎ Complete ✎✎. Inside the Sun Half Book, write characteristics of the Sun.

Penny-Sized Sun

Focus Skill: drawing conclusions

Activity Materials: penny

Activity: One person holds up the penny, as shown. Another person will stand in front of the penny, facing it. Carefully back away from the penny. Discuss the activity. What happens as you back away from the penny? Does the penny appear smaller as you step farther away? Did the size of the penny change? What can you conclude about the size of the Sun from this activity?

Investigative Loop – Colorful Sunset Lab 4–1

Focus Skill: explaining a concept
Lab Materials: a clear glass one-gallon container water bleach flashlight
Paper Handouts: 8.5" x 11" sheet of paper a copy of Lab Graphic 4-1
Graphic Organizer: Make a Large Question and Answer Book. Glue it side–by–side to the Lab Book. Glue Lab Graphic 4–1 on the left tab.

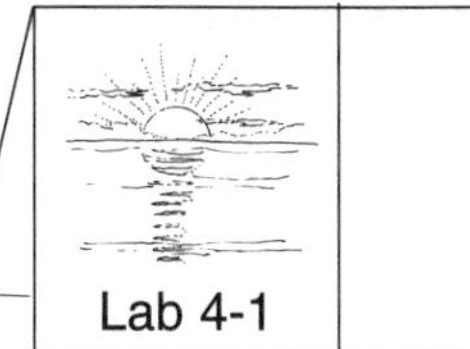

Question: Why are sunsets colorful?
Research: Read the *Lots of Science Library Book #4* and review the Question.
Procedure: Add water to the gallon container until it is half full. Add 1 tablespoon of bleach, and mix well. Although you cannot see the bleach in the water, it acts like the tiny particles in Earth's atmosphere. The flashlight represents the Sun and the water represents Earth's atmosphere. Set the gallon container on the table. Shine the flashlight at the top of the gallon container as someone faces the container, eyes level with the water. Gradually move the flashlight down toward the table while shining the light in the container. At the same time, the observer will gradually move upward, looking through the water. Trade positions and complete the activity again.
Observations: What was observed through the "atmosphere"? What colors appeared and in what order?
Record the Data: On the inside top section, under the tab, write the observations.
Conclusions: What does this lab indicate about the setting of the Sun? Why do colors appear?
Possible answer: As the light goes down, the person is looking through a thicker atmosphere, causing colors to appear. As the Sun appears to move lower in the sky, its light is going through a dense atmosphere to reach Earth's surface.
Communicate the Conclusions: On the lower section, write a description of a sunset using the concepts observed in this lab.
Spark Questions: Discuss any questions sparked by this lab.
New Loop: Choose one question to investigate further.
✎✎✎ **Design Your Own Experiment:** Select a topic based upon the experiences in the *Investigative Loop*. See page viii for more details.

Timeline

Paper Handouts: Space Timeline Book a copy of Graphics 4D–F
Graphic Organizer: Glue Graphics 4D–F to the correct pages in the Space Timeline Book.

Experiences, Investigations, and Research

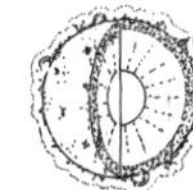
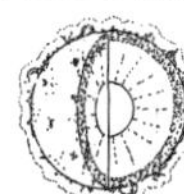
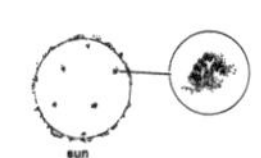

Select one or more of the following activities for individual or group enrichment projects. Allow your students to determine the format in which they would like to report, share, or graphically present what they have discovered. This should be a creative investigation that utilizes your students' strengths.

1. This activity requires adult supervision. Go outside with a magnifying glass and a piece of chocolate. Tip the magnifying glass at an angle to capture the rays of the Sun and direct them onto the chocolate. Describe what happens.

2. Take time to view a sunrise or sunset. Explain how and why the sky changes color.

3. Read and discuss *The Day We Saw the Sun Come Up* by Alice Goudey. ✎ ✎✎

4. Read *Amy Loves the Sun* by Julia Hoban. ✎✎ ✎✎✎

What are galaxies?

Space Concepts:

- A galaxy is a huge collection of stars, dust, and gas held together by gravity.
- Galaxies are classified into three general categories: irregular, elliptical, and spiral.
- Earth is located on one of the spiral arms of the Milky Way galaxy.
- Distances in space are measured in light–years. A light–year is the distance light travels in one year, about 5.9 trillion miles (9.5 trillion km) a year at approximately 186,000 miles (299,338 km) per second.

Teacher's Note: An alternative assessment suggestion for this lesson is found on pages 82–84. If Graphic Pages are being consumed, photocopy the assessment graphics that are needed first.

Vocabulary:
stars galaxy cluster spiral Milky Way *irregular *elliptical *light–year

Read:
Lots of Science Library Book #5.

Activities:

Types of Galaxies – Graphics Organizer

Focus Skill: defining
Paper Handouts: 8.5" x 11" sheet of paper
a copy of Graphics 5A–C
Graphic Organizer: Make a Hot Dog 3 Tab Book. Glue a graphic on each tab. Under each tab:

✎ Write/copy the name of each type of galaxy: *irregular, elliptical, spiral.* Draw an example under the name.

✎✎ Complete ✎. Write clue words about each galaxy:
irregular galaxy– no set shape, many new stars
elliptical galaxy – egg–shaped, very old stars
spiral galaxy – arms from a central bulge, old and new stars

✎✎✎ Complete ✎✎. Research the three types of galaxies and find an example of each type.

Investigative Loop – Spiraling Galaxy Lab 5–1

Focus Skill: observing
Lab Materials: hole puncher various colored construction paper (or confetti)
1 quart jar water
Paper Handouts: Lab Book a copy of Lab Graphic 5–1
Graphic Organizer: Glue Lab Graphic 5–1 on the right tab.
Concept: The stars in a spiral galaxy have arms that swirl.

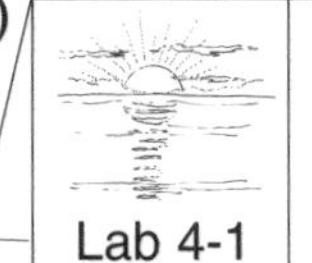
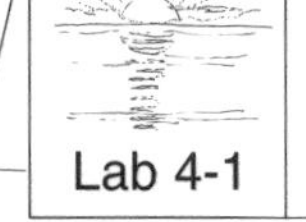

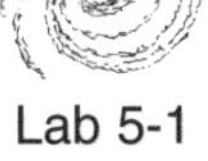

Research: Read *Lots of Science Library Book #5* and review spiral galaxies.

Procedure: Using the hole puncher, cut out about 30 colored circles, or use confetti. Fill the jar half full of water. Drop the colored circles in the water. Gently stir the water.

Observations: When the colored circles are moving in a swirling manner, observe their design. Are the colored circles in the swirling arms all on one level or in several levels?

Record the Data: Identify the type of galaxy that most closely resembles the paper in the jar.

Conclusions: What does this lab show about the Milky Way?

Communicate the Conclusions: Write your conclusions under the tab in the Lab Book.

Spark Questions: Discuss any questions sparked by this lab.

New Loop: Choose one question to investigate further.

✎✎✎ **Design Your Own Experiment:** Select a topic based upon the experiences in the *Investigative Loop*. See page viii for more details.

Timeline

Paper Handouts: Space Timeline Book a copy of Graphics 5D–E

Graphic Organizer: Glue Graphics 5D–E to the correct pages in the Space Timeline Book.

Experiences, Investigations, and Research

Select one or more of the following activities for individual or group enrichment projects. Allow your students to determine the format in which they would like to report, share, or graphically present what they have discovered. This should be a creative investigation that utilizes your students' strengths.

1. Using a marker, draw different types of galaxies on a large balloon. Blow up the balloon. What happens to the galaxies on the balloon as you inflate it? Investigate how this represents galaxies in space. The galaxies on the balloons move apart, just as they do in space.

2. Read *A Wind in the Door* by Madeleine L'Engle. ✎✎✎

3. Explain why galaxies are sometimes described as "islands in an ocean of space."

4. Make a galaxy timeline that outlines what we know about galaxies and when we discovered it.

5. Until the twentieth century, mankind thought the Milky Way galaxy was space in total. How did the discovery of the Andromeda galaxy, and then thousands of other galaxies, change attitudes as well as science?

6. Find an amateur astronomer who would be willing to help you go on a galaxy search. The Andromeda Galaxy, the brightest galaxy visible from the Northern Hemisphere, can be seen with binoculars as a blur of soft light, if one knows exactly where to look.

7. In 1986, a group of astronomers led by Margaret Geller discovered that galaxies tend to cluster. Use the Internet to discover the latest information on "galaxy clusters" and "superclusters."

8. Research the Milky Way. Sketch and label the parts of the Milky Way.

Notes

Space Concept Map

Lessons 6-20

Numbers Refer to Lesson Numbers

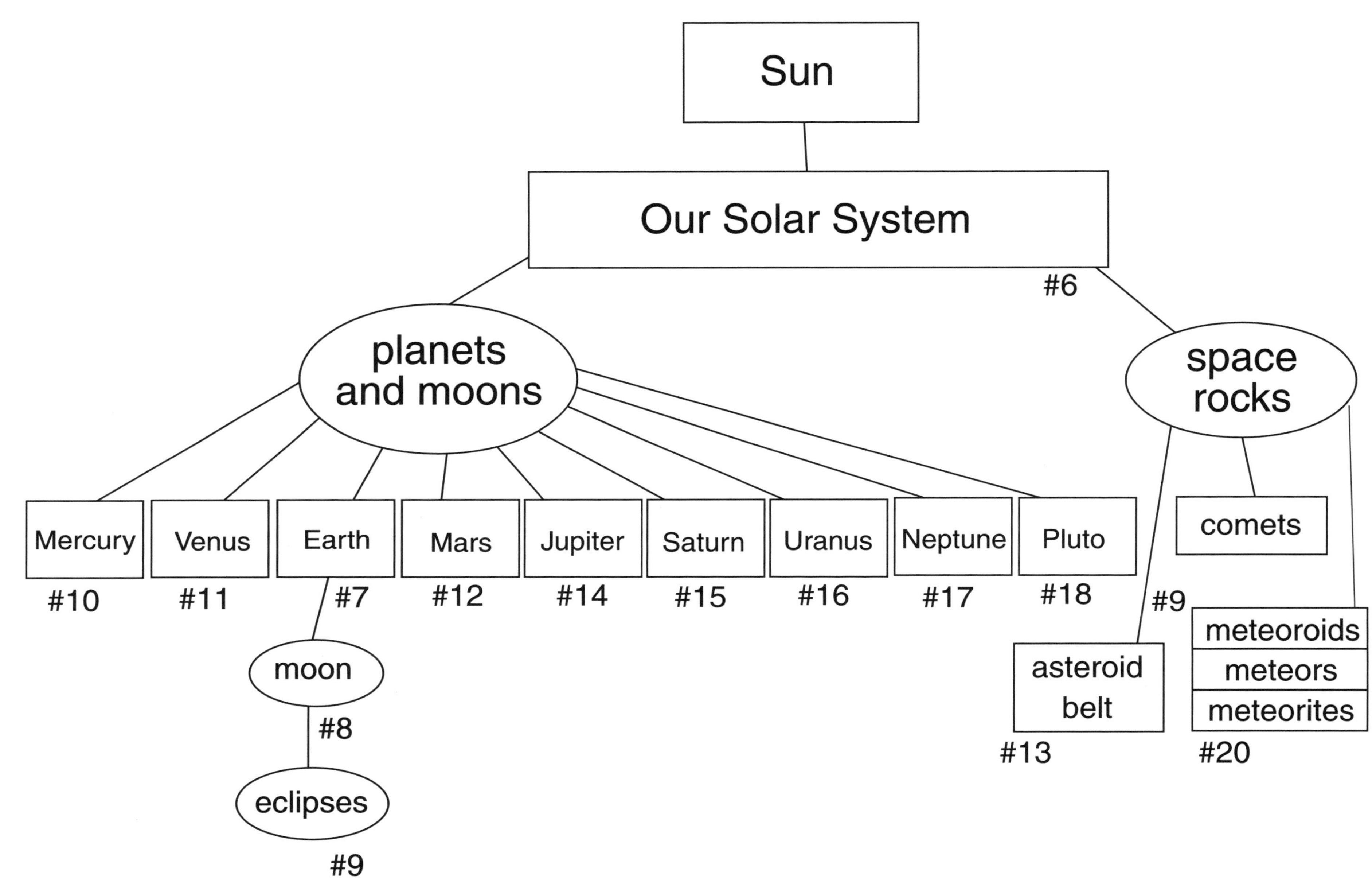

What is the solar system?

Space Concepts:

- The planets, moons, and asteroids orbiting the Sun make up our solar system.
- The first four planets are the solid, inner planets: Mercury, Venus, Earth, and Mars.
- The next four planets are the gaseous, outer planets: Jupiter, Saturn, Uranus, and Neptune.
- Distant Pluto is a very small solid planet.
- All planets revolve around the Sun and rotate on their own axis, while the entire solar system circles the Milky Way in a counterclockwise motion.

Vocabulary: solar system planet moon axis orbit rotate *asteroid *revolution *rotation

Read: *Lots of Science Library Book #6.*

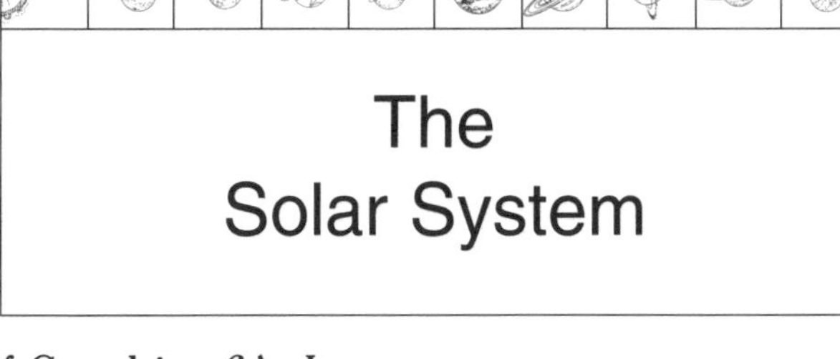

Activities:

The Solar System – Graphics Organizer

Focus Skill: recording data
Paper Handouts: 12 sheets of 8.5" x 11" paper a copy of Graphics 6A–J
Graphic Organizer: Make a 10 Tab Book, using the directions on page 5. Glue Graphic 6A, the Sun, on the first tab on the left. Glue Graphics 6B–J on the remaining tabs in the correct order.

The Sun – Graphic Organizer

Focus Skills: research, organizing information
Paper Handouts: Solar System Tab Book a copy of Graphics 6K–L
Graphic Organizer: On the Sun page of the Solar System Tab Book, glue Graphic 6 on the left side. Label the parts of the Sun, using information from the Lab Book. Glue Graphic 6L on the right side. Fill in the information about the Sun using *Lots of Science Library Book #4.*

Diameter: **865,000 miles/1,392,000 km**
Core Temperature: 30 million ºF/16,600,000 ºC
How heat and light are produced: **Inside the core, the transformation of hydrogen into helium produces heat and light.**
How long it takes light to travel to Earth: **8 minutes and 20 seconds**

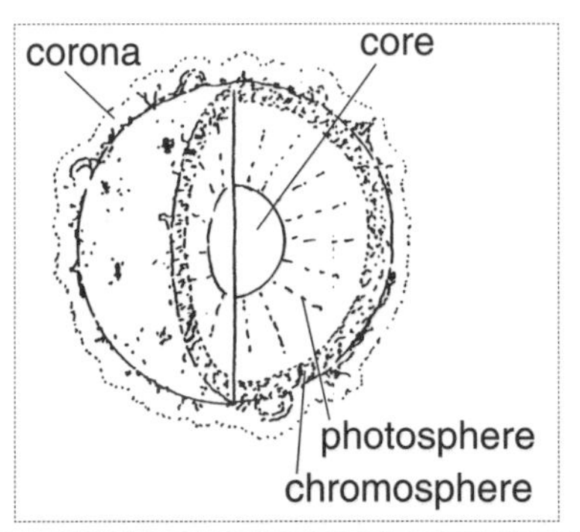

Fruity, Seedy Planets

Focus Skill: illustrating a concept
Activity Materials: grapefruit large orange two plums three peppercorns two peas index cards
Activity: Write the name of each planet on an index card. Arrange the items in the following order and place the correct index card next to it.

Peppercorn – Mercury	Large orange – Saturn	Pea – Venus
Plum – Uranus	Pea – Earth	Plum – Neptune
Peppercorn – Mars	Peppercorn – Pluto	Grapefruit – Jupiter

Observation Questions: Which planet is the largest? How many Earths do you think it would take to make one Jupiter? How many Mercurys do you think it would take to make one Saturn?

Distances From the Sun

Focus Skills: measuring, illustrating a concept
Paper Handouts: a copy of Graphic 6M
Activity Materials: basketball tape measure
Activity materials used in the Fruity, Seedy Planets activity
Activity: Place the basketball Sun at the end of a large field or parking lot. Use the chart of Graphic 6M to create a model of the Solar System.

Fruity, Seedy Planet	Distance from the basketball Sun
Peppercorn – Mercury	5 inches (12 cm)
Pea – Venus	9 inches (22 cm)
Pea – Earth	12 inches (30 cm)
Peppercorn – Mars	18 inches (46 cm)
Grapefruit – Jupiter	61 inches (156 cm)
Large orange – Saturn	112 inches (286 cm)
Plum – Uranus	226 inches (574 cm)
Plum – Neptune	354 inches (900 cm)
Peppercorn – Pluto	465 inches (1180 cm)

My Monster Named Zanet – Story and Graphic Organizer

Focus Skill: memorizing information
Read the poem: *Hungry Space Monster* by Dinah Zike

I imagine a monster whom I call Zanet,
Whose favorite snacks are moons and their planets!
My monster's as fierce as Godzilla or worse.
He spends his days traveling the Universe.
He is seeking a delicious, crunchy treat,
But in outer space there isn't much to eat.
So this monster gets hungrier every day.
If he doesn't eat something, he'll waste away.
He's too small to eat galaxies or their stars
But to him, the planets look like candy bars.
Help! Our Solar System comes into his view!
He's eating the planets and all their moons, too!
To remember the order of each planet,
Memorize this nine word phrase about Zanet:
My Very Empty Monster Just Swallowed Up Nine Planets.

Paper Handouts: 8.5" x 11" sheet of paper a copy of Graphic 6N
Graphic Organizer: Make a Half Book. Glue Graphic 6N on the cover. Inside, write/copy this humorous mnemonic to remember the planets in order from the Sun:
My **V**ery **E**mpty **M**onster **J**ust **S**wallowed **U**p **N**ine **P**lanets

My – Mercury
Very – Venus
Empty – Earth
Monster – Mars
Just – Jupiter
Swallowed - Saturn
Up - Uranus
Nine - Neptune
Planets - Pluto

Experiences, Investigations, and Research

Select one or more of the following activities for individual or group enrichment projects. Allow your students to determine the format in which they would like to report, share, or graphically present what they have discovered. This should be a creative investigation that utilizes your students' strengths.

1. To get an idea of our solar system's size, investigate *Voyager 2's* journey through our solar system and beyond.

2. Use the Internet to investigate the discovery of other "solar systems" in our galaxy. Use what you learn to compare and contrast our solar system with another solar system.

3. Define "heliocentric" and describe a heliocentric solar system.

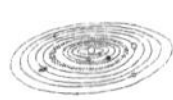

4. Hypothesize as to why all the inner planets are solid and the outer planets are gaseous.

5. http://www.jpl.nasa.gov/

6. http://www.seds.org/nineplanets/nineplanets/nineplanets.html

Notes

What do we know about Earth?

Space Concepts:

- Earth is the third planet from the Sun, about 93 million miles (150 billion km) from it.
- Earth's orbital position is "just right." It is neither too close nor too distant from the Sun for life to exist.
- Earth's rotation takes about 24 hours; and its orbit takes about 365 days.
- Earth's surface is about 79% water and 21% land.
- Earth has a protective atmosphere that surrounds the planet.
- Earth is composed of a center core of solid iron surrounded by a layer of liquid iron, a soft rock mantle, and a thin, rocky crust.
- Earth's diameter is about 7,926 miles (12,753 km).

Vocabulary:
Earth atmosphere spin *organic *inorganic *hemisphere *circumference

Read:
Lots of Science Library Book #7.

Activities:

Earth in the Solar System – Graphic Organizer

Focus Skills: research, recording data, organizing information

Paper Handouts: Solar System Top Tab Book made in Lesson 6
a copy of Graphics 7A–B

Graphic Organizer: On the Earth page of the Top Tab Book, glue Graphic 7A on the far left side and label each part of Earth: *core, mantle, crust.* Glue Graphic 7B on the right. This will leave space in the middle for a graphic to be added in Lesson 8. Fill in the information chart for Earth using the *Lots of Science Library Book #7.*

Under Graphics 7A–B:

✎ Write/copy the word *Earth.*

✎✎ Explain two new facts you learned about Earth in this lesson.

✎✎✎ Complete ✎✎. Research Earth and add two more new facts to the explanation.

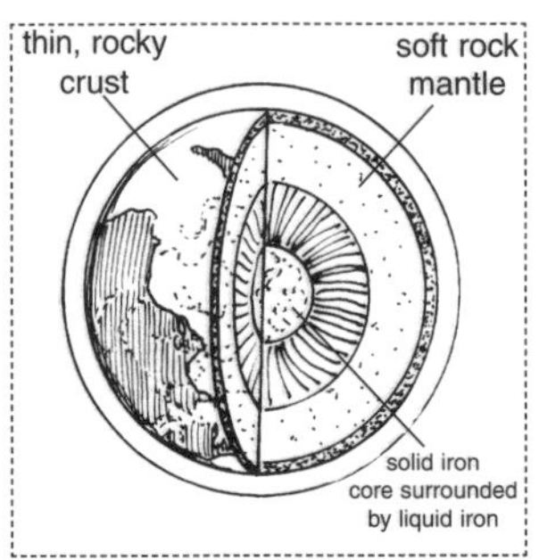

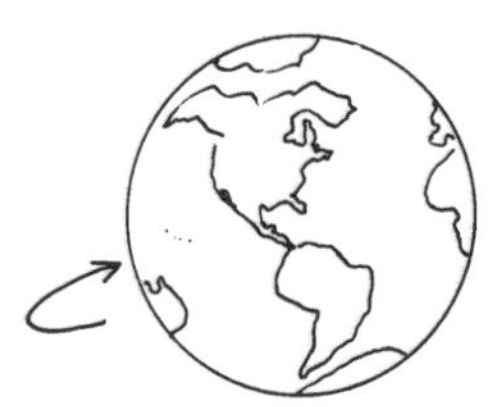

Distance from Sun: **93 million miles / 150 billion km**

Diameter: **7,926 miles / 12,753 km**

Rotation: **24 hours**

Revolution: **365 days**

Surface: **79% water / 21% land**

Known Moons: **1**

Interesting Information: **answers will vary**

Distances from the Sun

If you did not complete this activity in Lesson 6, complete it now for the Sun and Earth only. See Lesson 6 for specific information.

Investigative Loop – Day and Night   Lab 7–1

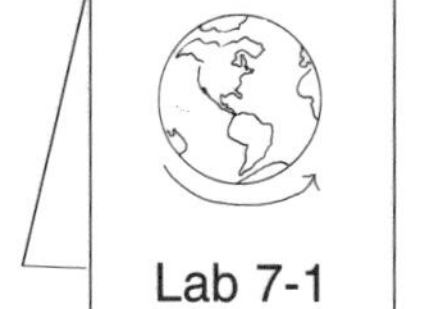

Focus Skill: draw a conclusion based on observations

Lab Materials: tennis ball   flashlight

Paper Handouts: 8.5" x 11" sheet of paper   a copy of Lab Graphic 7–1

Graphic Organizer: Make a Large Question and Answer Book. Glue it side–by–side to the Lab Book. Glue Graphic 7–1 on the left tab.

Concept: Earth experiences days and nights.

Research: Read *Lots of Science Library Book #7* and review the concept.

Procedure: The ball represents Earth and the flashlight represents the Sun. Hold the ball with your fingertips. Ask someone to shine the flashlight directly at the ball. Slowly turn Earth counterclockwise.

Observations: What is observed on the surface of the Earth that faces the sun? What happens to the surface of the Earth on the other side?

Record the Data: Draw a picture of the lab on the top section under the tab, with an emphasis on how the light shines on the ball.

Conclusions: Draw a conclusion from your observations.

Communicate the Conclusions: On the bottom section under the tab, explain how and why we experience days and nights on Earth.

Spark Questions: Discuss any questions sparked by this lab.

New Loop: Choose one question to investigate further.

✎✎✎ **Design Your Own Experiment:** Select a topic based upon the experiences in the *Investigative Loop*. See page viii for more details.

Sun and Shadow

Focus Skills: observing, recording data

Activity Materials: yardstick or wooden dowel   modeling clay   marker   newspaper   rocks

Activity: Find an open area and lay out newspapers. Weight the edges with rocks so they do not blow away. Form the clay into a ball to make a base. Stick the yardstick or wooden dowel in the clay. Hold the yardstick on end in the middle of the newspaper. The yardstick will make a shadow. Using a marker, trace the shadow of the yardstick. Every 30 minutes, repeat the same procedure. At the end of three hours, observe the shadow markings.

Discuss the Activity: Was there a pattern in the shadows? What can be concluded from the observations? **Possible answer: The shadows move in a clockwise direction because of Earth's rotation.**

Experiences, Investigations, and Research

Select one or more of the following activities for individual or group enrichment projects. Allow your students to determine the format in which they would like to report, share, or graphically present what they have discovered. This should be a creative investigation that utilizes your students' strengths.

1. Read *Journey to the Center of the Earth* by Jules Verne. ✎✎✎

2. Read *Journey to the Center of the Earth* by Raymond James (Troll illustrated classic). ✎✎ ✎✎✎

3. Travel back in time to debate the following: "Earth is the center of the universe."

4. Explain the "Goldilocks Theory" as it relates to Earth. "Earth is neither too hot nor cold, nor too large or small; Earth is just right."

5. Define *ellipse* and explain how it can be used to describe Earth.

6. Use the Internet to gather information on Earth's yearly average high and low temperatures. Make a table to record past and present averages. Are there any changes? Are changes predicted?

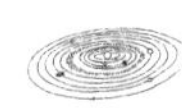
7. Why do people joke that "Earth" should have been called "Ocean"?

8. Explain: "Planet Earth is made of matter not commonly found in the Universe." Nearly everything known in the universe is dark matter, degenerate matter, or plasma. Of these three, Earth has only a small amount of plasma; so its composition is rare.

9. http://www.nasm.edu/ceps/ (Smithsonian National Air and Space Museum, Center for Earth and Planetary Studies)

Notes

Great Science Adventures

Lesson 8

What do we know about the Moon?

Space Concepts:

- The Moon is Earth's natural satellite.
- It is about $1/4$ the size of Earth.
- It does not have light of its own, but reflects the light of the Sun.
- It revolves around Earth and rotates on its axis at approximately the same speed; therefore, the same side of the moon always faces Earth.
- The Moon is always round, but appears to change shape because we see its sunlight side from different angles as it revolves around Earth. These regular size and shape changes are called phases.

Vocabulary: moon sky reflect satellite phases *luminous *crescent moon *full moon *waning *waxing

Read: *Lots of Science Library Book #8.*

Activities:

Solar System Top Tab Book – Graphic Organizer

Focus Skill: recording information
Paper Handouts: Solar System Top Tab Book a copy of Graphic 8A
Graphic Organizer: On the Earth page, glue Graphic 8A and record the information about Earth's Moon using the *Lots of Science Library Book #8.*

Investigative Loop – The Moon is not Luminous Lab 8–1

Lab 7-1 Lab 8-1

Focus Skill: compare and contrast
Lab Materials: mirror hand lotion flashlight
Paper Handouts: Lab Book a copy of Lab Graphic 8–1
Graphic Organizer: Glue Lab Graphic 8-1 on the right tab.
Concept: Earth and the Moon reflect the light of the Sun.
Research: Read *Lots of Science Library Book #8* and review the Concept.
Procedure: Look at a mirror in a dark room. The mirror is not luminous because it does not produce its own light. Shine a flashlight onto the mirror. Rub hand lotion on the mirror. Shine the light onto the lotion–covered mirror.
Observations: Describe the mirror without the flashlight shining on it. Describe the reflection of the light without the lotion on the mirror. Describe the reflection with the light with the lotion on the mirror. How is the reflection the same? How is it different?
Record the Data: Draw the three phases of the lab on the top section under the tab: 1) mirror without flashlight 2) mirror with flashlight 3) lotion on mirror with flashlight
Write clue words under each drawing.

Conclusions: Draw conclusions about the types of reflections each body has in space and why.
Possible answers: The Moon reflects light like the mirror with lotion on it. Earth reflects light like the mirror without the lotion.

Communicate the Conclusions: On the bottom section under the tab, write your conclusions using *Lots of Science Library Book #8,* if needed.

Spark Questions: Discuss questions sparked by this lab.

New Loop: Choose one question to investigate further.

✎✎✎ **Design Your Own Experiment:** Select a topic based upon the experiences in the *Investigative Loop*. See page viii for more details.

Investigative Loop – Craters on the Moon Lab 8–2

Focus Skill: compare and contrast

Lab Materials: plaster of Paris™ water tray bowl spoon rock ruler

Lab 8-2

Note: This activity can be messy, so complete it outside or place newspaper under the tray. Also, do not pour plaster down the drain.

Paper Handouts: 8.5" x 11" sheet of paper a copy of Lab Graphic 8–2 Lab Book

Graphic Organizer: Make a Large Question and Answer Book. Glue it side–by–side to the Lab Book. Glue Lab Graphic 8–2 on the left tab.

Question: How are Moon craters formed?

Research: Read *Lots of Science Library Book #8* and review craters on the Moon.

Prediction: Predict how craters were created on the moon. What do you think the size of the crater has to do with its creation? Write the prediction on the top section, under the tab in the Lab Book.

Procedure: Mix 2 cups of plaster of Paris with just enough water to make a consistency of thick batter. Work quickly so the plaster does not solidify. Spread the mixture onto the tray to represent the surface of the Moon. Fling the rock, which represents a meteorite, onto the tray.

Observations: Measure the crater and the rock to compare the sizes. Compare the size of the rock, or meteorite, to the size of the crater. How are they alike? How do they differ?

Record the Data: On the top section, under the tab, draw the lab. Record measurements taken during the lab.

Conclusions: Draw conclusions about Moon craters based on this lab. **Possible answer: The impact of the meteorite hitting the Moon causes a crater much larger than the meteorite itself.**

Communicate the Conclusions: Write the conclusions on the bottom section under the tab.

Spark Questions: Discuss questions sparked by this lab.

New Loop: Choose one question to investigate further.

✎✎✎ **Design Your Own Experiment:** Select a topic based upon the experiences in the *Investigative Loop*. See page viii for more details.

Moon Phases

Focus Skill: illustrating

Paper Handouts: pencil 30 pieces of paper (3" x 5") stapler Lab Book

Graphic Organizer: Store the paper in a legal–size envelope until the activity is completed.

Activity: Observe the Moon each night for the duration of its cycle, a little less than one month. Draw a picture of the Moon each night on a piece of paper. On the back of the paper, write the date. When the Moon cycle is completed, stack the papers in order and staple one end. Flip the pages to watch the phases of the Moon.

Timeline

Paper Handouts: Space Timeline Book a copy of Graphic 8B
Graphic Organizer: Glue Graphics 8B to the correct page in the Space Timeline Book.

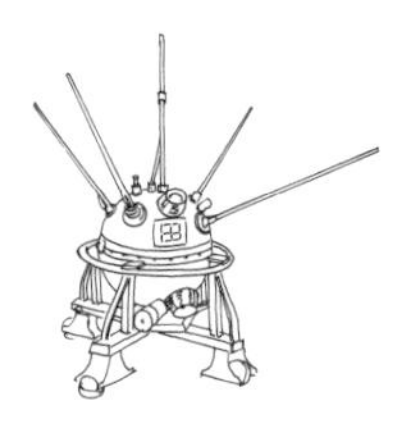

Experiences, Investigations, and Observations

Select one or more of the following activities for individual or group enrichment projects. Allow your students to determine the format in which they would like to report, share, or graphically present what they have discovered. This should be a creative investigation that utilizes your students' strengths.

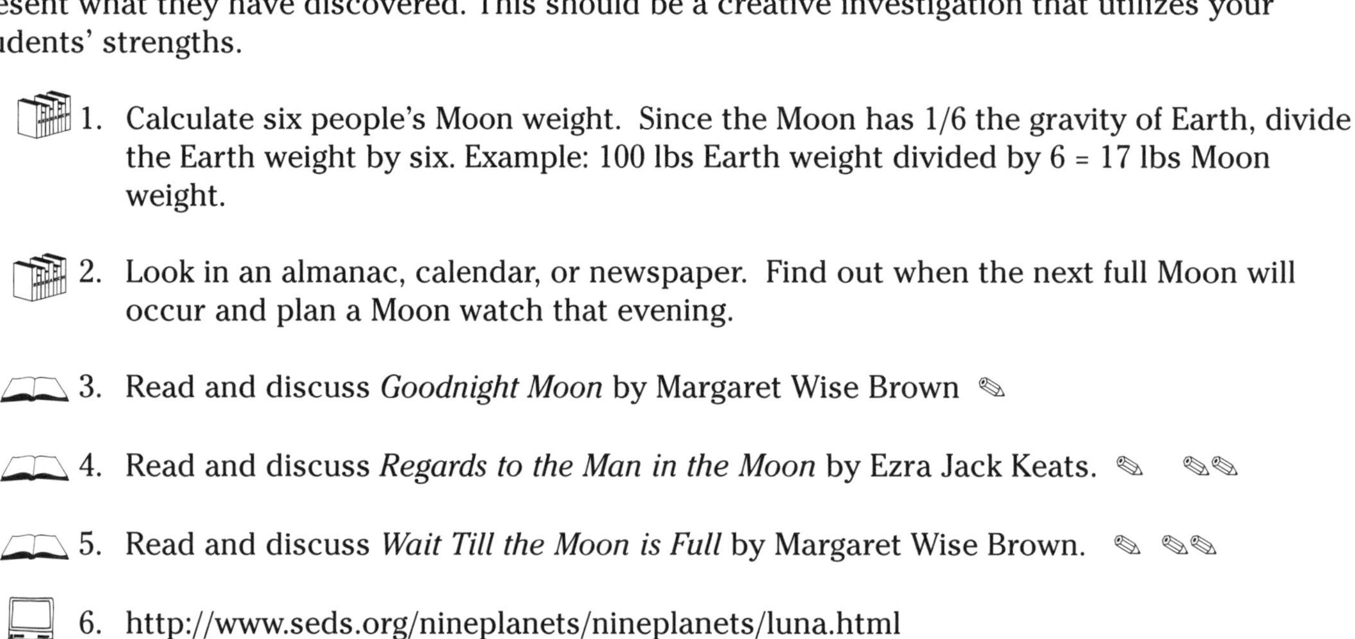

1. Calculate six people's Moon weight. Since the Moon has 1/6 the gravity of Earth, divide the Earth weight by six. Example: 100 lbs Earth weight divided by 6 = 17 lbs Moon weight.
2. Look in an almanac, calendar, or newspaper. Find out when the next full Moon will occur and plan a Moon watch that evening.
3. Read and discuss *Goodnight Moon* by Margaret Wise Brown ✎
4. Read and discuss *Regards to the Man in the Moon* by Ezra Jack Keats. ✎ ✎✎
5. Read and discuss *Wait Till the Moon is Full* by Margaret Wise Brown. ✎ ✎✎
6. http://www.seds.org/nineplanets/nineplanets/luna.html

Notes

Great Science Adventures

Lesson 9

What is an eclipse?

Space Concepts:

- When the Sun, Earth, and Moon line up and the Moon passes through Earth's shadow, a lunar eclipse occurs.
- When the Moon passes between Earth and the Sun, it blocks the Sun's light and casts a shadow on Earth, resulting in a solar eclipse.

Teacher's Note: An alternative assessment suggestion for this lesson is found on pages 82–84. If Graphic Pages are being consumed, photocopy the assessment graphics that are needed first.

Vocabulary: eclipse sunlight lunar solar *umbra *penumbra

Read: *Lots of Science Library Book #9.*

Activities:

Solar and Lunar Eclipse – Graphics Organizer

Focus Skill: recording information
Paper Handouts: 2 sheets of 8.5" x 11" paper a copy of Graphics 9A–D
Graphic Organizers: Make two Trifold Books. Glue Graphic 9A on one cover and Graphic 9B on the other cover. Open each Trifold Book and on the top section, draw the formation of the Sun, Earth, and Moon for each eclipse. Include shadows and sunlight in the drawings. On the middle section, glue Graphics 9C–D, appropriately. On the bottom section:

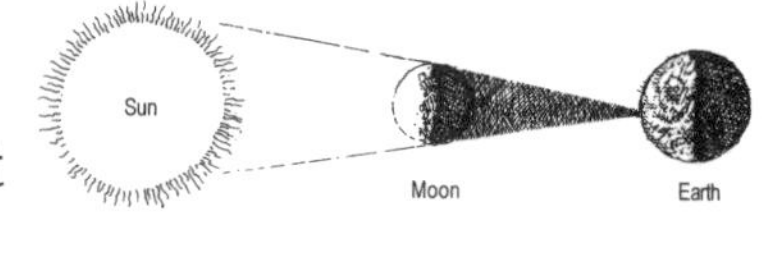

✎ Copy the words *Solar Eclipse* and *Lunar Eclipse* on the appropriate book.
✎✎ Describe each type of eclipse in two sentences.
✎✎✎ Research each type of eclipse and write an explanation of it.

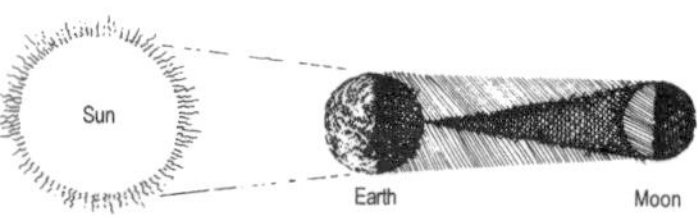

Investigative Loop – Lunar Eclipse Lab 9–1

Focus Skill: applying information
Lab Materials: styrofoam ball approximately $1^1/_2$ inches in diameter
styrofoam ball approximately 3 inches in diameter
modeling dough or putty desk lamp
2 wooden skewers strip of cardboard about 24" x 4"
Paper Handouts: Lab Book a copy of Lab Graphic 9–1
Graphic Organizer: Glue Lab Graphic 9–1 on the right tab.

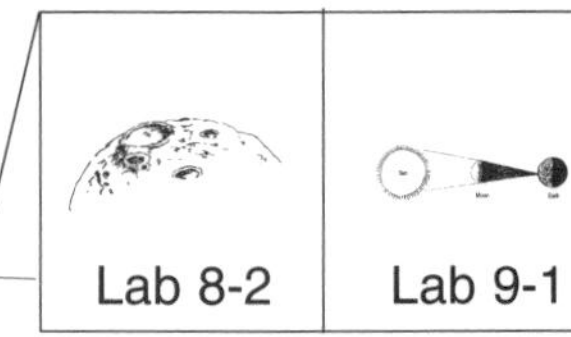

Concept: Observe how the Sun, Earth, and Moon line up during a lunar eclipse.
Research: Read *Lots of Science Library Book #9* and review the Concept.

Procedure: The large styrofoam ball represents Earth, the small styrofoam ball represents the Moon, and the lamp represents the Sun. Push a skewer into each ball. Form the dough into two balls to make bases for the skewers. Place Earth on one end of the cardboard strip and the Moon on the other end. Adjust the skewers so that the centers of the balls are at the same height. Place the lamp in front of Earth about 16" away. Adjust the lamp so that it is at the same height as the Earth and the Moon. Make a lunar eclipse by adjusting the cardboard strip and styrofoam balls.

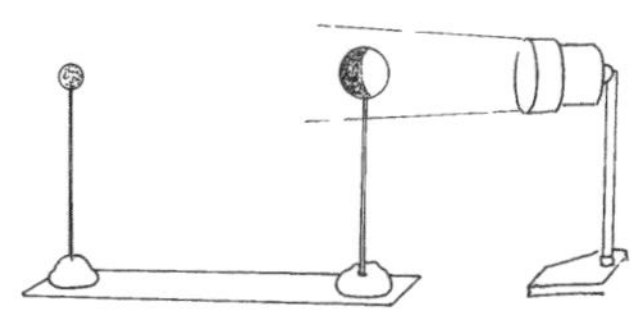

Observations: What are the positions of the Sun, Earth, and Moon to create a lunar eclipse?

Record the Data: Compare the pictures of a lunar eclipse in the *Lots of Science Library Book #9* with the lab. Make a drawing of the lab on the top section, under the tab.

Conclusions: Draw conclusions about a lunar eclipse based on the lab.

Communicate the Conclusions: On the bottom section, under the tab, explain a lunar eclipse.

Spark Questions: Discuss questions sparked by this lab.

New Loop: Choose one question to investigate further, or develop a New Loop with the following procedure.

Procedure: Form a 1-inch ball out of modeling dough to represent the Moon. Form a base with dough. Stick the skewer in the ball and stick it in to the base. Place the Moon on the table. Place a lamp, which represents the Sun, in front of the Moon at the same height. Place poster board behind the Moon. Turn on the lamp. The Moon's shadow is cast on the posterboard. With a pencil, mark the center of the shadow. Mark two points around the edge of the shadow. Using the skewer, punch a hole through these marks. Get behind the poster board and look through each hole.

✎✎✎ **Design Your Own Experiment:** Select a topic based upon the experiences in the *Investigative Loop*. See page viii for more details.

How Can the Small Moon Cover the Large Sun?

Focus Skill: inferring

Activity: Go outside with a partner and stand about 30' apart. Hold your finger straight in front of you and close one eye. Cover the image of your partner with your finger by walking forward or backward.

Discuss the Activity: Did your finger completely cover the image of your partner? Is your finger larger than your partner? Why did your finger cover a larger image? What does this explain about a solar eclipse?

Timeline Glue

Paper Handouts: Space Timeline Book   a copy of Graphic 9E

Graphic Organizer: Glue Graphic 9E to the correct page in the Space Timeline Book.

Experiences, Observations, and Research

Select one or more of the following activities for individual or group enrichment projects. Allow your students to determine the format in which they would like to report, share, or graphically present what they have discovered. This should be a creative investigation that utilizes your students' strengths.

1. Check an almanac to see if/when a lunar or solar eclipse is predicted this year.

2. Mark your calendar.

Total Lunar Eclipse Dates	Total Solar Eclipse Dates
Jan. 9, 2001	Jan. 21, 2001
May 16, 2003	Dec. 4, 2002
Nov. 8–9, 2003	Nov. 23, 2003
May 4, 2004	April 5, 2005
Oct. 28, 2004	March 29, 2006
March 3–4, 2007	Aug. 1, 2008
Aug. 28, 2007	July 22, 2009

3. Make a model depicting a lunar eclipse or a solar eclipse.

4. Survey twenty people and document how many have actually seen a solar eclipse and/or a lunar eclipse. Graph the results.

5. Find out how Christopher Columbus used his knowledge of eclipses to save his life and the lives of his men on the island of Jamaica.

6. http://sunearth.gsfc.nasa.gov/eclipse/eclipse.html

7. http://sunearth.gsfc.nasa.gov/eclipse/SEhelp/link.html#eclipse

Notes

What do we know about Mercury?

Space Concepts:

- Mercury is the closest planet to the Sun. It is about 36,000,000 miles (58,000,000 km) away.
- It is the second-smallest planet, less than half the size of Earth, about 3,030 miles (4,875 km) in diameter.
- Mercury is composed of a liquid iron core, a rocky molten mantle, and a thin, rocky crust.
- Its surface is about 50% craters and 50% plains.
- It has almost no atmosphere.
- Mercury has less than half of Earth's gravity.
- Its rotation is about 59 Earth days, and its orbit is about 88 Earth days.

Vocabulary: rocky mantle crater helium hydrogen *ellipse *elongated

Read: *Lots of Science Library Book #10.*

Activities:

Solar System Top Tab Book – Graphic Organizer

Focus Skills: researching, recording information, organizing data
Paper Handouts: Solar System Top Tab Book a copy of Graphics 10A–B
Graphic Organizer: On the Mercury page, glue Graphic 10A on the left side and label the parts of the planet. Glue Graphic 10B on the right side and fill in the information about Mercury.

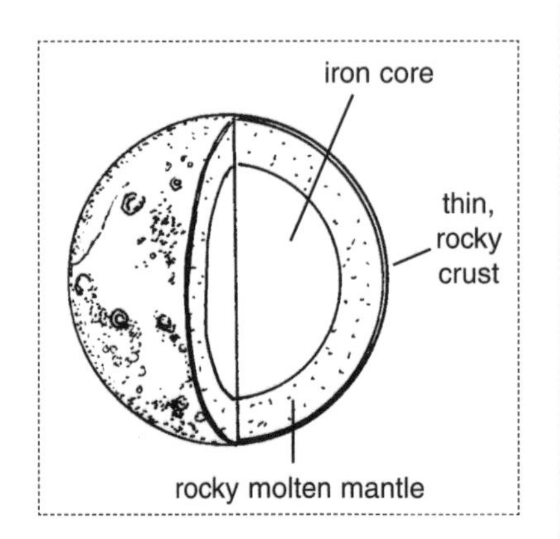

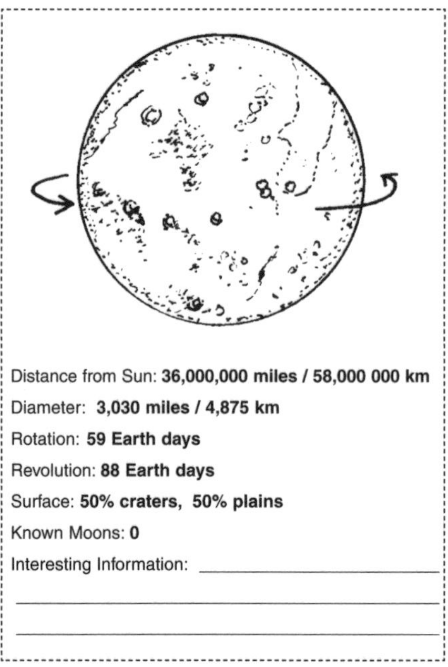

Mercury's Orbit

Note: This activity works best when one person is shorter than the other.
Focus Skill: demonstrating a concept
Activity Materials: 2 pieces of rope (8' and 20')
Activity: Use a clothesline pole, flagpole, or a tall, narrow tree. Loosely tie the shorter rope around the pole. Loosely tie the longer rope in a higher position around the pole. The shorter person should hold the short rope and walk around the pole. This represents Mercury's orbit. The taller person will hold the longer rope and walk around the pole. This represents an orbit of a more distant planet. The pole represents the Sun.
Discuss the Activity: Which planet completed its orbit first? Why do you think that happened?

Timeline

Paper Handouts: Space Timeline Book a copy of Graphic 10C
Graphic Organizer: Glue Graphic 10C to the correct page in the Space Timeline Book.

Experiences, Investigations, and Research

Select one or more of the following activities for individual or group enrichment projects. Allow your students to determine the format in which they would like to report, share, or graphically present what they have discovered. This should be a creative investigation that utilizes your students' strengths.

1. Since Mercury is much closer to the Sun than Earth, describe what you think the Sun looks like in Mercury's sky.

2. What do you think happens to the temperature on Mercury's surface when the Sun sets? What happens when the Sun rises? Research Mercury to confirm your ideas.

3. Compare and contrast the revolution of Mercury to the revolution of the other planets.

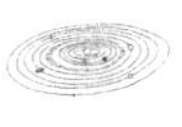

4. Use 3 pieces of paper to make a Bound Book. Entitle your journal "Solar System Weather Journal" and use one page for each planet. Record the weather conditions on Mercury on the first page. Record the weather conditions on Earth on the third page. Compare and contrast the weather conditions on Mercury and Earth. You may add information for other planets in future lessons.

5. Write about a situation in which you are the first person to visit Mercury. Imagine that new materials have been invented to make this trip possible. Describe these materials and explain how they help you, the visiting astronaut, to survive.

6. http://www.seds.org/nineplanets/nineplanets/mercury.html

What do we know about Venus?

Space Concepts:

- Venus is the second planet from the Sun, about 67,200,000 miles (108,100,000 km) away.
- It is about 7,500 miles (12,100 km) in diameter.
- Venus is composed of a semisolid metal core, a rocky mantle, and a thin, rocky crust.
- Its surface is the hottest of all the planets because of its gaseous clouds.
- Venus has a high atmospheric pressure.
- It has less gravity than Earth.
- Venus' rotation is about 243 Earth days. Its orbit is about 225 Earth days, so its day is longer than its year.

Vocabulary: diameter gaseous gravity *atmospheric pressure

Read: *Lots of Science Library Book #11.*

Activities:

Solar System Top Tab Book – Graphic Organizer

Focus Skills: researching, recording information, organizing data
Paper Handouts: Solar System Top Tab Book a copy of Graphics 11A–B
Graphic Organizer: On the Venus page, glue Graphic 11A on the left side and label the parts of the planet. Glue Graphic 11B on the right side and fill in the information about Venus.

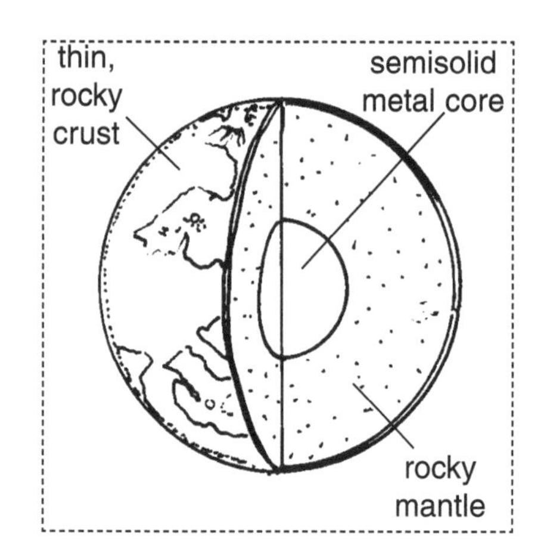

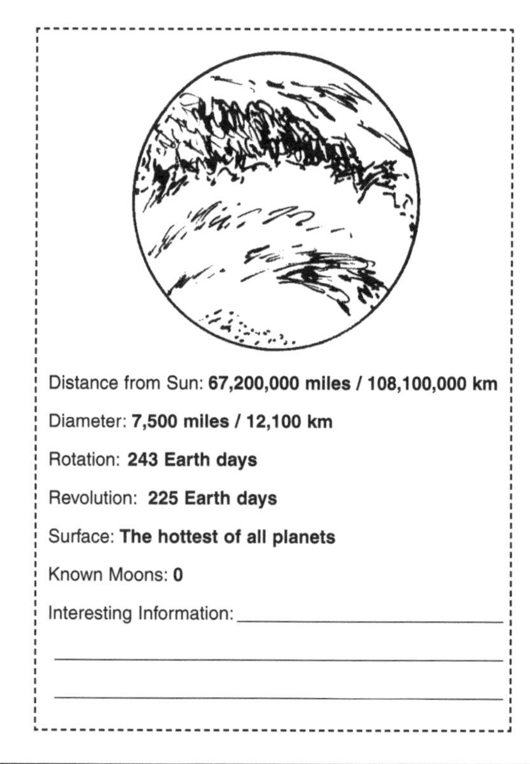

Compare Venus and Earth – Graphic Organizer

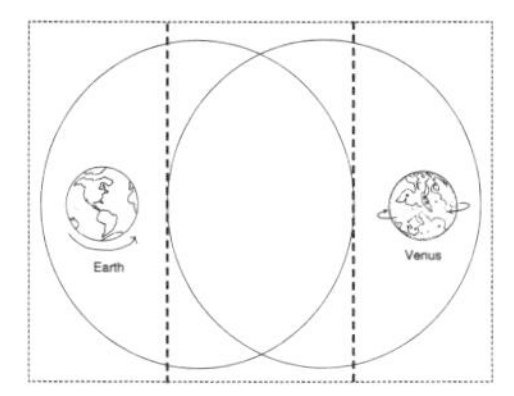

Focus Skill: comparing and contrasting
Paper Handouts: 8.5" x 11" sheet of paper a copy of Graphic 11C
Graphic Organizer: Make a Half Book. Glue Graphic 11C on the cover and cut on the dotted lines. Review *Lots of Science Library Books #7, #8,* and *#11.* Under the tabs:

✎ Draw a picture of Earth and Venus under the appropriate tabs. Write/dictate clue words about how Earth and Venus are alike under the middle tab.

✎✎ Write clue words about Earth and Venus under the appropriate tab. Write clue words about how Earth and Venus are alike under the middle tab.

✎✎✎ Research the two planets. Describe each planet under the appropriate tabs. Compare them under the middle tab.

Investigative Loop – Hot Venus Lab 11–1

Focus Skill: identifying variables
Lab Materials: 2 thermometers 2 glass jars plastic wrap rubber band
Paper Handouts: 8.5" x 11" sheet of paper a copy of Lab Graphic 11–1
Graphic Organizer: Make a Large Question and Answer Book. Glue it side–by–side to the Lab Book. Glue Lab Book Graphic 11–1 on the left tab of the Lab Book.

Lab 11-1

Question: Why is Venus the hottest planet?
Research: Read *Lots of Science Library Book #11* and review Venus' atmosphere.
Predictions: Predict how trapped gases affect the temperature of an atmosphere. Write your prediction on the top section under the tab.
Procedure: Place one thermometer in a glass jar and seal it with plastic wrap and a rubber band. Place the other thermometer in another jar. Place both jars in the sun.
Observations: Check the temperatures in the two jars after one hour. Check them every hour for the rest of the day.
Record the Data: On the bottom section, under the tab, record the temperatures. Make 2 graphs of the temperature changes in each jar.
Conclusions: Review the data. Draw conclusions about the effect of trapped gases on the temperature of an atmosphere.
Communicate the Conclusions: On the bottom section under the tab, write your conclusions about this lab. Include how this applies to the atmosphere of Venus.
Spark Questions: Discuss questions sparked by this lab.
New Loop: Choose one sparked question to investigate further.

✎✎✎ **Design Your Own Experiment:** Select a topic based upon the experiences in the *Investigative Loop*. See page viii for more details.

Timeline

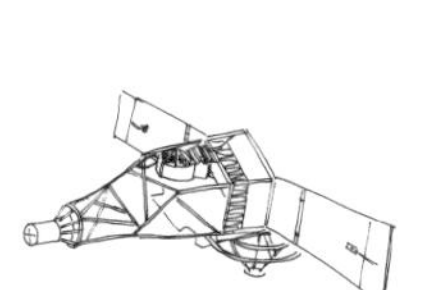

Paper Handouts: Space Timeline Book a copy of Graphic 11D
Graphic Organizer: Glue Graphic 11D to the correct page in the Space Timeline Book.

Experiences, Investigations, and Research

Select one or more of the following activities for individual or group enrichment projects. Allow your students to determine the format in which they would like to report, share, or graphically present what they have discovered. This should be a creative investigation that utilizes your students' strengths.

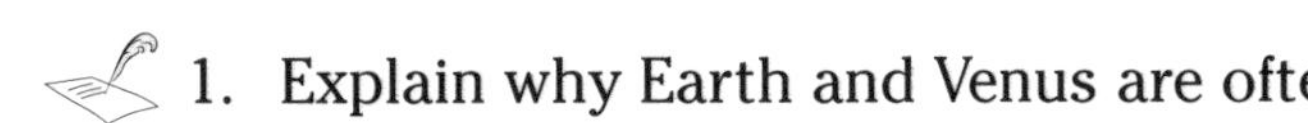

1. Explain why Earth and Venus are often referred to as sisters or "twins."

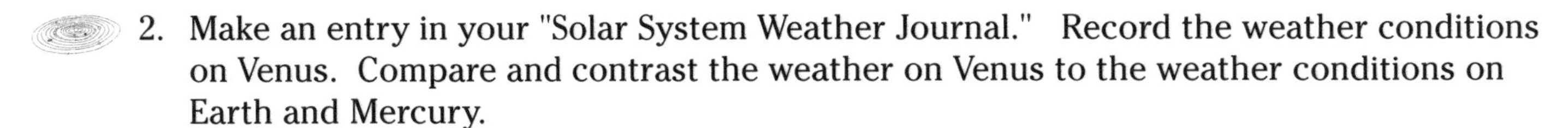

2. Make an entry in your "Solar System Weather Journal." Record the weather conditions on Venus. Compare and contrast the weather on Venus to the weather conditions on Earth and Mercury.
3. Explain why "the Morning Star" is not a star, but a planet, either Venus or Mercury.

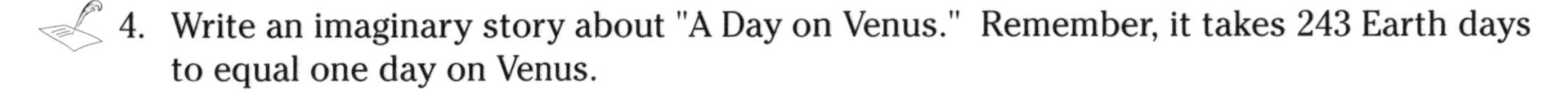

4. Write an imaginary story about "A Day on Venus." Remember, it takes 243 Earth days to equal one day on Venus.
5. Compare and contrast the surface of Venus to a greenhouse on Earth.

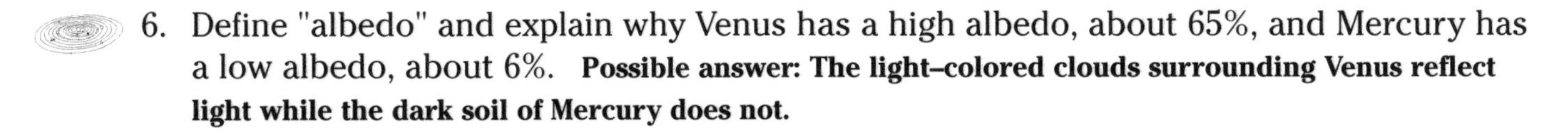

6. Define "albedo" and explain why Venus has a high albedo, about 65%, and Mercury has a low albedo, about 6%. **Possible answer: The light-colored clouds surrounding Venus reflect light while the dark soil of Mercury does not.**

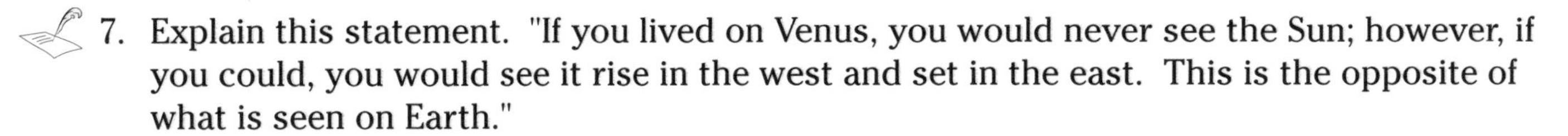

7. Explain this statement. "If you lived on Venus, you would never see the Sun; however, if you could, you would see it rise in the west and set in the east. This is the opposite of what is seen on Earth."
8. http://www.seds.org/nineplanets/nineplanets/venus.html

Notes

What do we know about Mars?

Space Concepts:

- Mars is the fourth planet from the Sun, about 141,600,000 miles (227,830,000 km) away.
- It is about 4,220 miles (6,790 km) in diameter.
- Mars is composed of a solid, rocky core, a thick, rocky mantle, and a solid, rocky crust.
- Its surface soil contains iron, giving it a red color.
- It has a thin atmosphere consisting primarily of carbon dioxide.
- Mars has less than half of Earth's gravity.
- Its rotation is about $24\frac{1}{2}$ Earth days, and its orbit is about 687 Earth days.
- Mars has two small moons.

Vocabulary: volcano

dust storm *carbon dioxide

Read: *Lots of Science Library Book #12.*

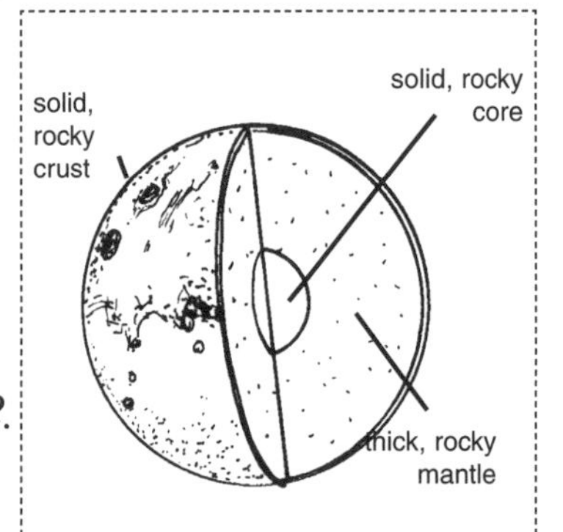

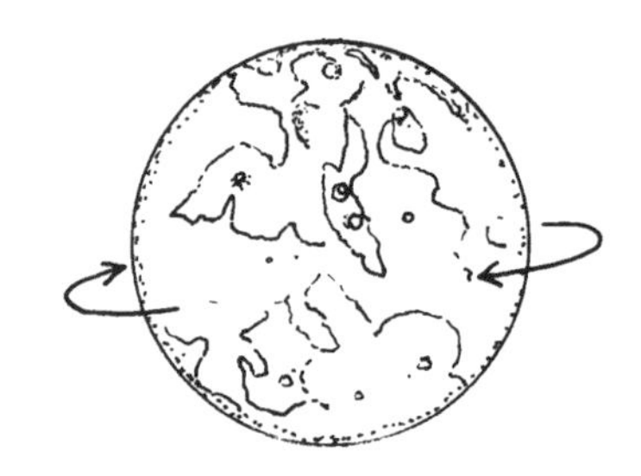

Distance from Sun: **141,600,000 miles / 227,830,000 km**

Diameter: **4,220 miles / 6,790 km**

Rotation: **24 3/4 Earth days**

Revolution: **687 Earth days**

Surface: **Iron in the soil gives a red color**

Known Moons: **2**

Interesting Information: ____________________

____

Activities:

Solar System Top Tab Book – Graphic Organizer

Focus Skills: researching, recording information, organizing data
Paper Handouts: Solar System Top Tab Book
a copy of Graphics 12A–B
Graphic Organizer: Glue Graphic 12A on the left side of the Mars page and label the parts of the planet. Glue Graphic 12B on the right side and fill in the information about Mars.
Note: Be sure to leave 2" on the far right side for an activity in Lesson 13.

Olympus Mons – Graphics Organizer

Focus Skill: compare and contrast
Paper Handouts: 8.5" x 11" sheet of paper a copy of Graphics 12C–E
9" x 12" sheet of red construction paper
Graphic Organizer: Make a Pop–Up Book with two tabs from the sheet of paper. Cut the first pop-up tabs 2" from the left edge, $3\frac{1}{2}$" long and $\frac{3}{4}$" wide. Cut the second pop-up tabs, $1\frac{1}{2}$" from the right edge, 2" long and $\frac{3}{4}$" wide. Glue Graphic 12C on the left pop–up tab and Graphic 12D on the right one. Make a Half Book from the red construction paper. Apply glue along the edges of the Pop–Up Book and firmly press inside the Half Book. On the cover, glue Graphic 12E or copy the poem "Martian Giants." Memorize the poem.
✎✎✎ Research Olympus Mons. Either orally or on the back of the Red Half Book, present data located in the research.

Investigative Loop – The Red Planet   Lab 12–1

Lab 11-1 Lab 12-1

Focus Skills: qualitative observations, drawing conclusions
Lab Materials: sand   steel wool   rubber gloves   baking dish
scissors
Paper Handouts: a copy of Lab Graphic 12–1   Lab Book
Graphic Organizer: Glue Lab Graphic 12–1 on the right tab.
Question: Why does Mars have a rusty red color?
Research: Read *Lots of Science Library Book #12* and review the Question.
Predictions: Predict why Mars has a red color. Write the prediction on the top section under the tab.
Procedure: Fill the baking dish half full of sand. Put on the rubber gloves and cut the steel wool into small pieces. Mix it in the sand. Pour just enough water to cover the sand mixture. Set aside and check it daily. Keep the sand mixture moist by adding water as needed.
Observations: Describe the appearance of the dirt each day.
Record the Data: Record your observations on the top section under the tab.
Conclusions: Review the data for this lab. Draw conclusions about the surface of Mars based on this lab and your knowledge of Mars.
Communicate the Conclusions: On the bottom section under the tab, write the conclusions of the lab. Option: Write the conclusions in first person as if you were the planet Mars.
Spark Questions: Discuss questions sparked by this lab.
New Loop: Choose one sparked question to investigate further.
✎✎✎ **Design Your Own Experiment:** Select a topic based upon the experiences in the *Investigative Loop*. See page viii for more details.

Testing Martian Soil

Focus Skill: evaluating results
Activity Materials: 3 glass containers   salt   yeast   baking powder   clean sand
sugar   permanent marker
Activity: With the permanent marker, label the containers A, B, and C. Fill each container a third full with sand. Add 3 tablespoons of salt to container A and mix. Add 3 tablespoons of baking powder to container B and mix. Add 3 tablespoons, or packages, of yeast to container C and mix. Place the containers in the refrigerator overnight, simulating the cold temperature on Mars.
On day two, mix 2 cups of warm water and $^1/_2$ cup sugar. Remove the containers from the refrigerator. Pour equal amounts of the sugar solution into each container.
After one hour, observe the containers. After three hours, observe the containers.
Discuss the Activity: Describe the solution in each container. Which container do you think contains life?
Teacher's Note: If living cells are present, such as in yeast, a reaction will occur slowly and continually as they multiply. Other chemicals may cause a reaction for a short period of time only.

Timeline

Paper Handouts: Space Timeline Book
a copy of Graphic 12G
Graphic Organizer: Glue Graphic 12G to the correct page in the Space Timeline Book.

Experiences, Investigations, and Research

Select one or more of the following activities for individual or group enrichment projects. Allow your students to determine the format in which they would like to report, share, or graphically present what they have discovered. This should be a creative investigation that utilizes your students' strengths.

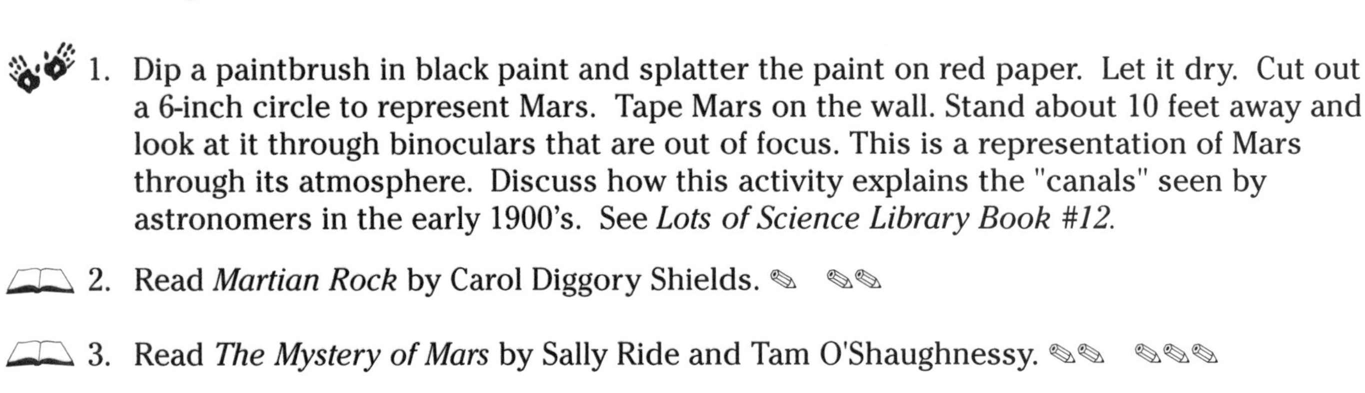

1. Dip a paintbrush in black paint and splatter the paint on red paper. Let it dry. Cut out a 6-inch circle to represent Mars. Tape Mars on the wall. Stand about 10 feet away and look at it through binoculars that are out of focus. This is a representation of Mars through its atmosphere. Discuss how this activity explains the "canals" seen by astronomers in the early 1900's. See *Lots of Science Library Book #12.*

2. Read *Martian Rock* by Carol Diggory Shields. ✎ ✎✎

3. Read *The Mystery of Mars* by Sally Ride and Tam O'Shaughnessy. ✎✎ ✎✎✎

4. Read *The War of the Worlds* by Robert Blaisdell (Dover Children's 1–1–Thrift Classics; abridged from H.G. Wells). ✎✎ ✎✎✎

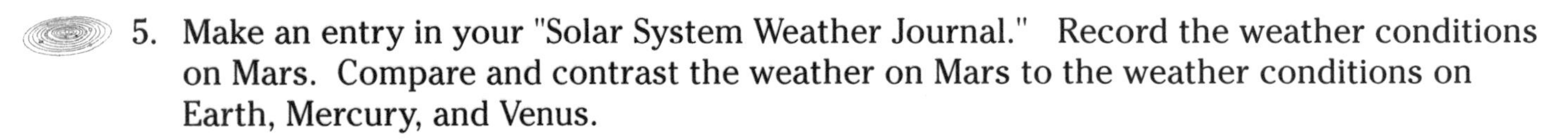

5. Make an entry in your "Solar System Weather Journal." Record the weather conditions on Mars. Compare and contrast the weather on Mars to the weather conditions on Earth, Mercury, and Venus.

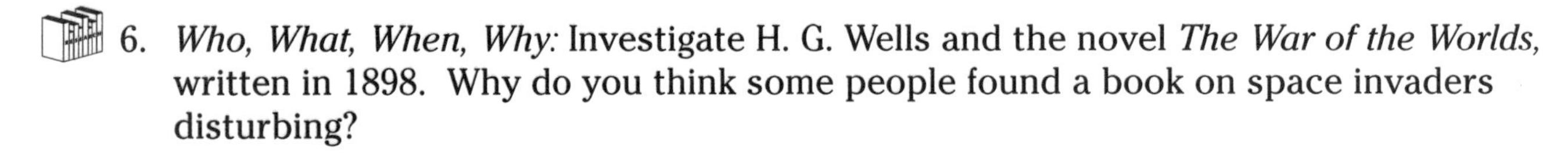

6. *Who, What, When, Why:* Investigate H. G. Wells and the novel *The War of the Worlds,* written in 1898. Why do you think some people found a book on space invaders disturbing?

7. At least 12 of the meteorites found on Earth are known to be crust broken away from Mars by impacts. Review current publications and use the Internet to discover more about these Martian meteorites and specifically the one that might show signs of fossilized microscopic life.

8. Compare and contrast the polar caps on Mars with the polar caps on Earth.

9. Research and report on any number of the gigantic geological features of Mars: Thargus Bulge, Olympus Mons, or Valles Marineris (Mariner Valley).

10. Explain the purpose of the *Mars Global Surveyor* (MGS) spacecraft currently in orbit around the planet.

11. http://www.seds.org/nineplanets/nineplanets/mars.html

12. http://spaceflight.nasa.gov/mars/index.html (NASA Exploring Mars)

Notes

Great Science Adventures

Lesson 13

What do we know about the asteroid belt?

Space Concepts:

- "Asteroid" comes from the Greek word meaning "starlike."
- The asteroid belt is between Mars and Jupiter and contains most of the asteroids in our solar system.
- Most asteroids are pebble–sized, but some are about the size of small cars.
- Asteroids are composed of metal, rock, or a combination of both and have varying reflective qualities, or albedo.
- There are three main types of asteroids:
    - About 75% of asteroids are C Type: They are composed mostly of carbon; they are dark because they have a low albedo (they do not reflect the Sun's light well); and most are found in the outer region of the asteroid belt.
    - About 17% of asteroids are S Type: They are composed of nickel, iron, and silicate; somewhat reddish in color with a high albedo; and found mostly in the inner region of the asteroid belt.
    - About 7% of asteroids are M Type: They are composed of nickel and iron; silvery in color, allowing them to reflect sunlight well; and found mostly in the middle region of the asteroid belt.

Teacher's Note: An alternative assessment suggestion for this lesson is found on pages 82–84. If Graphic Pages are being consumed, photocopy the assessment graphics that are needed first.

Vocabulary: carbon nickle belt *albedo

Read: *Lots of Science Library Book #13.*

Activities:

Solar System Top Tab Book - Graphic Organizer

Focus Skills: researching and recording information
Paper Handouts: Solar System Top Tab Book a copy of Graphics 13A
Graphic Organizer: On the Mars page, glue Graphic 13A on the far right side and label it *Asteroid Belt.*

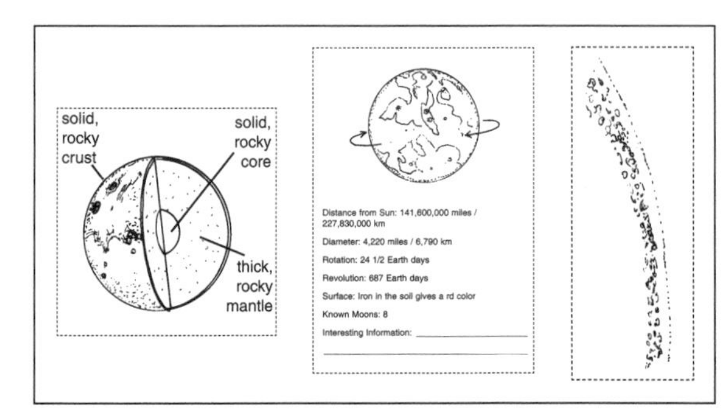

Asteroid Riddle – Graphic Organizer

Mystery Riddle

We are made of rock or metal,
Or combinations of the two.
We are planetary matter
That never formed and grew.
Travel from Mars to Jupiter
and there's a chance we'll hit you.
What are we?

C Type
S Type
M Type

Focus Skill: classifying

Paper Handouts: 2 sheets of 8.5" x 11" paper   a copy of Graphics 13B–E

Graphic Organizer: Make a Layered Look Book. On the top page, glue Graphic 13B or copy the poem "Mystery Riddle." On the bottom of the next tab, write *C Type.* On the bottom of the next tab, write *S Type,* and write *M Type* on the last tab. Draw/glue Graphics 13C–E accordingly.

✎ Color each type of asteroid as it is described. Read the poem and answer the riddle. **Answer: asteroids**

✎✎ On each tab, describe the asteroid.

✎✎✎ Complete ✎✎. Choose one type of asteroid to research. Write a paragraph on the back of the Layered Look Book explaining the data.

Experiences, Investigations, and Research

Select one or more of the following activities for individual or group enrichment projects. Allow your students to determine the format in which they would like to report, share, or graphically present what they have discovered. This should be a creative investigation that utilizes your students' strengths.

1. Read *The Little Prince* by Antoine de Saint–Exupéry. ✎✎✎
2. Write and illustrate a story about a spacecraft flying through the asteroid belt. There are between 40,000 and 50,000 asteroids in this main belt, but because space is so vast there is a great distance between each. **Note: During discussion, lead students to understand that it might not be as dangerous as they might imagine.**
3. Use the Internet to investigate "killer asteroids" and try to determine if the media hype concerning them is justified.
4. Not all asteroids are in the asteroid belt. Research the more than 300 small "trans–Neptunian" bodies found beyond Neptune.
5. In October 2000, astronomers announced the discovery of a double asteroid in our solar system. Investigate the double asteroid called Antiope.
6. At least two asteroids are known to have moons. Define the word "moon" as you explain how objects as small as asteroids can have moons.
7. http://www.seds.org/nineplanets/nineplanets/asteroids.html

What do we know about Jupiter?

Space Concepts:

- Jupiter is the fifth planet from the Sun, about 483,600,000 miles (778,112,400 km)away.
- It is the largest planet in our solar system, about 88,850 miles (142,960 km) in diameter.
- Jupiter is composed of a rocky core and metallic hydrogen mantle, surrounded by liquid hydrogen and helium.
- Jupiter has a hydrogen and helium atmosphere in layers that bulge at its equator, causing a ring.
- It has $2^1/_2$ times Earth's gravity.
- Its rotation is about 10 Earth hours, and its orbit is about 12 Earth years.
- Jupiter has 16 known moons.

Vocabulary: equator ring solid cloud *bulge

Read: *Lots of Science Library Book #14.*

Activities:

Solar System Top Tab Book – Graphic Organizer

Focus Skills: researching, recording information, organizing data
Paper Handouts: Solar System Top Tab Book a copy of Graphics 14A–B
Graphic Organizer: On the Jupiter page, glue Graphic 14A on the left side and label the parts of the planet. Glue Graphic 14B on the right side and fill in the information about Jupiter.

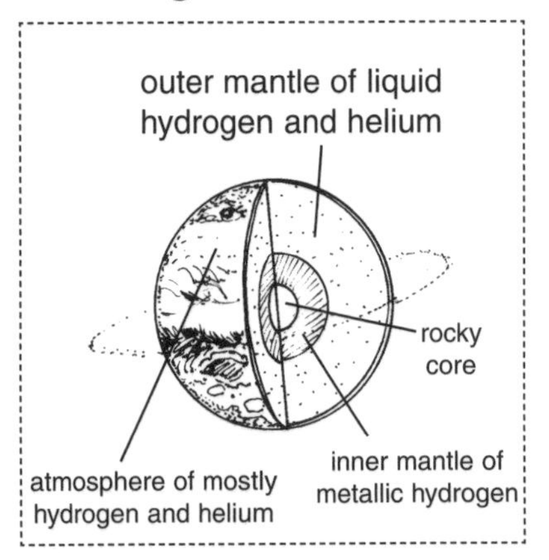

Distance from Sun: **483,600,00 miles / 778,112,400 km**
Diameter: **88,850 miles / 142,960 km**
Rotation: **10 Earth hours**
Revolution: **12 Earth years**
Surface: **hydrogen and helium atmosphere**
Known Moons: **16**
Interesting Information: ____________________
____
____

Investigative Loop – Stormy Jupiter Lab 14–1

Focus Skill: applying information
Lab Materials: $^1/_2$ cup whole milk red and yellow food coloring
dishwashing liquid clear bowl

Paper Handouts: 8.5" x 11" sheet of paper a copy of Graphic 14–1
Graphic Organizer: Make a Large Question and Answer Book. Glue it side–by–side to the Lab Book. Glue Lab Graphic 14–1 on the left tab.
Concept: Jupiter's surface is stormy.
Research: Read *Lots of Science Library Book #14* and review Jupiter's surface.

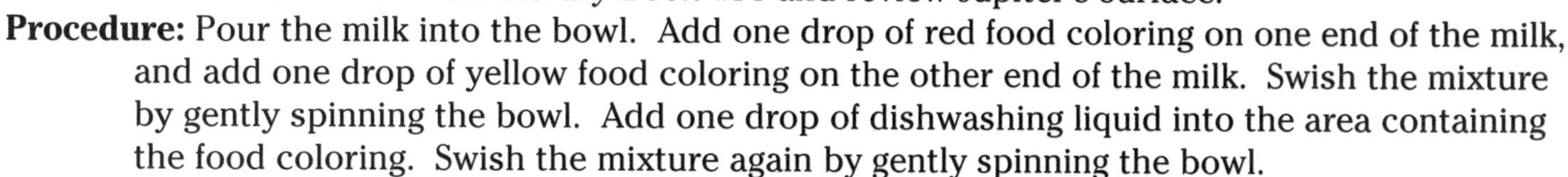

Procedure: Pour the milk into the bowl. Add one drop of red food coloring on one end of the milk, and add one drop of yellow food coloring on the other end of the milk. Swish the mixture by gently spinning the bowl. Add one drop of dishwashing liquid into the area containing the food coloring. Swish the mixture again by gently spinning the bowl.
Observations: Describe the milk in the bowl as it spins.
Record the Data: On the top section under the tab, draw/describe the lab.
Conclusion: This lab gives an idea of the "stormy" surface of Jupiter. Draw conclusions about the surface of Jupiter based on the observations of this lab.
n the bottom section under the tab, write the

ıs sparked by this lab.
› investigate further.
ıent: Select a topic based upon the experiences in the
e viii for more details.

3ook a copy of Graphics 14H
14H to the correct page in the Space Timeline Book.

ions, and Research

g activities for individual or group enrichment projects. Allow
rmat in which they would like to report, share, or graphically
d. This should be a creative investigation that utilizes your

"Solar System Weather Journal." Record the weather conditions
ınd contrast the weather on Jupiter to the weather conditions on
, and Mars.

ıld take to turn Jupiter into a star. **Hint:** It would need to be about
ıan it is now to increase the pressure and temperature in its core
could take place to turn it into a star.

tiate between Jupiter's belts and zones.

4. Investigate the ... and effect of Jupiter's rapid rotation and its oblate shape.

5. In July 1994, astronomers for the first time observed large objects crashing into a planet. Use the Internet to research the comet Shoemaker–Levy 9.

6. http://www.seds.org/nineplanets/nineplanets/jupiter.html

7. http://nssdc.gsfc.nasa.gov/planetary/comet.html

What do we know about Saturn?

Space Concepts:

- Saturn is the sixth planet from the Sun, about 886,000,000 miles (1,426,000,000 km) away.
- It is the second largest, about 74,900 miles (120,500 km) in diameter.
- Saturn is composed of a hot, rocky core; an inner mantle of liquid; metallic hydrogen; an outer mantle of liquid hydrogen; and an atmosphere of mostly hydrogen and helium.
- Its rings are composed of fragmented ice, rocks, and frozen gas.
- Saturn has a gaseous atmosphere.
- It has a little more gravity than Earth.
- Its rotation is about 10.7 Earth hours, and its orbit is about 29.5 Earth years.
- Saturn has 22 known moons.

Vocabulary: ice rock gas *fragmented *density

Read: *Lots of Science Library Book #15.*

Activities:

Solar System Top Tab Book – Graphic Organizer

Focus Skills: researching and recording information
Paper Handouts: Solar System Top Tab Book a copy of Graphics 15A–B
Graphic Organizer: On the Saturn page, glue Graphic 15A on the left side and label the parts of the planet. Glue Graphic 15B on the right side and fill in the information about Saturn.

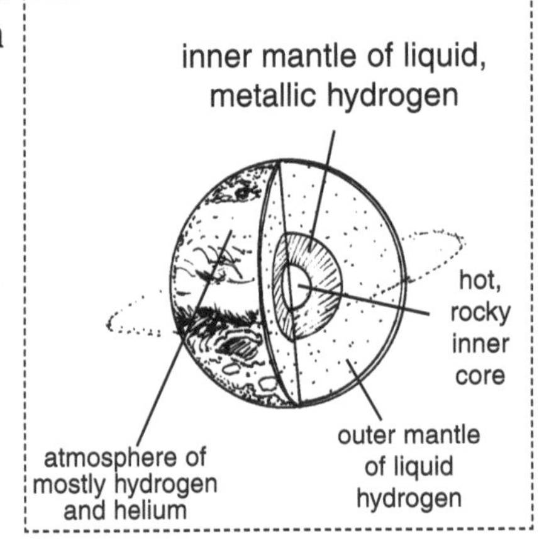

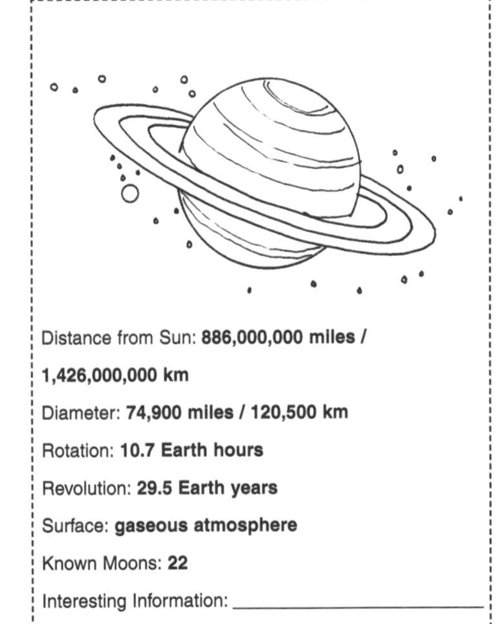

Investigative Loop – Density of Saturn

Lab 14-1 | Lab 15-1

Note: This activity is designed to compare the density of Earth and Saturn. The size of the marble and ball is not to scale.

Focus Skills: compare and contrast, draw conclusions

Lab Materials: clear bowl   water   marble   ping–pong ball (or any other plastic ball)

Paper Handouts: a copy of Graphic 15–1   Lab Book

Graphic Organizer: Glue Graphic 15–1 on the right tab of the Lab Book.

Question: How do Saturn and Earth compare in density?

Research: Review *Lots of Library Books #7 and #15* and review the density of each planet.

Procedure: Fill the bowl with water. Drop the marble, representing Earth, and ping–pong ball, representing Saturn, into the water.

Observation: Observe the size of each item. What happened when they each were put into the water?

Record the Data: On the top section under the tab, describe each item in the lab, including size and weight. Describe the lab.

Conclusions: Draw conclusions about the lab, based on the data recorded.

Communicate the Conclusions: On the bottom section under the tab, explain why the lab proceeded as it did. Define the word "density" in the explanation.

Possible answer: The marble sinks because it is more dense than water. The ping–pong ball floats because it is less dense than water. Saturn is made up mostly of light gases and is therefore less dense than Earth, which is a solid planet.

Spark Questions: Discuss questions sparked by this lab.

New Loop: Choose one question to investigate further.

✎✎✎ **Design Your Own Experiment:** Select a topic based upon the experiences in the *Investigative Loop*. See page viii for more details.

Timeline

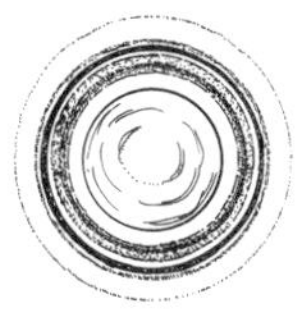

Paper Handouts: Space Timeline Book   a copy of Graphics 15C–D

Graphic Organizer: Glue Graphics 15C–D to the correct pages in the Space Timeline Book.

Experiences, Investigations, and Research

Select one or more of the following activities for individual or group enrichment projects. Allow your students to determine the format in which they would like to report, share, or graphically present what they have discovered. This should be a creative investigation that utilizes your students' strengths.

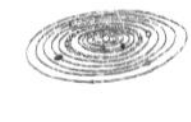

1. Make an entry in your "Solar System Weather Journal." Record the weather conditions on Jupiter. Compare and contrast the weather on Saturn to the weather conditions on Earth, Mercury, Venus, Mars, and Jupiter.

2. Compare and contrast the rings of Saturn with the rings of the other gaseous planets.

3. http://www.seds.org/nineplanets/nineplanets/saturn.html

What do we know about Uranus?

Space Concepts:

- Uranus is the sixth planet from the Sun, about 1,786,000,000 miles (2,874,000,000 km) away.
- It is the third largest planet, about 31,750 miles (51,086 km) in diameter.
- Uranus is composed of a solid, rocky core surrounded by a dense mantle of water, ammonia, and methane gas and an atmosphere of methane, hydrogen, and helium.
- It has a little less gravity than Earth.
- Its rotation is about 17 Earth hours, and its orbit is about 84 Earth years plus 25 Earth days long.
- Uranus is tilted on its axis at about 98° so it appears to be on its side.
- It has about 11 thin rings.
- Uranus has 21 known moons.

Vocabulary: *methane

Read: *Lots of Science Library Book #16.*

Activities:

Solar System Top Tab Book – Graphic Organizer

Focus Skills: researching and recording information
Paper Handouts: Solar System Top Tab Book a copy of Graphics 16A–B
Graphic Organizer: On the Uranus page, glue Graphic 16A on the left side and label the parts of the planet. Glue Graphic 16B on the right side and fill in the information about Uranus.

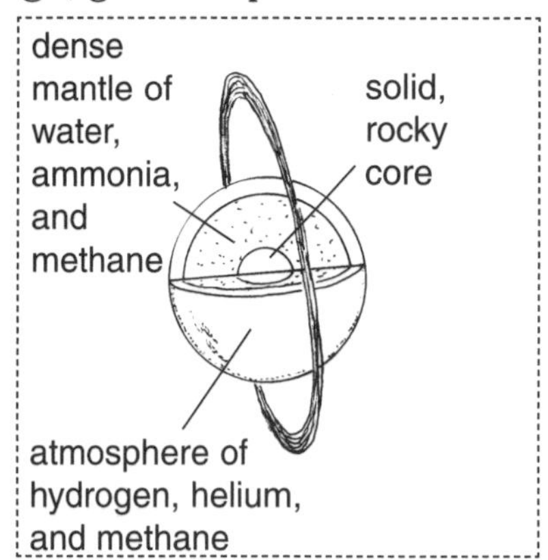

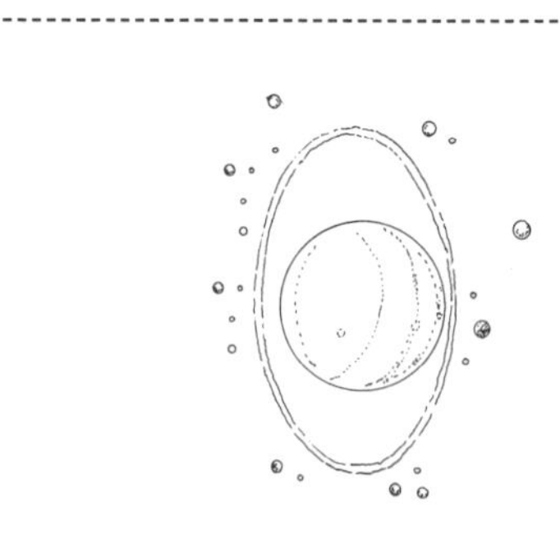

Distance from Sun: **1,786,000,000 miles / 2,874,000,000 km**

Diameter: **31,750 miles / 51,086 km**

Rotation: **17 Earth hours**

Revolution: **84 Earth years and 25 Earth days**

Surface: **gaseous atmosphere**

Known Moons: **21**

Interesting Information: ______________________

____

Investigative Loop – The Rings of Uranus Lab 16–1

Focus Skill: communication

Lab Materials: plastic 2-liter soda bottle with cap   flashlight
candle   matches

Paper Handouts: 8.5" x 11" sheet of paper   a copy of Lab Graphic 16–1
Lab Book

Graphic Organizer: Make a Large Question and Answer Book. Glue it side–by–side to the Lab Book. Glue Lab Graphic 16–1 on the left tab.

Concept: The rings of Uranus can be seen better when light is shining behind them.

Research: Read *Lots of Science Library Book #16* and review the rings of Uranus.

Procedure: Light a candle and blow it out. Quickly drop it into the plastic bottle and seal it with the cap. Shine the flashlight into the bottle from the front. Then shine the flashlight from behind the bottle.

Observations: What did you see when the light shone in front of the bottle? What did you see when the light shone from behind the bottle?

Record the Data: On the top section under the tab, record the observations made in this lab.

Conclusions: Explain why Uranus' rings can be seen better when the Sun shines behind them.

Communicate the Conclusions: On the bottom section under the tab, write your conclusions about the lab. Draw a picture to illustrate the conclusions. Explain the conclusions orally.

Spark Questions: Discuss questions sparked by this lab.

New Loop: Choose one question to investigate further.

✎✎✎ **Design Your Own Experiment:** Select a topic based upon the experiences in the *Investigative Loop*. See page viii for more details.

Timeline

Paper Handouts: Space Timeline Book
a copy of Graphics 16C–D

Graphic Organizer: Glue Graphics 16C–D to the correct pages in the Space Timeline Book.

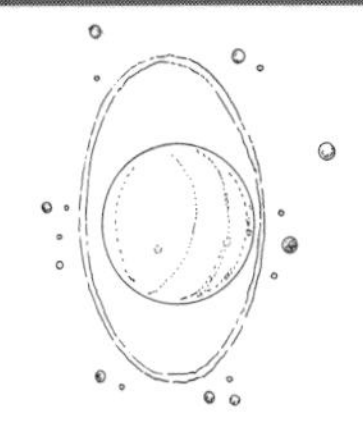

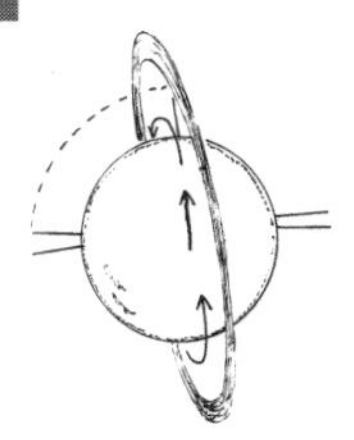

Experiences, Investigations, and Research

Select one or more of the following activities for individual or group enrichment projects. Allow your students to determine the format in which they would like to report, share, or graphically present what they have discovered. This should be a creative investigation that utilizes your students' strengths.

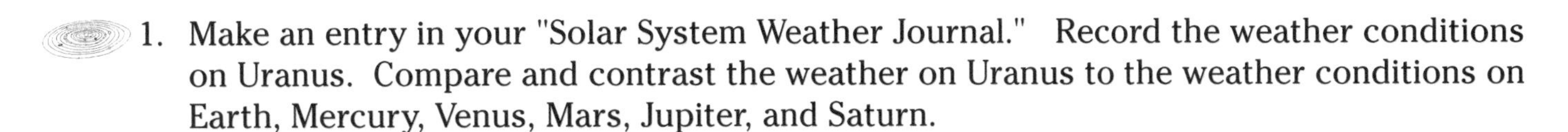

1. Make an entry in your "Solar System Weather Journal." Record the weather conditions on Uranus. Compare and contrast the weather on Uranus to the weather conditions on Earth, Mercury, Venus, Mars, Jupiter, and Saturn.

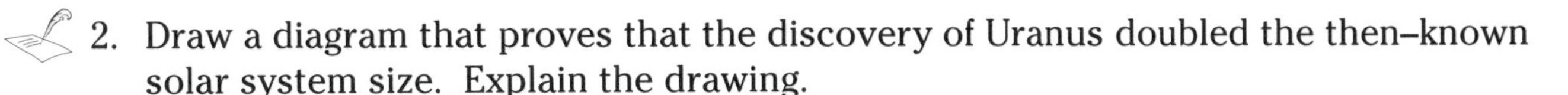

2. Draw a diagram that proves that the discovery of Uranus doubled the then–known solar system size. Explain the drawing.

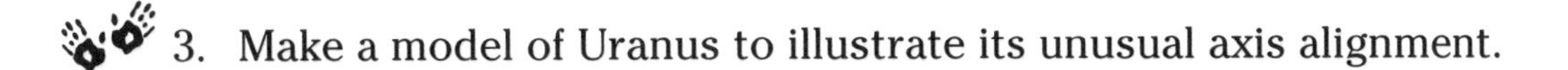

3. Make a model of Uranus to illustrate its unusual axis alignment.

4. http://www.seds.org/nineplanets/nineplanets/uranus.html

Great Science Adventures

What do we know about Neptune?

Space Concepts:

- Neptune is the eighth planet from the Sun, about 2,798,800,000 miles (4,503,300,000 km) away.
- It is about 30,800 miles (49,500 km) in diameter.
- It is composed of a small, rocky core surrounded by icy water and gases, with an atmosphere of hydrogen, helium, and methane.
- Neptune's surface is gaseous and covered with currents and strong winds.
- It has a little less gravity than Earth.
- Neptune's rotation is about 16 Earth hours, and its orbit is about 164 Earth years.
- It has 8 known moons.

Vocabulary: Review vocabulary words from previous lessons.

Read: *Lots of Science Library Book #17.*

Activities:

Solar System Top Tab Book – Graphic Organizer

Focus Skills: researching and recording information
Paper Handouts: Solar System Top Tab Book a copy of Graphics 17A–B
Graphic Organizer: On the Neptune page, glue Graphic 17A on the left side and label the parts of the planet. Glue Graphic 17B on the right side and fill in the information about Neptune.

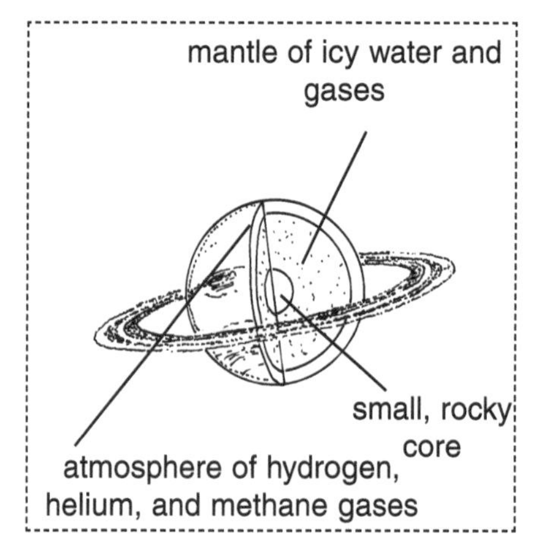

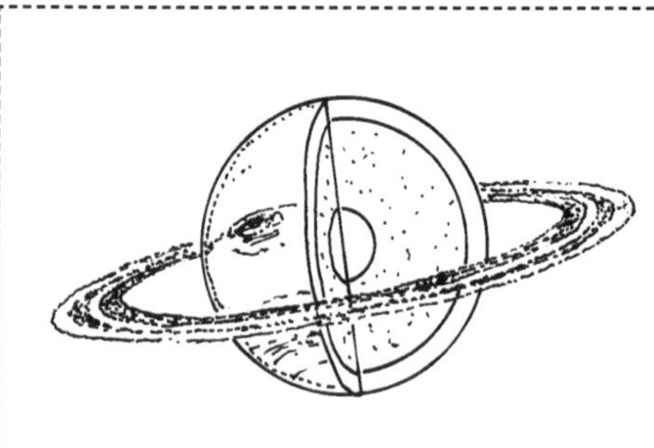

Distance from Sun: **2,798,800,000 miles / 4,503,300,000 km**
Diameter: **30,800 miles / 49,500 km**
Rotation: **16 Earth hours**
Revolution: **164 Earth years**
Surface: **strong winds and currents**
Known Moons: **8**
Interesting Information: ____________________
____

Investigative Loop – Icy Triton Lab 17-1

Lab 16-1 Lab 17-1

Note: Adult supervision is necessary for this lab.
Focus Skills: demonstrating a concept, explaining a demonstration
Lab Materials: modeling clay, string, thin wooden dowel or skewer, saucepan, water
Paper Handouts: a copy of Lab Graphic 17–1, Lab Book
Graphic Organizer: Glue Lab Graphic 17–1 on the right tab.
Concept: The temperatures on Neptune's moon, Triton, are so cold that gases in its atmosphere freeze without becoming a liquid.
Research: Read *Lots of Science Library Book #17* and review the Concept.
Procedure: Make a model of Triton by forming a ball from modeling clay. Tie a piece of string to the ball and tie the other end to the end of the wooden dowel. Place it in a freezer overnight. The next day, boil water in the saucepan. Hold the skewer over the boiling water, placing frozen Triton in the steam. Be careful not to burn your hand.
Observations: Observe the Triton ball. What changes do you observe when it is in the steam?
Possible answer: Water vapor forms a thin layer of ice on Triton.
Record the Data: On the top section under the tab, draw the lab. Record the observations about the Triton ball in the steam.
Conclusions: Explain why the thin layer of ice forms on the ball. How does this lab demonstrate what happens on Neptune's moon, Triton? **Possible answer: Triton's atmosphere, which is mostly nitrogen, freezes preventing it from turning into a liquid state.**
Communicate the Conclusions: On the bottom section under the tab, illustrate the lab and explain the conclusions drawn from it. Write it as a news report, if desired.
Spark Questions: Discuss questions sparked by this lab.
New Loop: Choose one question to investigate further.
✎✎✎ **Design Your Own Experiment:** Select a topic based upon the experiences in the *Investigative Loop*. See page viii for more details.

Timeline

Paper Handouts: Space Timeline Book, a copy of Graphic 17C
Graphic Organizer: Glue Graphic 17C to the correct page in the Space Timeline Book.

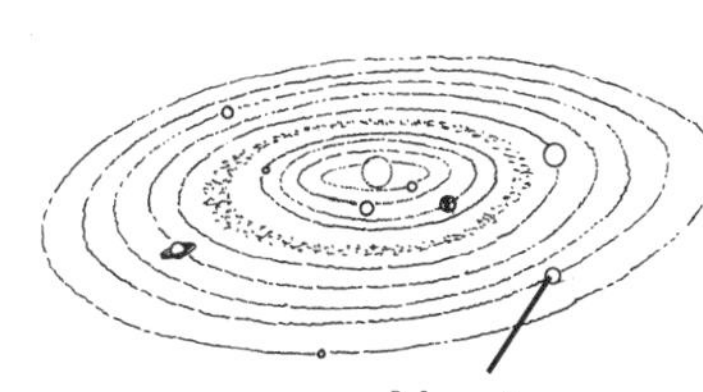

Experiences, Investigations, and Research

Select one or more of the following activities for individual or group enrichment projects. Allow your students to determine the format in which they would like to report, share, or graphically present what they have discovered. This should be a creative investigation that utilizes your students' strengths.

1. Make an entry in your "Solar System Weather Journal." Record the weather conditions on Neptune. Compare and contrast the weather on Neptune to the weather conditions on other planets studied.
2. Compare and contrast Neptune and Uranus.
3. Investigate Neptune's moon, Triton.
4. http://www.seds.org/nineplanets/nineplanets/neptune.html

What do we know about Pluto?

Space Concepts:

- Pluto is the ninth planet from the Sun, about 3,670,000,000 miles (5,905,000,000 km) away.
- It is the smallest planet, about 1,430 miles (2,300 km) in diameter.
- Pluto is composed of a rock-and-ice-covered mantle with a layer of icy water and methane.
- Its atmosphere is primarily nitrogen, carbon monoxide, and methane.
- Pluto has very little gravity.
- Its rotation is about 6 Earth days, and its orbit is about 248 Earth years.
- Pluto has one known moon.

Teacher's Note: An alternative assessment suggestion for this lesson is found on pages 82–84. If Graphic Pages are being consumed, photocopy the assessment graphics that are needed first.

Vocabulary: *carbon monoxide

Read: *Lots of Science Library Book #18.*

Activities:

Solar System Top Tab Book - Graphic Organizer

Focus Skills: researching and recording information
Paper Handouts: Solar System Top Tab Book a copy of Graphics 18A–B
Graphic Organizer: On the Pluto page, glue Graphic 18A on the left side and label the parts of the planet. Glue Graphic 18B on the right side and fill in the information about Pluto.

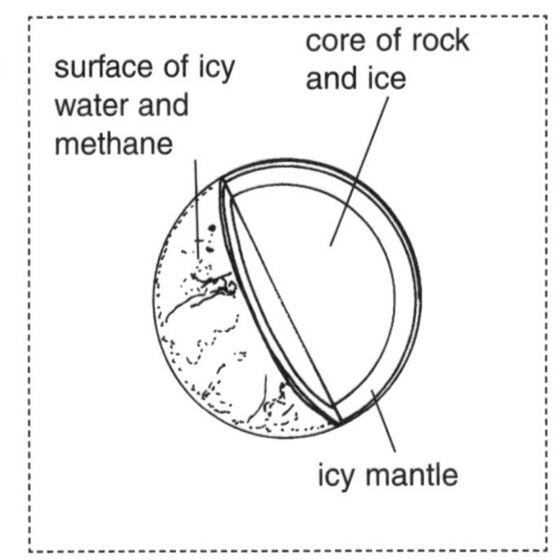

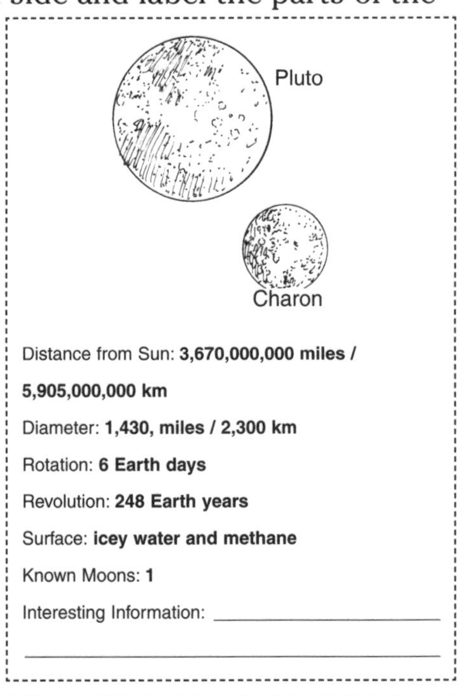

The Wonders of a Solar System Table - Graphic Organizer

Focus Skills: making and reading a table
Paper Handouts: 5 sheets of 9" x 12" construction paper
Solar System Top Tab Book
Graphic Organizer: Make a 5-paper Layered Look Book. Draw lines to make 5 columns down the book. Cut up on the lines from the bottom of tab 9 through tab 2. Label the top, beginning at the left: *Planet, Distance from Sun, Diameter, Rotation, Revolution.* List the planets under the Planet column, one on each tab. Use the Solar System Top Tab Book to fill in the information for each planet.
Chart Reading: Use the Solar System Chart and the Solar System Top Tab Book to answer these questions: Which planet is the largest? Which is the third largest? Which planet is about 67,000,000 miles from the Sun? Continue asking comparison questions. Which is easier to use for answering the questions: the Solar System Top Tab Book or the Solar System Table?

Planet	Distance from Sun	Diameter	Rotation	Revolution	
Mercury	36,000,000 miles	3,030 miles			Tab 2
Venus					
Earth					
Mars					
Jupiter					
Saturn					
Uranus					
Neptune					Tab 9
Pluto					

Planet Riddles – Graphic Organizer

Focus Skill: apply information
Paper Handouts: 9"x12" sheet of black construction paper a copy of Graphic 18E
Graphic Organizer: Make a Pocket Book. With a white crayon or white-out liquid write *Space* on the cover. On the left pocket write *Planets* and on the right pocket write *Riddles.* Cut out each card. Match the riddle card with the correct planet card. Play a memory game with the cards. Store the cards in the correct pocket.

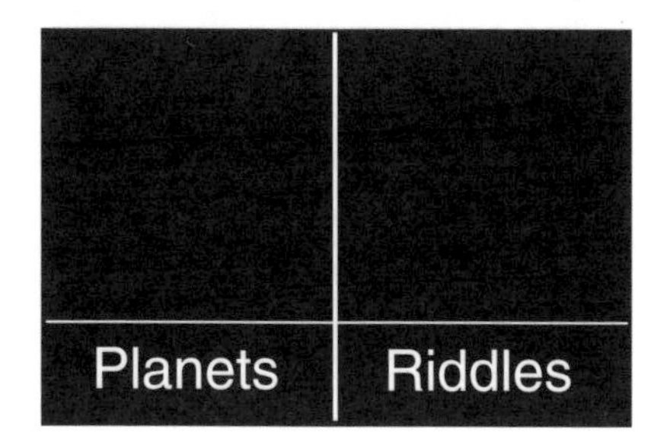

Which planet am I?

For centuries it has been said.
That this planet appears bright red.
But *Viking I* recently found
A rusty-brown, dark colored ground.
It's cold at night and days are hot
With a sky thats, colored apricot.
Mars

Which planet am I?

The gaseous planets
All have rings,
But none of them has
More than I.
Scientists learned
interesting things
when *Voyager* made a fly by.
Saturn

Which planet am I?

I have a circular orbit
And a thick, cloudy atmosphere.
From my surface Earth can't be seen,
And no planets appear.
Venus

Which planet am I?

I appear to be aquamarine;
eleven thin rings can be seen.
My axis is tilted in a way
that points my poles sunward everyday.
Uranus

Which planet am I?

I'm invisible
I'm so close to the Sun;
View me when it's
Below the horizon.
Mercury

Which planet am I?

The fastest winds
in the Solar System whip around me.
I'm a gaseous planet,
but look like a turquoise sea.
Neptune

Which planet am I?

78% nitrogen, 21% oxygen
in my atmosphere;
lots of liquid water
and life forms everywhere.
Earth

Which planet am I?

I am the most recent planet discovery.
I'd been predicted for a century.
A famous dog that's cartoon-y
has the same name as little 'ol me.
Pluto

Which planet am I?

I am a gas giant,
As big as a planet can be.
I have lots of weather.
But no geography!
Jupiter

Compare the Size of Pluto to the Other Planets

Note: This model indicates the planets' sizes to scale only. To demonstrate the distance between each planet correctly, see Lesson 6.
Activity Materials: thick needle or pin variously colored construction paper
7 sheets of colored poster board
string
a pole at least 8 feet long (a tall garden stake)

Activity: Cut out the following planets from poster board or construction paper using the diameters listed. Cut 2 of each planet. Use colors that represent each planet, if desired. (Mars out of red paper. Use the *Lots of Science Library Books* for the information.) Cut a slit in each circle from the outer edge to the middle. Slot together the two circles of each planet. Make a hole at the top of each planet, using a thick needle. Thread each planet with string. Discuss the activity and then tie the strings to the long pole in the correct order from the Sun.

Mercury – $^1/_8$ in.	Venus – $1^5/_8$ in.	Earth – $1^5/_8$ in.	Mars – $^1/_4$ in.
Jupiter – 19 in.	Saturn – 15 in.	Uranus – 8 in.	Neptune – 8 in.
Pluto – $^1/_4$ in.			

Optional: Make the Sun with a diameter of 13 ft. You can tape newspapers together to make paper that large.

Discuss the Activity: Compare the various planets to one another. Put the planets in order by size, largest to smallest. Put the planets in order by density.

Timeline

Paper Handouts: Space Timeline Book a copy of Graphics 18C–D

Graphic Organizer: Glue Graphics 18C–D to the correct pages in the Space Timeline Book.

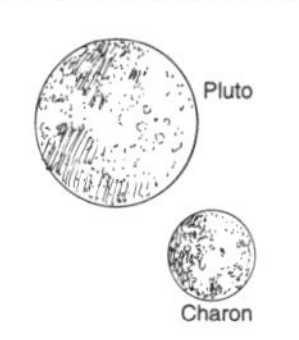

Experiences, Investigations, and Research

Select one or more of the following activities for individual or group enrichment projects. Allow your students to determine the format in which they would like to report, share, or graphically present what they have discovered. This should be a creative investigation that utilizes your students' strengths.

1. Make an entry in your "Solar System Weather Journal." Record what little is known of the weather conditions on Pluto. Compare and contrast the weather on Pluto with the weather on Mercury.

2. Investigate the debate over Pluto's status as a planet. Recently, some astronomers have argued that Pluto is not a planet. Why? If it is not a planet, what is it? In February 1999 the IAU, International Astronomical Union, reaffirmed that Pluto is a planet.

3. Compare and contrast Pluto's orbit before and after March 1999.

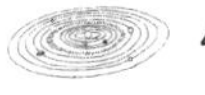

4. Mercury has greater extremes in temperature highs and lows than Pluto. Why?

5. Research the discovery of "mini–Pluto," a space rock, object 2000 EB173, that orbits the Sun in the same amount of time as Pluto. It isn't a planet, and it isn't a moon. What is it?

6. http://www.seds.org/nineplanets/nineplanets/pluto.html7.

7. http://dosxx.Colorado.edu/plutohome.html

Notes

What are comets?

Space Concepts:

- Comets are large masses of water, ice, and frozen gases with dust particles imbedded within.
- They usually originate in an area beyond Neptune or in the Oort Cloud.
- Collisions and gravitational pull of the planets pull some comets toward the Sun.
- Comets do not have their own light; they reflect sunlight.
- As they near the Sun, heat vaporizes their outer layers, resulting in a gas and dust tail.
- Comets consist of three parts: nucleus, coma, and tail.
- Some comets travel near the Sun, and then their elongated orbits take them back to the outer solar system.

Vocabulary: comet tail coma *nucleus

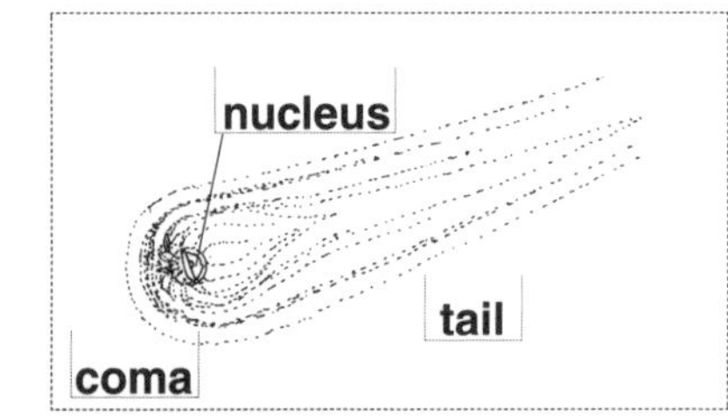

Read: *Lots of Science Library Book #19.*

Activities:

Parts of a Comet – Graphic Organizer

Focus Skill: labeling parts

Paper Handouts: 9” x 12” sheet of construction paper a copy of Graphic 19A

Graphic Organizer: Cut on the dotted lines of Graphic 19A, forming three tabs. Fold the tabs open. Make a Half Book from the construction paper. Put glue on the back of Graphic 19A, being careful not to glue the tabs. Glue the graphic on the cover of the Half Book. Do not glue down the tabs.

✎ On the tabs, write/copy the parts of the comet: *nucleus, coma, tail.* Review the parts of the comet. Draw a comet inside the book.

✎✎ Label each part of the comet on the tab. Inside, describe comets and explain how they travel in the solar system.

✎✎✎ Label each part of the comet on the tab. Describe each part inside the book. Research specific comets and list them inside the Half Book. Write about each one, such as: When was it first seen? When was it last seen? When is it predicted to return?

Make a Comet Tail

Focus Skill: demonstrating a concept

Activity Materials: small plastic tray or cookie sheet plastic dishpan tempera paint paintbrush watering can with water

Activity: Place one end of the tray in the dishpan at an angle. Using a paintbrush, place a thick blob of paint on the top of the tray. The paint blob represents a comet. Gently pour water from the watering can over the paint blob comet. The water represents the solar wind.

Discuss the Activity: What happens to the blob of paint as you pour the water over it? How does this demonstrate a comet? **Possible answer: The water should form a tail from the paint blob, just as solar winds sweeps gas from the comet.**

A Comet's Tail Always Points Away from the Sun

Focus Skill: demonstrating

Activity Materials: blow dryer colored tissue paper ping–pong ball wooden skewer

Activity: Cut colored tissue paper into 15 – 8" x 1/4" strips. Line the strips side-by-side and tape together. Tape the line of tissue strips to the middle of the ping-pong ball. This represents the tail of a comet. Push the skewer into the ping-pong ball, which represents a comet. Hold the comet in the air. Ask someone to point the blow dryer at the ping-pong ball and turn it on low. The blow dryer represents the solar winds from the Sun. Move the comet around the Sun as the solar winds continue to point towards the nucleus, or head, of the comet.

Discuss the Activity: Why does the tail of a comet always point away from the Sun?

Timeline

Paper Handouts: Space Timeline Book a copy of Graphics 19B–C

Graphic Organizer: Glue Graphics 19B–C to the correct pages in the Space Timeline Book.

Experiences, Investigations, and Research

Select one or more of the following activities for individual or group enrichment projects. Allow your students to determine the format in which they would like to report, share, or graphically present what they have discovered. This should be a creative investigation that utilizes your students' strengths.

1. Make a Halley's Comet Timeline that illustrates and describes sightings and discoveries. Note that comets are named after the people who discover them. Add other famous comets to your Halley's Comet Timeline as you learn about them.

2. Compare and contrast comets and meteors.

3. Explain how a comet's tail can tell astronomers on Earth which way solar winds are blowing in space.

4. Read *Maria's Comet* by Deborah Hopkinson. Maria Mitchell was an American astronomer who discovered a telescopic comet around 1900. ✎ ✎✎

5. http://www.seds.org/nineplanets/nineplanets/comets.html

6. encke.jpl.nasa.gov

7. www.skypub.com/sights/comets/comets.html

What are meteoroids, meteors, and meteorites?

Space Concepts:

- Meteoroids are pieces of comets, asteroids, and space dust moving in deep space.
- Sometimes a meteoroid is pulled into Earth's atmosphere. When it enters Earth's atmosphere, it is a meteor.
- Most meteors burn up in the atmosphere, but those that land on Earth are called meteorites.

Teacher's Note: An alternative assessment suggestion for this lesson is found on pages 82–84. If Graphic Pages are being consumed, photocopy the assessment graphics that are needed first.

Vocabulary: meteoroid meteor meteorite

Read: *Lots of Science Library Book #20.*

Activities:

Meteor, Meteoroid, Meteorite – Graphics Organizer

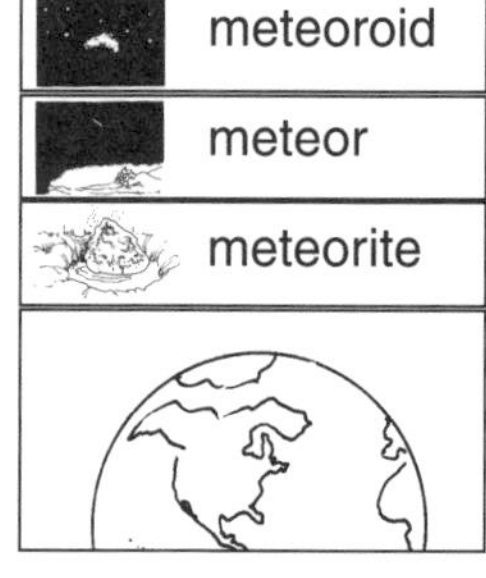

Focus Skill: classifying
Paper Handouts: 2 sheets of 8.5" x 11" paper a copy of Graphics 20A–D
Graphic Organizer: Make a Layered Look Book with 1" tabs. Turn the book so the fold is at the bottom. Glue Graphic 20A on the cover, 20B on the next tab up, 20C on the second tab up, and 20D on the top tab.

✎ On each tab, write/copy the name of the object, starting at the top: *meteoroid, meteor, meteorite.*

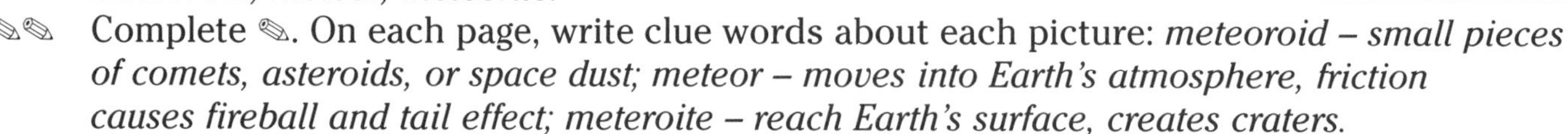

✎✎ Complete ✎. On each page, write clue words about each picture: *meteoroid – small pieces of comets, asteroids, or space dust; meteor – moves into Earth's atmosphere, friction causes fireball and tail effect; meteroite – reach Earth's surface, creates craters.*

✎✎✎ Complete ✎✎. Explain why the tail appears on the meteor. Research the Ahnighito, Hoba, or Great Barringer Crater. Write a short paragraph on the back of the Layered Look Book about the research.

Meteorites Make Craters

Focus Skill: drawing conclusions
Activity Materials: deep plastic pan or a sandbox sand
balls of various weights and sizes (steel ball, marble, billiard ball, etc.)
Activity: Fill the pan with sand. Drop one ball into the sand. Carefully remove the ball and look at the crater. Drop another ball and do the same. Compare the craters. Try dropping the balls from different heights.
Discuss the Activity: What size crater did the small ball make? What size crater did the large ball make? What size crater did the heavy ball make? What size crater did the light ball make? What can you conclude about crater size in relation to the various sizes of balls?

Meteors Spread Out – Observation Activity

Focus Skill: explaining a concept
Activity Materials: uncooked spaghetti modeling clay or dough flat plate
Activity: Flatten the clay on the plate so that most of the plate is covered. One by one, stand pieces of spaghetti vertically into the clay, covering the plate. The spaghetti represents dust particles in a meteor shower as they enter Earth's atmosphere. Look down on the plate full of spaghetti.
Discuss the Activity: What do you see? The spaghetti pieces should look like they are spreading out from the center of the plate. How does this illustrate the appearance of a meteor shower from Earth? **Possible answer: Although meteors travel in parallel paths, as they burn up they appear to spread out from a single point.**

Timeline

Paper Handouts: Space Timeline Book a copy of Graphic 20E
Graphic Organizer: Glue Graphic 20E to the correct page in the Space Timeline Book.

Experiences, Investigations, and Research

Select one or more of the following activities for individual or group enrichment projects. Allow your students to determine the format in which they would like to report, share, or graphically present what they have discovered. This should be a creative investigation that utilizes your students' strengths.

1. Observe the night sky, watching for a "falling star" or meteor. Keep track of your observations, noting if more meteors are seen after midnight or before.
2. Obtain the dates of possible meteor showers in your area and mark your calendar. Plan an observation party.
3. Investigate how the Great Barringer meteor crater in Arizona was named and why it should be called the Great Barringer meteorite crater. Note that all meteorites are named after a geographic location. Meteorites belong to the owners of the property on which they fall. Metorites that fall on government property in the U.S. belong to the Smithsonian Institute.
4. Compare and contrast the two types of meteoroids: cometary meteoroids (particles shed from comets), and asteroidal meteoroids (microscopic to large particles of asteroids).
5. Use the Internet to discover what micrometeorites are and where they are found.
6. Make a table recording the name, location, size, weight, and composition of famous meteorites.

7. Read and discuss *Call Me Ahnighito* by Pam Conrad. ✎ ✎✎

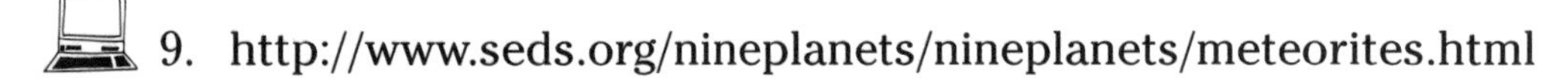
8. Read an excerpt from "The Rime of the Ancient Mariner" by Samuel Taylor Coleridge. Do you think seeing a meteor shower may have inspired him? ✎✎✎

> The upper air burst into life!
> And a hundred fire–flags sheen,
> To and fro they were hurried about!
> And to and fro, and in and out,
> The wan stars danced between.
> And the coming wind did roar more loud,
> And the sails did sigh like sedge;
> And the rain poured down from one black cloud;
> The Moon was at its edge.

9. http://www.seds.org/nineplanets/nineplanets/meteorites.html

Space Concept Map

Lessons 21-24

Numbers Refer to Lesson Numbers

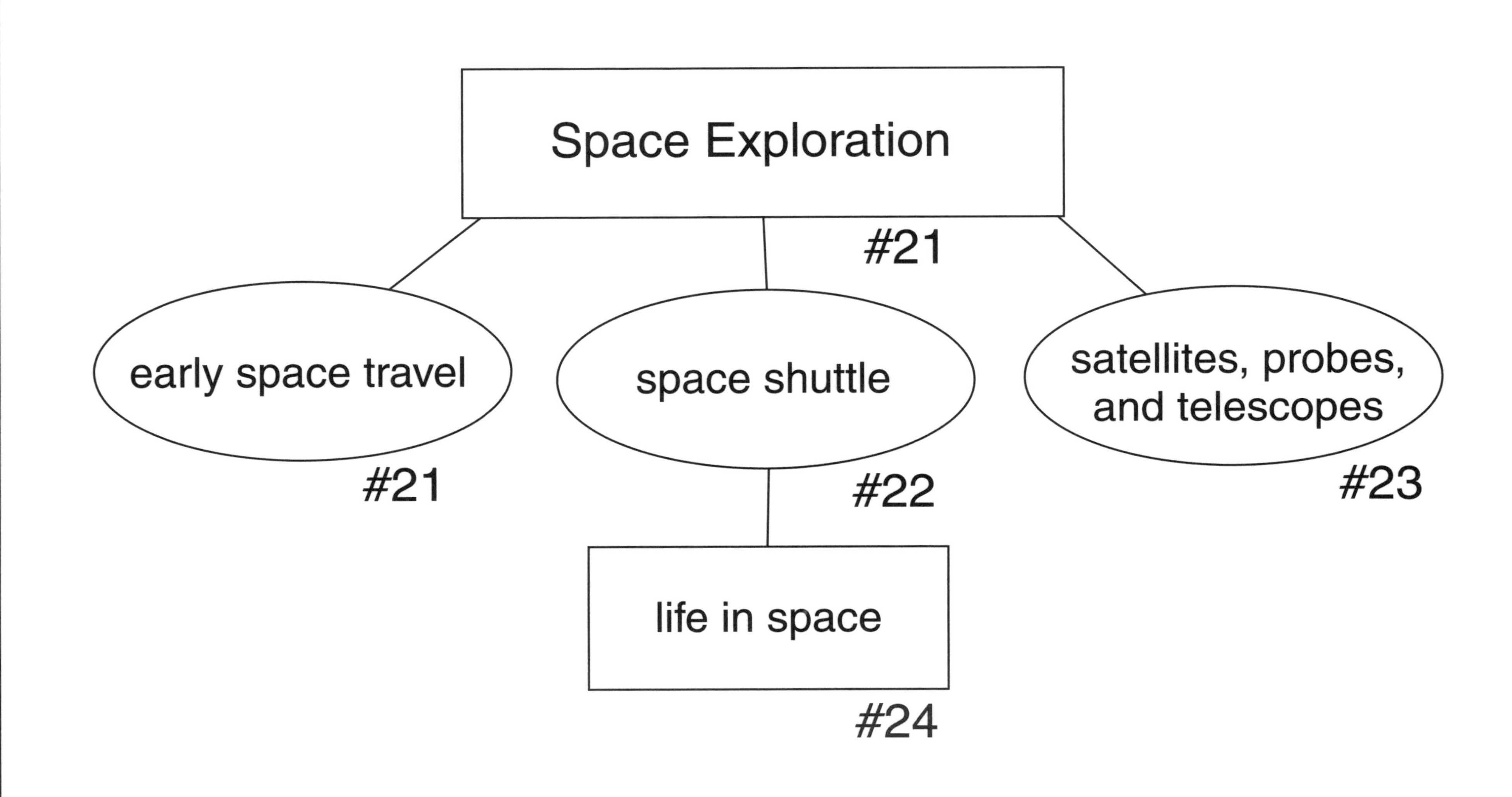

When did people begin space explorations?

Space Concepts:

- Only rockets are powerful enough to escape Earth's gravity and facilitate space travel.
- The first milestone in space exploration occurred when the USSR launched *Sputnik 1* in October 1957.
- Numerous space exploratory missions took place between 1957 and July 1969, when the USA landed two men on the Moon.

Vocabulary:
explore vehicle rocket spacecraft *tether *excursion

Read:
Lots of Science Library Book #21.

Activities:

Investigative Loop – Balloon Rocket Lab 21–1

Focus Skill: demonstrating a concept

Lab Materials: a brick or any heavy object; 5 yards of string; clamp; long, thin balloon; tape; drinking straw

Paper Handouts: 8.5" x 11" sheet of paper; a copy of Lab Graphic 21-1

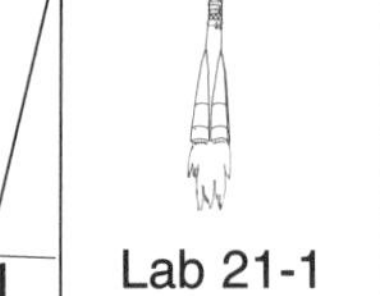

Graphic Organizer: Make a Large Question and Answer Book. Glue it side–by–side to the Lab Book. Glue Lab Graphic 21-1 on the left tab.

Concept: Force is needed for a rocket to launch.

Research: Read *Lots of Science Library Book #21* and review the Concept.

Procedure: Blow up the balloon and ask someone to hold it so the air does not escape. Cut two 2-inch lengths of drinking straw and tape one on each end of the balloon. Thread the string through both pieces of straw. Tie one end of the string to a brick on the floor. Tape the other end of the string to a high location, like the top of a door. Move the balloon to the bottom of the string and release it.

Observations: Observe the balloon when it is released. How far did the balloon fly? How fast did it move?

Record the Data: On the top section under the tab, draw the lab. Draw arrows to indicate how the balloon traveled. Record the observations.

Conclusions: Review the data and conclude why the balloon responded as it did when the air was released.

Communicate the Conclusions: On the bottom section under the tab, explain why the balloon reacted as it did. Relate the lab to a rocket used in space travel.

Spark Questions: Discuss questions sparked by this lab.

New Loop: Choose one question to investigate further.

Design Your Own Experiment: Select a topic based upon the experiences in the *Investigative Loop*. See page viii for more details.

Timeline

Paper Handouts: Space Timeline Book a copy of Graphics 21A-L
Graphic Organizer: Glue Graphics 21A-L to the correct pages in the Space Timeline Book.

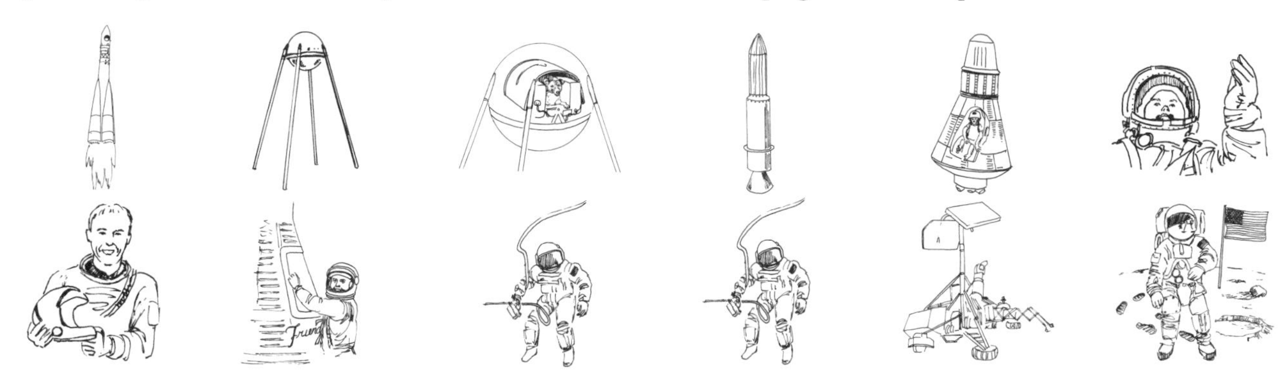

Experiences, Investigations, and Research

Select one or more of the following activities for individual or group enrichment projects. Allow your students to determine the format in which they would like to report, share, or graphically present what they have discovered. This should be a creative investigation that utilizes your students' strengths.

1. Build your own rocket from one of the kits found in most hobby stores. Follow the directions in the kit.

2. Pour $^{1}/_{2}$ cup of water and $^{1}/_{2}$ cup of vinegar in a plastic bottle. With a pushpin, attach streamers or ribbons to the top of a cork that fits in the bottle. Place 1 tablespoon of baking soda in the middle of a piece of paper towel, roll it up, and twist the ends. Drop the baking soda "fuel" into the bottle. Immediately, plug the bottle with the cork and put the bottle on level ground. Move at least 10 feet from the bottle and watch the rocket blast off.

3. Read *A Swiftly Tilting Planet* by Madeleine L'Engle.

4. Read *Neil Armstrong: Young Flyer* (Childhood of Famous Americans series) by Montrew Dunham.

5. Read *John Glenn – Young Astronaut* (Childhood of Famous Americans series) by Michael Burgan.

6. http://education.nasa.gov/

What is the Space Shuttle?

Space Concepts:

- Early spacecraft were not reusable, so they were very expensive.
- The Space Shuttle is the world's first manned, reusable spacecraft.
- The Space Shuttle consists of four main parts: orbiter, external fuel tank, two solid rocket boosters, and main engines.
- The payload bay, inside the orbiter, is as large as a bus. It holds space equipment that is being transported.
- Today's Space Shuttle can transport a crew of ten people.

Vocabulary: reusable orbiter external booster engine *manipulator

Read: *Lots of Science Library Book #22.*

Lab 21-1 Lab 22-1

Activities:

Robotic Arm - Investigative Loop – Lab 22–1

Focus Skill: demonstrating

Lab Materials: thick cardboard, 2 brads, 2 paper clips, modeling clay, thin, wooden dowel, 24 inches long, thick nail, small cup hook

Paper Handouts: a copy of Lab Graphic 22–1, Lab Book

Graphic Organizer: Glue Lab Graphic 22–1 on the right tab.

Concept: Space missions require the use of the remote manipulator system (RMS). The astronaut inside the orbiter controls the arm to perform various activities in space.

Research: Read *Lots of Science Library Book #22* and review the Concept.

Procedure: Cut the cardboard into three 11" x 2" strips. Using the nail, punch a hole 1" from the end of each strip. Join the strip with brads. Bend a paper clip into an S-shape and put it in the last hole of the cardboard strips. Screw the cup hook into one end of the dowel. Slip the cup hook into the last hole on the cardboard strips so that you can manipulate the end of the strips with the dowel. You may have to ask a partner to hold the cardboard strips for you as you manipulate the dowel. Form a ball with the modeling clay, and insert the other paper clip, S-shaped, into it. Place the ball on a table with the paper clip sticking up in the air. Use the dowel to manipulate the cardboard strips so that you can pick up the ball with the S-shaped paper clip on the end of the cardboard strips.

cardboard
paper clip
cup hook
dowel
paper clip
modeling clay

Observations: Observe the procedure. Was it easier or more difficult than you thought it would be? What made it easy? What made it difficult? What would have made it easier?

Record the Data: On the top section, under the tab, draw the lab and describe the observations.

Conclusions: Based on the lab, draw conclusions about the use of RMS in a space mission.
Using the RMS is a specialized job requiring much practice.
Communicate the Conclusions: On the bottom section under the tab, record the conclusions.
Include why is it necessary to use the RMS in space.
Spark Questions: Discuss questions sparked by this lab.
New Loop: Choose one question to investigate further.
✎✎✎ **Design Your Own Experiment:** Select a topic based upon the experiences in the *Investigative Loop*. See page viii for more details.

The Space Shuttle – Graphic Organizer

Focus Skill: explaining a process
Paper Handouts: 3 sheets of 8.5" x 11" paper a copy of Graphics 22A–F
Graphic Organizer: Make a Layered Look Book with 3/4 inch tabs. Glue Graphic 22A on the cover, 22B on the next page, and so on, with 22F on the last page.

✎ On each page, color the picture and discuss that stage in the Space Shuttle's trip.

✎✎ Write clue phrases about each step on that page: *Space Shuttle takes off, solid rocket boosters separate, external tank separates, orbital mission landing.* Explain each step in the Space Shuttle's mission.

✎✎✎ Explain each step in the Space Shuttle's mission on the appropriate tab. Research one shuttle mission and report the findings on the back of the Layered Look Book.

The Robot and the Controller

Focus Skills: communicating and following directions
Activity Materials: wastebasket ball blindfold
Activity: Choose a person to be the robot and one to be the controller. Blindfold the robot. The controller's mission is to direct the robot to drop the ball into the basket by giving commands such as "Turn right," "Go five paces," "Stop."
Options: Rather than saying "Turn right" say, "Make a 20° turn to the right."
Discuss the Activity: What did you observe as the robot? What did you observe as the controller? How important is it to be exact? In what areas would a robot be helpful in a space mission? What do you think is the future of robots in space missions?

Timeline

Paper Handouts: Space Timeline Book a copy of Graphic 22G
Graphic Organizer: Glue Graphic 22G to the correct pages in the Space Timeline Book.

Experiences, Investigations, and Research

Select one or more of the following activities for individual or group enrichment projects. Allow your students to determine the format in which they would like to report, share, or graphically present what they have discovered. This should be a creative investigation that utilizes your students' strengths.

1. Use a liter soft drink bottle and other recyclable materials to design your own space shuttle or to make a model of the current shuttle.
2. Read *To Space and Back* by Sally Ride and Susan Okie. ✎ ✎✎
3. http://spaceflight.nasa.gov/shuttle/index.html (NASA Space Shuttle)

What are satellites, space probes, and the Hubble Telescope?

Space Concepts:

- A satellite is an object orbiting around another object. Moons are natural satellites.
- Artificial satellites orbit Earth for various purposes: weather predictors, navigation tools, communications, monitors of Earth's geological concerns, and more.
- The Hubble Telescope is a type of orbiting observatory that can produce clear images that are not distorted by Earth's atmosphere.
- Space probes are unmanned spacecraft that travel great distances into space over long periods of time. As they explore space, they send information back to Earth.

Vocabulary: probe telescope *observatory

Read: *Lots of Science Library Book #23.*

Activities:

Stationary Satellites

Focus Skill: demonstrating a concept
Activity Materials: white chalk yellow chalk
Activity: Find an open area where you can mark with chalk on the ground, such as a driveway or parking lot. With the white chalk, draw a small circle. With the yellow chalk, draw a larger circle outside the white one. Stand on the white line of the inner circle. Ask someone else to stand on the yellow line of the outer circle. Hold each other's arms. The white inner circle represents Earth, and the yellow outer circle represents the orbit of a satellite. Move slowly around the inner circle as Earth, and ask the human satellite to keep pace with you.

Discuss the Activity: What did you observe, in relationship to the satellite, as you moved around the circle? How does this observation activity explain why a satellite dish on Earth does not have to move?

Send and Receive Messages

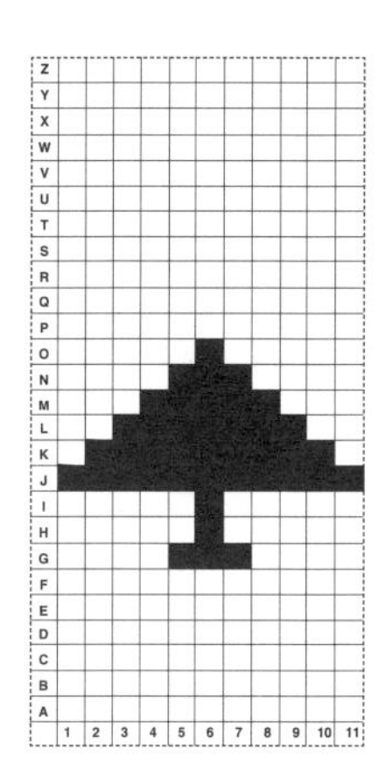

Focus Skill: graphing
Paper Handouts: a copy of Graphic 23A
Activity: Two people are needed to work together on this activity. Cut Graphic 23A into two pieces. Each person uses one piece. One person is the sender and one is the receiver. The sender will make a simple drawing on Graphic 23A, such as a happy face or a tree. Do not let the receiver see the picture. Now send messages, such as "D5," to the receiver. The receiver fills in the square. Continue this procedure until all the squares have been "sent" to the receiver. Compare the pictures and then trade places.
Discuss the Activity: What did you observe as you transmitted signals? What did you observe as you received signals?

Timeline

Paper Handouts: Space Timeline Book a copy of Graphics 23B
Graphic Organizer: Glue Graphics 23B to the correct page in the Space Timeline Book.

Experiences, Investigations, and Observations

Select one or more of the following activities for individual or group enrichment projects. Allow your students to determine the format in which they would like to report, share, or graphically present what they have discovered. This should be a creative investigation that utilizes your students' strengths.

1. Make your own time capsule. If you could send a time capsule into space, think of the things you would include. Fill a box with items or make a video tape.

2. Describe at what point the space shuttle becomes an artificial satellite.

3. Sketch examples of artificial satellites. List the pros and cons of their use. Do you think the pros outweigh the cons? Explain.

4. Differentiate between functional and nonfunctional satellites.

5. Learn how to identify artificial satellites in the night sky. The International Space Station and Hubble Space Telescope can be seen as steadily moving points of light moving from west to east in the western sky.

6. www.skypub.com/sights/satellites/satellites.html (International Space Station)

7. www.gsoc.dlr.de/satvis/ (German Space Operations Centre)

8. http://www.stsci.edu/

What do we know about life in space?

Space Concepts:

- There is no gravity or oxygen in space.
- Astronauts wear air tanks and special spacesuits, called EMU.
- Most food in space is dehydrated.
- Liquids are consumed through tubes.
- Astronauts sleep in sleeping bags attached to the wall.
- Astronauts must exercise in space because the lack of gravity weakens their muscles.

Teacher's Note: An alternative assessment suggestion for this lesson is found on pages 82–84. If Graphic Pages are being consumed, photocopy the assessment graphics that are needed first.

Vocabulary: oxygen spacesuits

Read: *Lots of Science Library Book #24.*

Activities:

Investigative Loop – Working in Space Lab 24–1

Focus Skill: comparing and contrasting
Lab Materials: rubber gloves nuts and bolts plastic dishpan water
Paper Handouts: 8.5" x 11" sheet of paper Lab Book
a copy of Lab Graphic 24–1
Graphic Organizer: Make a Large Question and Answer Book. Glue it side–by–side to the Lab Book. Glue Lab Graphic 24–1 on the left tab.

Lab 24-1

Question: How is working in space different than working on Earth?
Research: Read *Lots of Science Library Books #22, #23, and #24* and review the Question.
Procedure: Place the nuts and bolts on the table. Screw the nuts and bolts together. Unscrew the nuts and bolts. Now, fill the dishpan with water. Drop the nuts and bolts into the water. Put on the rubber gloves. Screw the nuts and bolts together under the water.
Observations: Describe how it felt to work with the nuts and bolts on the table. Describe what it was like to work with the nuts and bolts underwater wearing rubber gloves.
Record the Data: On the top section under the tab, describe the experience with the nuts and bolts on the table and under the water.
Conclusions: Completing the task on the table is like completing it on Earth. Completing the task underwater with gloves is like working in space in a bulky spacesuit. Explain the difference between the two types of work. Draw a conclusion about the preparation of an astronaut. **Possible answer: Working in space is difficult because there is no gravity. Wearing a bulky spacesuit makes it even more difficult.**

Communicate the Conclusions: On the bottom section, under the tab, write your conclusions. Include suggestions for preparing an astronaut for outer space work.
Spark Questions: Discuss questions sparked by this lab.
New Loop: Choose one question to investigate further.
✎✎✎ **Design Your Own Experiment:** Select a topic based upon the experiences in the *Investigative Loop*. See page viii for more details.

Timeline

Paper Handouts: Space Timeline Book   a copy of Graphics 24A–D
Graphic Organizer: Glue Graphics 24A–D to the correct pages in the Space Timeline Book.

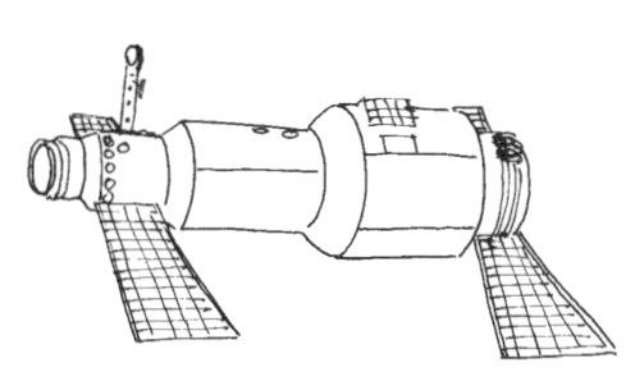 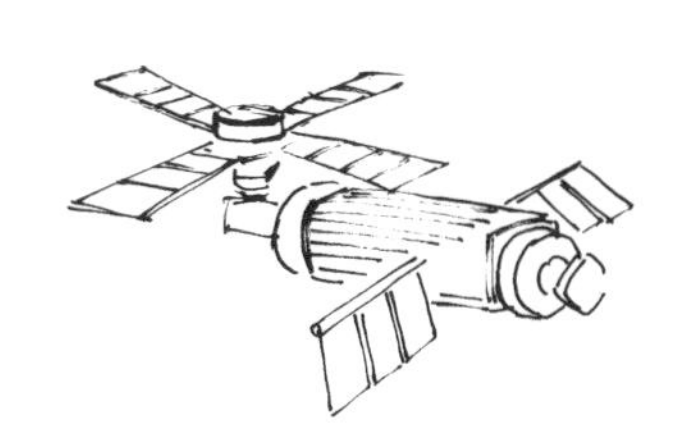 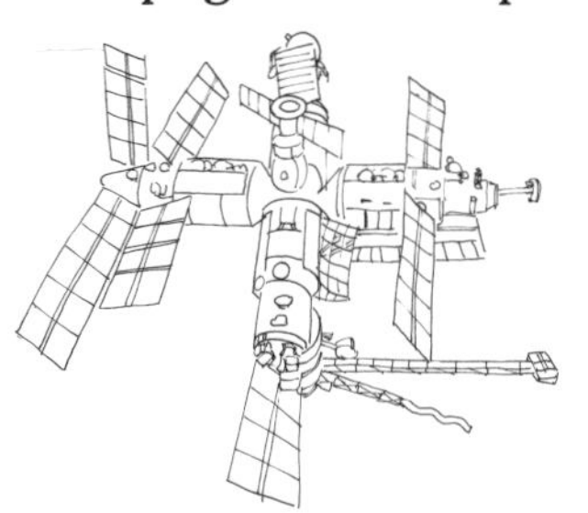 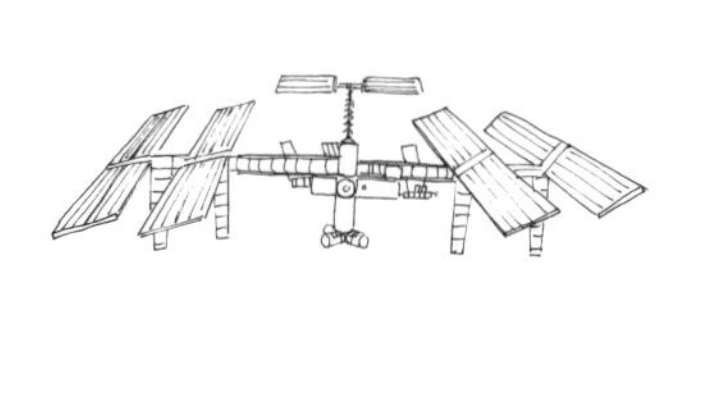

Experiences, Investigations, and Research

Select one or more of the following activities for individual or group enrichment projects. Allow your students to determine the format in which they would like to report, share, or graphically present what they have discovered. This should be a creative investigation that utilizes your students' strengths.

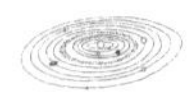

1. Design your own space station and create an imaginary crew. As you design, keep in mind the purpose of the space station and the "wants and needs" of the humans who will have to live there.

2. *Who, What, When, Where:* Investigate the international team of astronauts who have been working on the International Space Station.

3. Investigate the progress made in the construction of the International Space Station.

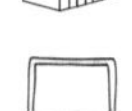

4. http://nyelabs.kcts.org/openNyeLabs.html

5. http://www.spaceflight.nasa.gov/station/index.html (NASA International Space Station)

6. Make a cumulative project using all or some of the activities in this program. Use *The Big Book of Books and Activities* by Dinah Zike for display ideas. Visit www.dinah.com or call 1-210-698-0123 for a free catalog.

Assessment: An Ongoing Process

Students do not have to memorize every vocabulary word or fact presented in these science lessons. It is more important to teach them general science processes and cause and effect relationships. Factual content is needed for students to understand processes, but it should become familiar to them through repeated exposure, discussion, reading, research, presentations, and a small amount of memorization. You can determine the amount of content your students have retained by asking specific questions that begin with the following words: *name, list, define, label, identify, draw,* and *outline.*

Try to determine how much content your students have retained through discussions. Determine how many general ideas, concepts, and processes your students understand by asking them to describe or explain them. Ask leading questions that require answers based on thought and analysis, not just facts. Use the following words and phrases as you discuss and evaluate: *why, how, describe, explain, determine,* and *predict.* Questions may sound like this:

What would happen if ____________?
Why do you think _________ happens?
What do you think about ___________?

Compare _________ to ___________.
What does ___have in common with __?
What is the importance of __________?

Alternative Assessment Strategies

If you need to know specifically what your students have retained or if you need to assign your students a grade for the content learned in this program, we suggest using one of the following assessment strategies.

By the time your students have completed a lesson in this program, they will have written about, discussed, observed, and discovered the concepts of the lesson. However, it is still important for you to review the concepts that you are assessing prior to the assessment. By making your students aware of what you expect them to know, you provide a structure for their preparations for the assessments.

1) At the end of each lesson, ask your students to restate the concepts taught in the lesson. For example, if they have made a 4 Door Book showing the steps of process, ask them to tell you about each step, using the pictures as a prompt. This assessment can be done by you or by a student.

2) At the end of each lesson, ask your students to answer the questions on the inside back cover of the *Lots of Science Library Book* for that lesson. The answers to these questions may be done verbally or in writing. Ask older students to use their vocabulary words in context as they answer the questions. This is a far more effective method to determine their knowledge of the vocabulary words than a matching or multiple choice test on the words.

3) Provide your students with Space Concept Maps that have been partially completed. Ask them to fill in the blanks. Example for Lesson 20:

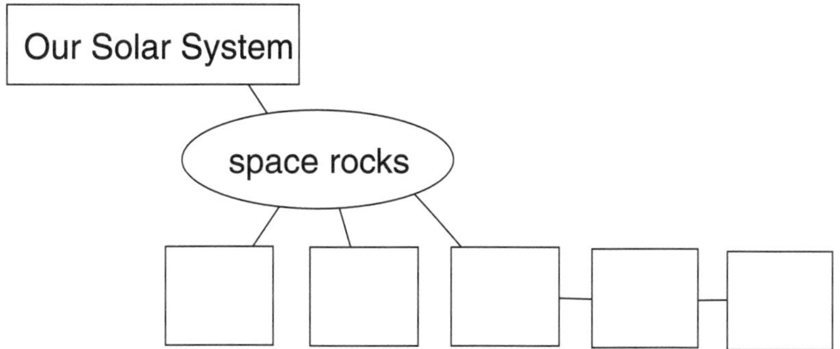

4) Use the *3D Graphic Organizers* to assess your students' understanding of the concepts. Use the *Space Concepts* listed on the teachers' pages to determine exactly what you want covered in the assessments. Primary and beginning students may use the pictures found on the Graphics Pages as guides for their assessments. By using the pictures, your students are sequencing and matching while recalling information. Older students should draw their own pictures and use the vocabulary words in their descriptions of the concepts. Below are suggestions for this method of assessment.

   a) Lesson 4 - Make a Large Question and Answer Book. On the left tab, write *Astronomy*. On the right tab, write *Stars*. Under the left tab, define astronomy, explain how ancient man used it, and track the developments that took place from 350 B.C. to the 1930's. Under the right tab, explain the life stages of a star. Include information about the star closest to Earth.

   b) Lesson 5 - Make a 4 Door Book. On the front, write *Galaxies*. Write these words on the tabs: *galaxies, irregular galaxy, elliptical galaxy, and spiral galaxy*. Define the words under the appropriate tab and explain details of it.

   c) Lesson 9 - Make a Large Question and Answer Book. On the left tab, write *Solar Eclipse*. Under the tab, sketch this eclipse and explain what occurs during a solar eclipse. On the right tab, write *Lunar Eclipse*. Under the tab, sketch this eclipse and explain what occurs during a lunar eclipse.

   d) Lesson 13 - Make a Half Book. On the cover, sketch the Sun and the first four planets in our solar system. Inside, describe these planets and compare and contrast their size, weather conditions, and movements. Describe where most of the asteroids in the solar system are contained.

   e) Lesson 18 - Make a Half Book. On the cover, sketch the Sun and the last five planets in our solar system. Inside, describe these planets and compare and contrast their size, weather conditions, and movements.

f) Lesson 20 - Make a Large Question and Answer Book. On the left tab, write *Comets.* On the right tab, write *Meteoroids.* Under each tab, describe the space rock and track its possible path as it nears Earth.

g) Lesson 24 - Make a two-page Layered Look Book. On the cover, write *Space Exploration.* On the first tab, write *Early Space Explorations.* On that page, describe early space explorations, up to the first lunar landing. Explain the progression in these explorations. On the second tab, write *Space Shuttle.* Describe the space shuttle and explain its importance in continued space explorations. Include an explanation of life in space. On the last tab, write *Satellites, Probes,* and *Telescopes.* Explain how each is used in the study of space. Compare their use and predict what equipment might be used for future space exploration.

Lots of Science Library Books

Each *Lots of Science Library Book* is made up of 16 inside pages, plus a front and back cover. All the covers to the *Lots of Science Library Books* are located at the front of this section. The covers are followed by the inside pages of the books.

How to Photocopy the *Lots of Science Library Books*

As part of their *Great Science Adventure,* your students will create *Lots of Science Library Books.* The *Lots of Science Library Books* are provided as consumable pages which may be cut out of the *Great Science Adventures* book at the line on the top of each page. If, however, you wish to make photocopies for your students, you can do so by following the instructions below.

To photocopy the inside pages of the *Lots of Science Library Books:*

1. Note that there is a "Star" above the line at the top of each *LSLB* sheet.

2. Locate the *LSLB* sheet that has a Star on it above page 16. Position this sheet on the glass of your photocopier so the side of the sheet which contains page 16 is facing down, and the Star above page 16 is in the left corner closest to you. Photocopy the page.

3. Turn the *LSLB* sheet over so that the side of the *LSLB* sheet containing page 6 is now face down. Position the sheet so the Star above page 6 is again in the left corner closest to you.

4. Insert the previously photocopied paper into the copier again, inserting it face down, with the Star at the end of the sheet that enters the copier last. Photocopy the page.

5. Repeat steps 1 through 4, above, for each *LSLB* sheet.

To photocopy the covers of the *Lots of Science Library Books:*

1. Insert "Cover Sheet A" in the photocopier with a Star positioned in the left corner closest to you, facing down. Photocopy the page.

2. Turn "Cover Sheet A" over so that the side you just photocopied is now facing you. Position the sheet so the Star is again in the left corner closest to you, facing down.

3. Insert the previously photocopied paper into the copier again, inserting it face down, with the Star entering the copier last. Photocopy the page.

4. Repeat steps 1 through 3, above, for "Cover Sheets" B, C, D, E, and F.

How to assemble the *Lots of Science Library Books*

Once you have made the photocopies or cut the consumable pages out of this book, you are ready to assemble your *Lots of Science Library Books.* To do so, follow these instructions:

1. Cut each sheet, both covers and inside pages, on the solid lines.

2. Lay the inside pages on top of one another in this order: pages 2 and 15, pages 4 and 13, pages 6 and 11, pages 8 and 9.

3. Fold the stacked pages on the dotted line, with pages 8 and 9 facing each other.

4. Turn the pages over so that pages 1 and 16 are on top.

5. Place the appropriate cover pages on top of the inside pages, with the front cover facing up.

6. Staple on the dotted line in two places.

You now have completed *Lots of Science Library Books.*

Who were the first astronomers?

Lots of Science Library Book #2

A GREAT EARTH SCIENCE STUDY

What is the Sun?

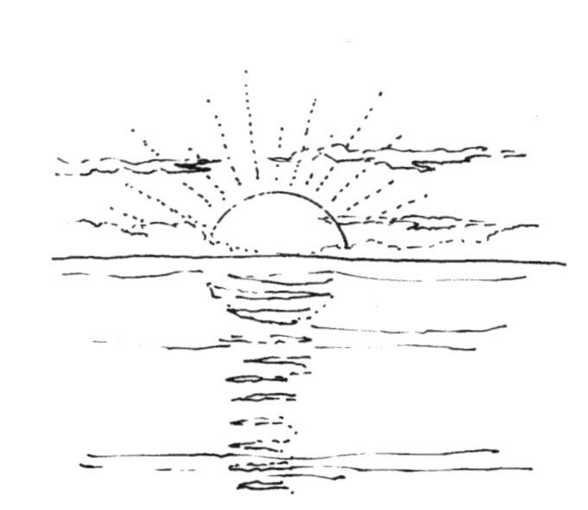
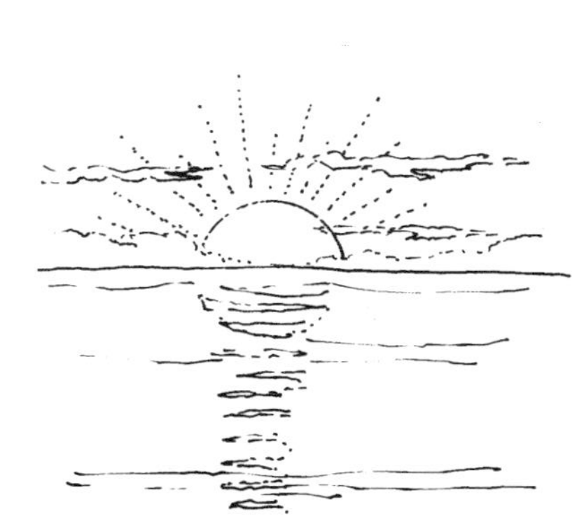

Lots of Science Library Book #4

What is astronomy?

Lots of Science Library Book #1

A GREAT EARTH SCIENCE STUDY

What are stars?

Lots of Science Library Book #3

A

heat
light
energy
core
sunspots

* photosphere
* chromosphere
* corona
* magnetic

Describe the Sun.

sun
planet
telescope

* astronomer

Describe three discoveries by early astronomers.

gas
hydrogen
spin
collide

* temperature
* supernova

Explain the life cycle of a star.

star
space

* astronomy
* constellation

Explain how people have used the stars.

Describe a constellation.

What is the solar system?

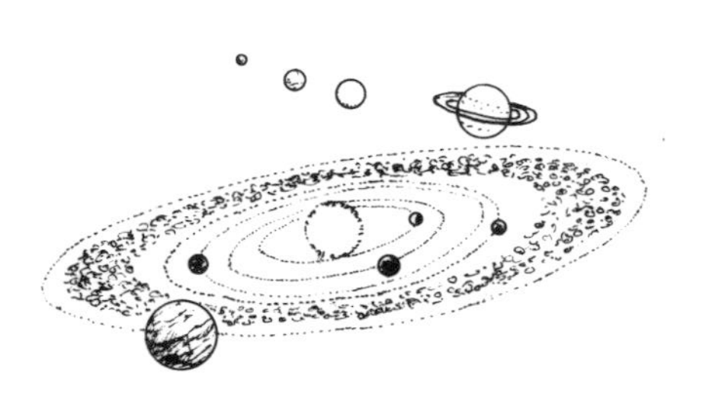

Lots of Science Library Book #6

What do we know about the Moon?

Lots of Science Library Book #8

What are galaxies?

Lots of Science Library Book #5

What do we know about Earth?

Lots of Science Library Book #7

B

moon
sky
reflect
satellite
phases

* luminous
* crescent moon
* full moon
* waning
* waxing

Describe the Moon.

solar system
planet
moon
orbit
rotate
axis

* asteroid
* revolution
* rotation

Describe our solar system.

Earth
atmosphere
spin

* organic
* inorganic
* hemisphere
* circumference

Describe Earth.

stars
galaxy
cluster
spiral
Milky Way

* irregular
* elliptical
* light-year

Describe the three
types of galaxies.

What do we know about Mercury?

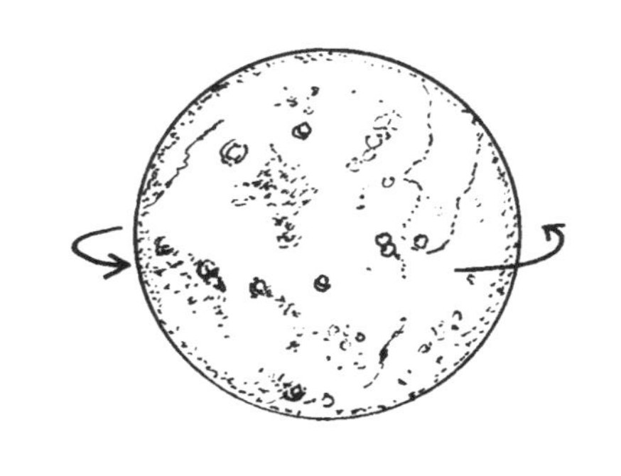

Lots of Science Library Book #10

What do we know about Mars?

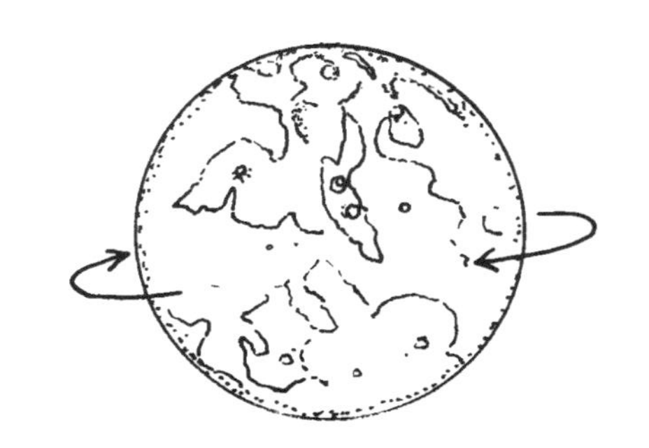

Lots of Science Library Book #12

What is an eclipse?

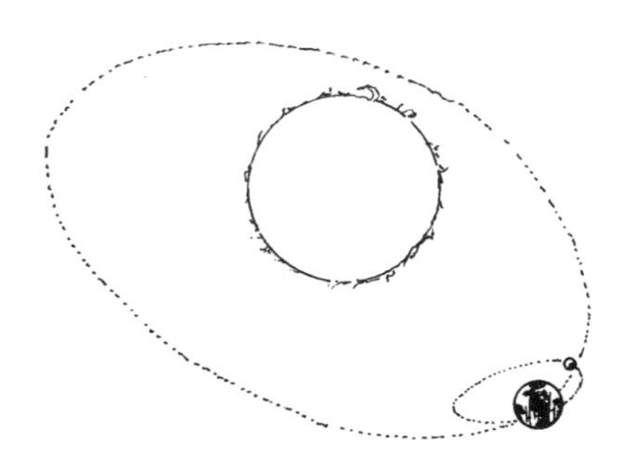

Lots of Science Library Book #9

What do we know about Venus?

Lots of Science Library Book #11

C

volcano
dust storm

* carbon dioxide

Describe Mars.

rocky
mantle
crater
helium
hydrogen

* ellipse
* elongated

Describe Mercury.

diameter
gaseous
gravity

* atmospheric pressure

Describe Venus.

eclipse
sunlight
lunar
solar

* umbra
* penumbra

Explain lunar eclipse.

Explain a solar eclipse.

A GREAT EARTH SCIENCE STUDY

What do we know about Jupiter?

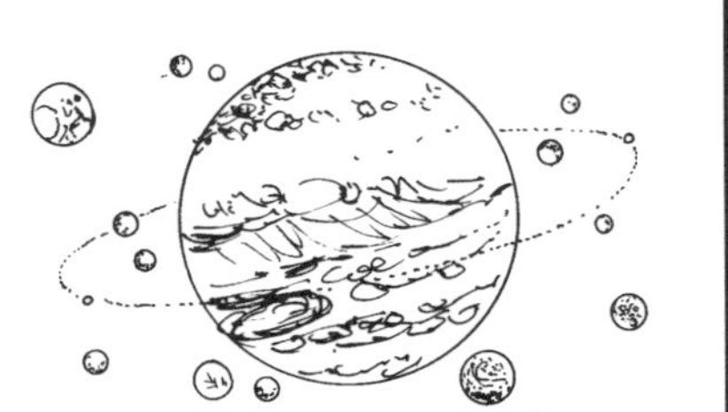

Lots of Science Library Book #14

A GREAT EARTH SCIENCE STUDY

What do we know about Uranus?

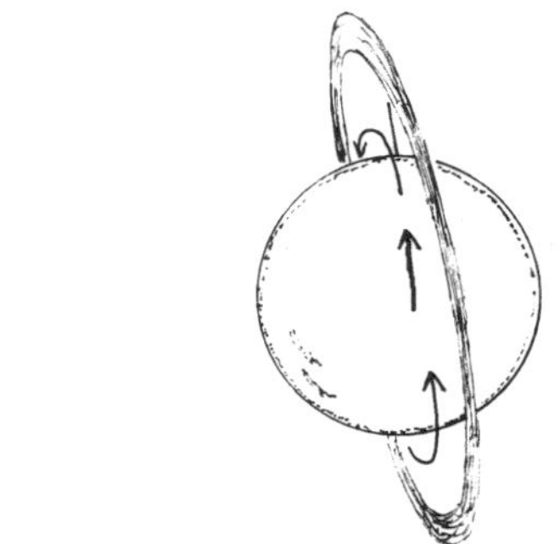

Lots of Science Library Book #16

A GREAT EARTH SCIENCE STUDY

What do we know about the asteroid belt?

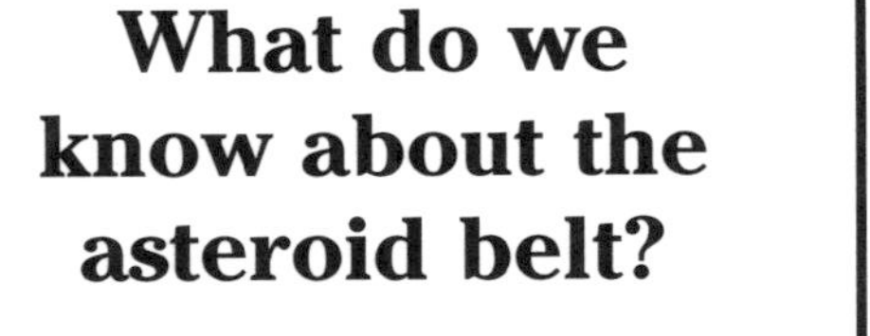

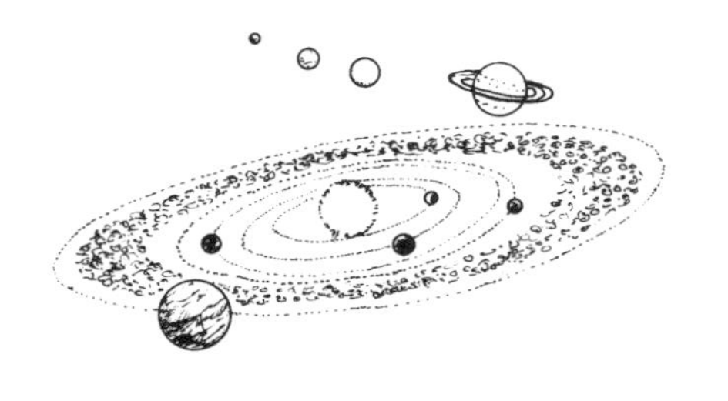

Lots of Science Library Book #13

A GREAT EARTH SCIENCE STUDY

What do we know about Saturn?

Lots of Science Library Book #15

D

* methane

Describe Uranus.

equator
ring
solid
cloud

* bulge

Describe Jupiter.

ice
rock
gas

* fragmented
* density

Describe Saturn.

carbon
nickel
belt

* albedo

Describe the asteroid belt.

What do we know about Pluto?

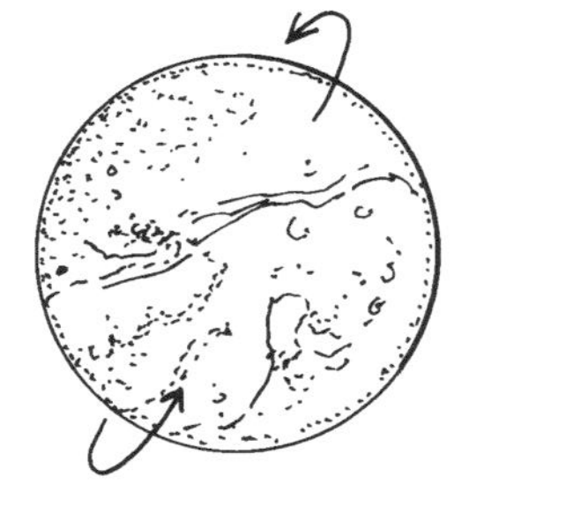

Lots of Science Library Book #18

What are meteoroids, meteors, and meteorites?

Lots of Science Library Book #20

What do we know about Neptune?

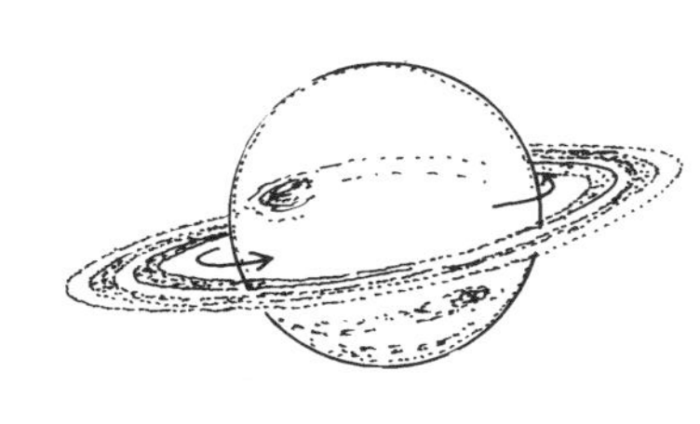

Lots of Science Library Book #17

What are comets?

Lots of Science Library Book #19

E

meteoroid
meteor
meteorite

Describe a meteoroid, meteor, and meteorite.

* carbon monoxide

Describe Pluto.

comet
tail
coma

* nucleus

Describe a comet.

Explain the movement of comets in the inner solar system.

Describe Neptune.

A GREAT EARTH SCIENCE STUDY

What is the space shuttle?

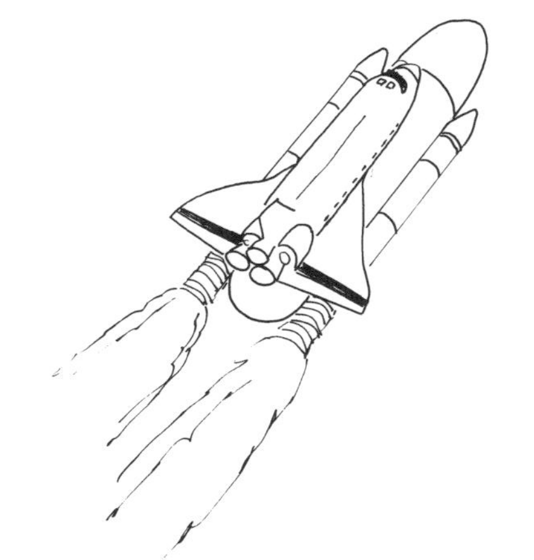

Lots of Science Library Book #22

A GREAT EARTH SCIENCE STUDY

What do we know about life in space?

Lots of Science Library Book #24

A GREAT EARTH SCIENCE STUDY

When did people begin space explorations?

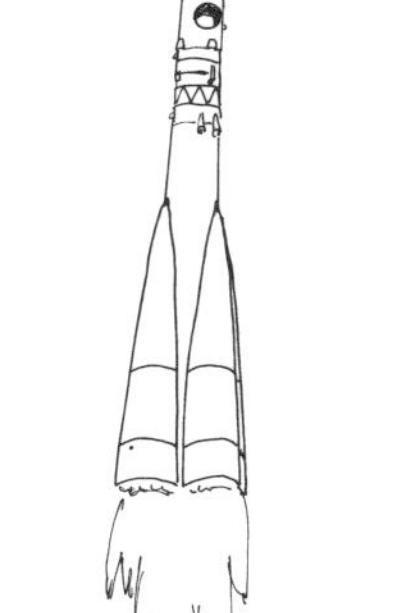

Lots of Science Library Book #21

A GREAT EARTH SCIENCE STUDY

What are satellites, space probes, and the Hubble Telescope?

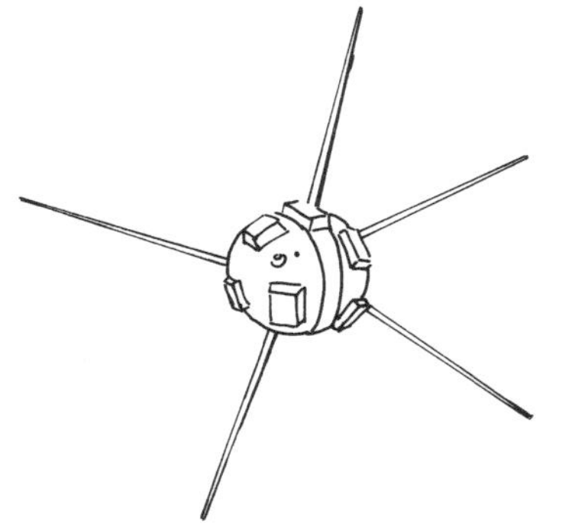

Lots of Science Library Book #23

F

oxygen
space suits

Describe life in space.

Explain the EMU and why
it is so important.

reusable
orbiter
external booster
engine

* manipulator

Describe the space shuttle.

Explain why the space
shuttle is important
to space exploration.

probe
telescope

* observatory

Explain three uses of
satellites.

Explain why the Hubble
Space Telescope is unique.

explore
vehicle
rocket
spacecraft

* tether
* excursion

Describe three early
space explorations.

The stars in a constellation look like they are close together, but in reality these stars are very far apart.

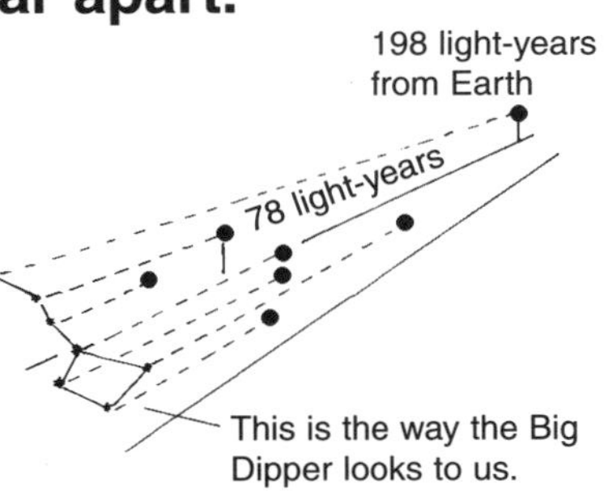

Hi. My name is Astronaut Al. I am your tour guide into space.

A building where people observe stars and other heavenly bodies is called an observatory. The oldest observatory still standing is the Chomsungdae Observatory in South Korea. It was built about 632 A.D. Other ancient observatories have been found in Mexico and India.

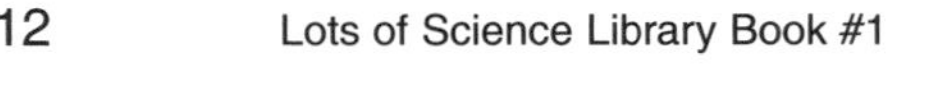

The study of space is called astronomy. Astronomy comes from the Greek word *astron*, meaning "star," and *nemein*, meaning "to name."

Clocks and calendars help us keep track of time.

Stonehenge, built about 2000 B.C. and located in England, contains large stones placed in a circular arrangement. Although Stonehenge remains a mystery, scientists believe that it was used as a type of clock or calendar.

The ancient Babylonians (2700 B.C. - 538 B.C.) kept records of the movements of planets and moon phases. These records enabled them to determine when to sow and harvest crops.

Ancient Babylonia is current-day Iraq.

When we want to know the time, we look at a clock. A clock divides a day into 24 hours.

When we want to know the date, we look at a calendar. A calendar divides a year into 12 months.

Early stargazers imagined that stars outlined pictures in the sky. The group of stars that form these patterns are called constellations.

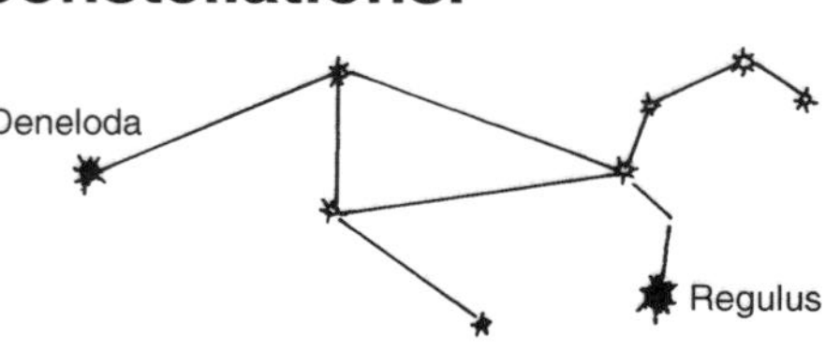

The ancient Greeks named 48 constellations. More recent stargazers have named about 40 more.

Long ago, sailors depended on the stars to guide them in navigation.

Ancient Egyptians marked the passage of time by observing the phases of the moon. They defined one month as the time between one new moon and another.

In ancient times, before there were clocks and calendars, people realized that the Sun, Moon, and stars moved in a regular manner. By observing these bodies in space, they were able to mark the passing of time.

Dedicated astronomers continue to study space.

Much of what we know about space was unknown thousands of years ago. In 150 A.D., a Greek astronomer named Ptolemy believed that Earth stood still and the Sun, stars, and planets circled around it.

This belief is called the Ptolemaic system.

3) The time it takes for a planet to complete one revolution around the Sun depends on its distance from the Sun. The closer the planet is to the Sun, the shorter the revolution.

Because telescopes had not been invented, Copernicus had to observe the sky with the naked eye. Copernicus' theory became very controversial and was banned by the authorities of the time.

Sir Isaac Newton (1642-1727), an English scientist, invented the reflecting telescope, which used mirrors instead of lenses. Newton's research was based on Kepler's three laws of planetary motion.

Newton's theory on universal gravitation was fundamental to astronomy through the 19th century.

Scientists who study the stars and planets are called astronomers. In 1543, Nicolaus Copernicus (1473-1543), a Polish monk and astronomer claimed that the Earth and the planets circled around a still Sun.

This is the heliocentric view of the universe.

2) Each planet's orbital speed depends on its distance from the Sun. The closer the planet is to the Sun, the faster it orbits.

About 70 years later, Galileo Galilei (1564-1642) proved Copernicus' theory by observing the planets with the first telescope. He was charged with heresy and his writings were banned. Gaileo invented the first refracting telescope, which used glass lenses to bend light.

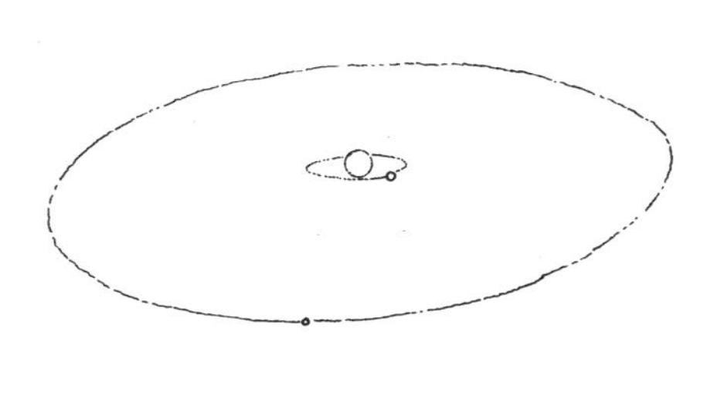

In 350 B.C., the Greek philosopher Aristotle argued that Earth was round, not flat. It would be hundreds of years before this fact came to be accepted.

Newton also made remarkable discoveries about gravity, motion, and light.

Johannes Kepler (1571-1630), a German mathematician, discovered three laws of planetary motion.

1) Planets orbit, or circle, the Sun in an elliptical pattern.

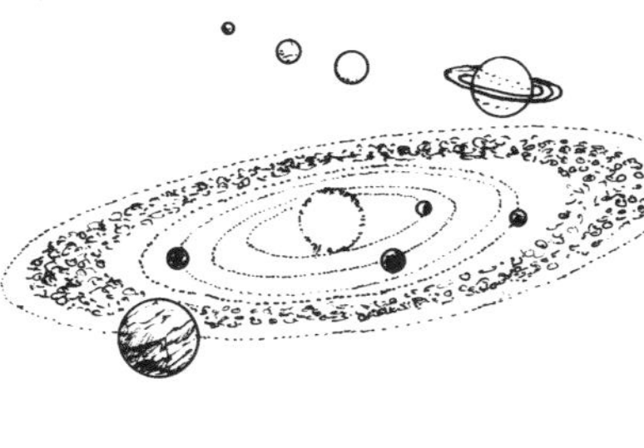

Sun

This planet takes about 59 Earth days to orbit the Sun.

This planet takes about 248 Earth years to orbit the Sun.

Most stars are so far away that it takes thousands of years for their light to reach Earth. The light can travel to Earth long after the star has died. When you look at a star, it is as though you are looking back in time.

"Twinkle, twinkle, little star ...."
This familiar rhyme and the appearance of stars may lead us to think that stars really do twinkle.

Proxima Centauri is the next closest star to Earth. Alpha Centauri and Alpha Centauri B are the third and fourth closest stars to Earth.

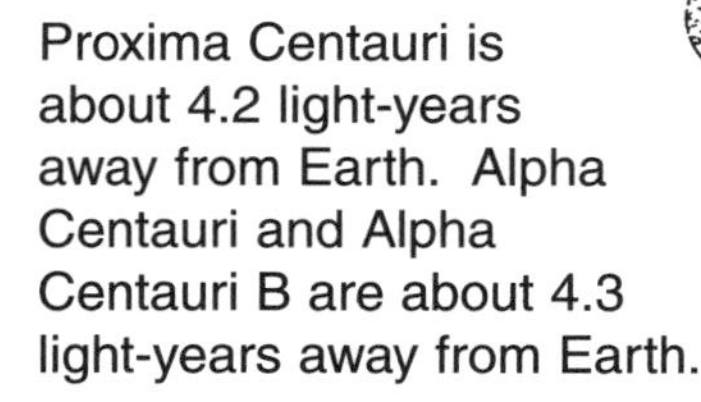

Proxima Centauri is about 4.2 light-years away from Earth. Alpha Centauri and Alpha Centauri B are about 4.3 light-years away from Earth.

The spinning causes the atoms to collide and heat up. As heat increases, the core of the new star is formed and starts to burn, or shine.

The first star brightness classification system was invented by the Greek astronomer Hipparchus in 134 B.C.

This system is called apparent magnitude. It classifies stars by how bright they appear from Earth.

Stars move through the Universe, because they move at the same rate as all the objects around them, they do not appear to be moving.

nebula

main sequence star

planetary nebula

black dwarf

A star's lifespan depends on its mass at birth and how quickly it burns up hydrogen. An average-sized star, like our Sun, will burn until it runs out of hydrogen. It then expands, cools, collapses, and dies. A "dead star" is called a black dwarf.

The Sun is the closest star to Earth. Because the Sun is so close to Earth, it appears large compared to other stars. This is also why we can see the Sun during the day but other stars are usually only seen at night.

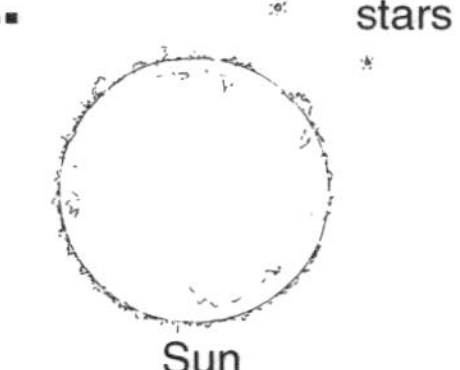

Stars actually glow with a steady light. When their light hits the Earth's atmosphere, gas molecules move the light around. This makes the stars look like they are twinkling in the night sky.

A more accurate way to measure the brightness of stars was developed by Ejnar Hertzsprung (1873-1967). This scale ranks the brightness of stars as if they were all exactly the same distance from Earth.

This classification system is called the absolute magnitude.

The death of a massive star is spectacular. As hydrogen burns up, the star expands, contracts, and then explodes with a brilliant flash. This is called a supernova.

The colors found in a star help to determine its temperature. Use this poem to help you remember what the colors in stars mean:

Cold stars
Orange and red,
Hot stars
Blue and white,
Medium stars
White and yellow,
All producing
Heat and light.
Dinah Zike

Most stars go through life stages. Stars are born in giant clouds of dust and gases, mostly hydrogen and helium. Gravity pulls the giant clouds together to form a spinning cloud.

Clouds of dust and gas that give birth to stars are called nebulae. Although stars are not living, most stars go through life stages: birth, childhood, adolescence, maturity, middle age, old age, and death.

Stars have different levels of brightness. The Sun looks much brighter than other stars because it is so close to Earth. However, the star Sirius A is a much brighter star than the Sun.

Never look directly at the Sun because it can damage your eyes. Remember this poem:

Be careful!
Our Sun is so bright,
We can be
Blinded by its light.
The safest Sun-viewing bet,
Is when it rises and as it sets

Dinah Zike

The Sun is a star that is located at the center of our solar system. Unlike most stars, it appears to be large. We can see it during the day because it is close to Earth.

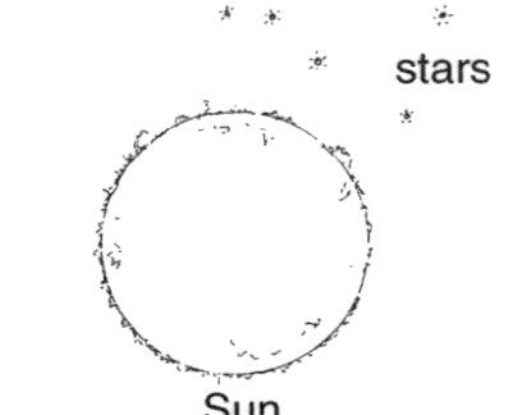

3) The next layer is the Sun's lower atmosphere, called the chromosphere. Solar flares are extremely powerful explosions that are unleashed from the chromosphere.

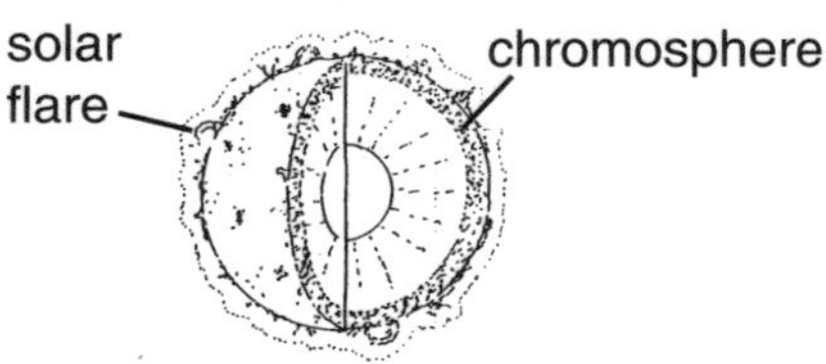

The Sun is not solid. It is a ball of hot gases. Heat in the Sun is produced by hydrogen being transformed into helium. Temperatures reach up to 30 million degrees F (16,600,000˚C) in the Sun's core.

Sunspots are cooler than the surrounding photosphere. They appear darker than the rest of the Sun's surface.

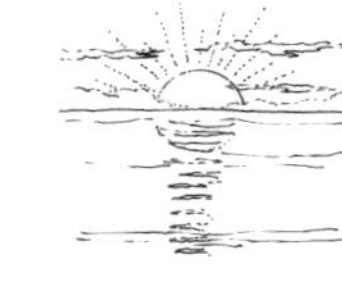

Sunspots are areas of magnetic force that are thousands of times more powerful than the magnetic field of the Sun. Though they vary in size, most of them are larger than Earth. Early Chinese astronomers recorded observations of sunspots in the 2nd century B.C.

Tiny bits of light called photons are produced and released from the Sun's core. These photons travel from the core to the surface of the Sun.

The Sun is made up of four main layers.
1) The core is the center of the Sun. The heat and light that we feel and see are produced in the Sun's core.

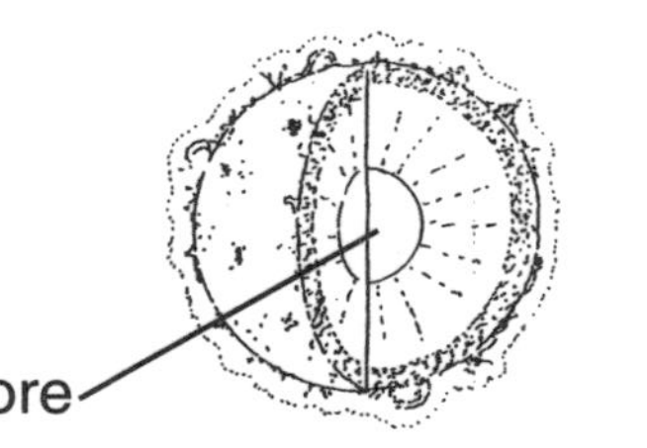

Look at this dot.

•

A dot this size, made up of the Sun's heat, could kill someone 90 miles away.

Sir Joseph Norman Lockyer (1836-1920), a British astronomer, observed the Sun and discovered a new element in 1868. He named it helium, after *helios*, which is a Greek word for Sun.

2) The next layer, the photosphere, is the Sun's surface. The energy produced in the core makes its way here, where it gives off heat, light, and electromagnetic radiation.

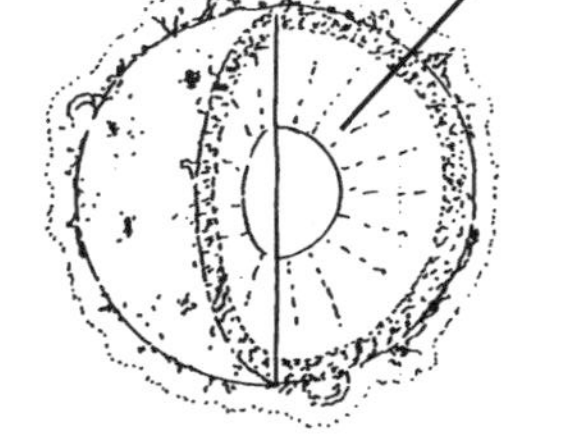

The Sun produces light and heat from its core. The light and heat are produced through nuclear fusion.

Nuclear fusion creates a release of tiny bits of light called photons.

When the Sun appears low in the sky, its light passes through extra atmosphere to reach Earth. This extra atmosphere is filled with dust and particles that scatter the Sun's light. This scattering of light makes the beautiful colors that we see at sunrise and sunset.

The Sun's diameter is about 865,000 miles (1,392,000 km). If the Sun were a hollow ball, it could hold over one million Earths.

The force that attracts one object to another is called gravity. The Sun's gravitational pull keeps nine planets and thousands of asteroids in orbit. The Sun's surface gravity is about 30 times stronger that that of Earth. An object that weighs 100 pounds on Earth would weigh about 3,000 pounds on the Sun.

It takes 8 minutes and 20 seconds for the light of the Sun to reach Earth. Compare that to our next closest star, Proxima Centauri. It takes about 4.2 years for the light from Proxima Centauri to reach Earth.

4) The outermost layer of the Sun's atmosphere is called the corona. It is constantly expanding and changing shape.

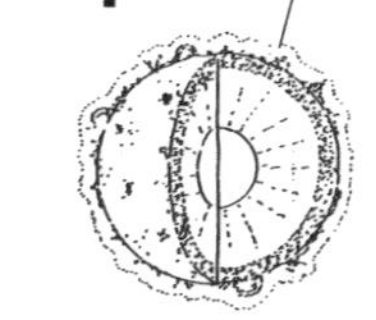

Francis Baily (1774-1844) named this layer the "corona" because it looked like a crown around the Sun.

The research of Henrietta Leavitt (1868-1921), an American astronomer who studied the stars and their brightness led the way for accurately determining the distances between galaxies.

Come aboard and fasten your seat belt. It is time to tour the universe.

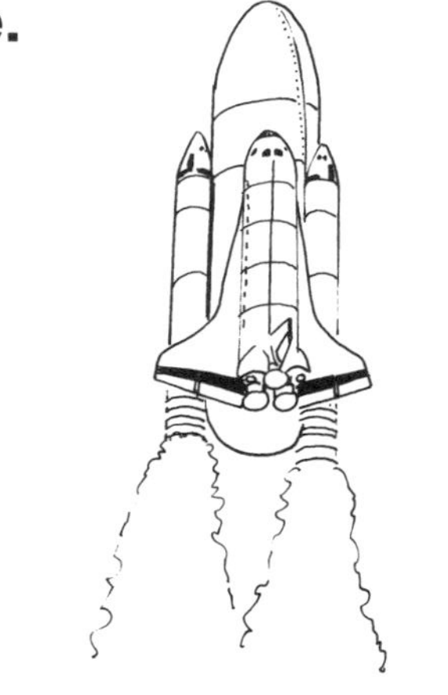

As we journey through the Milky Way, we can see its four main spiraling arms. The central bulge is made up mostly of older red and yellow stars. The stars in the spiral arms are mostly young blue stars.

Andromeda Galaxy

Many galaxies form groups called clusters. The Milky Way is part of a small cluster of galaxies called the Local Group. The Local Group is made up of approximately 30 known galaxies.

When clusters of galaxies form a group, they are called "superclusters."

Globular clusters contain hundreds of thousands of older stars arranged in ball shapes.

The center sphere of the Milky Way Galaxy is an example.

For years, people thought our solar system lay in the center of the galaxy. Dutch astronomer Jan Oort (1900-1992) discovered the true position of our Sun in the Milky Way. Jan Oort also discovered a cloud of comets surrounding our solar system, now named Oort Cloud.

3) A spiral galaxy has arms that extend out from a central bulge. It contains both old and new stars.

★

Galaxies are classified into three categories:

1) An irregular galaxy has no set shape and is made of many new stars.

2) An elliptical galaxy is egg-shaped and is made of very old stars.

Oort Cloud

Stars are not spread out evenly in space; they form groups, or clusters. The stars in each cluster were formed from the same cloud and are about the same age and composition. Open clusters of stars are made up of a few hundred very young and randomly arranged stars.

American astronomer Edwin Hubble (1889-1953) discovered that Andromeda was a galaxy separated by space from the Milky Way Galaxy. This discovery changed the science of astronomy forever since scientists had assumed the Milky Way was the only galaxy in the Universe.

We live in a spiral galaxy called the Milky Way. It is made up of over 200 billion stars, including our Sun. We cannot see the spirals because Earth is located in one of the spiral arms. The Milky Way, like all galaxies, is constantly moving in space. Not only is the whole galaxy moving, but all the stars within it are moving.

Galaxies are huge collections of stars, dust, and gas held together by gravity. Small galaxies contain about 100,000 stars. The Andromeda Galaxy contains more than 3,000 billion stars. Astronomers estimate that there are billions of galaxies in the universe.

Distances in space are so great that scientists use in light-years as units of measurement. A light-year does not measure time; it measures distance. A light-year is the distance light travels in a year. Light travels about 5.9 trillion miles (9.5 trillion km) in a year, at approximately 186,000 miles (299,338 km) per second.

Although Mercury is the closest planet to the Sun, Venus is the hottest planet in our solar system. Pluto is the farthest from the Sun and is the coldest planet. All the planets except Mercury and Venus have at least one moon. Saturn and Uranus have rings around their surface.

The planets, moons, and asteroids orbiting the Sun make up our solar system. These heavenly bodies orbit the Sun in a counterclockwise motion. The solar system is one small part of our galaxy, the Milky Way.

One trip around the Sun is called a revolution, and is measured as a year. It takes 365 $^{1}/_{4}$ days for Earth to complete one revolution. The planet with the shortest revolution in the solar system is Mercury at about 88 Earth days. Pluto has the longest revolution, is about 248 Earth years.

As planets orbit the Sun, they also spin on their axis. This is called rotation, and one rotation equals a day. It takes Earth 24 hours to complete one rotation.

The planet with the shortest rotation is Saturn at about 10 $^{1}/_{2}$ Earth hours. Venus has the longest rotation at about 243 Earth days.

Pluto
Neptune
Uranus
Saturn
Jupiter

He named the asteroid Ceres. At about 623 miles (1002 km) across, it is the largest known asteroid.

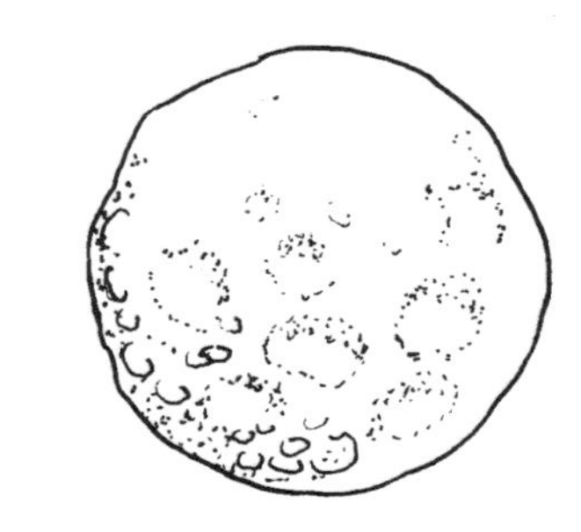

Asteroids are small, rocky bodies found orbiting the Sun. In 1801, Italian astronomer Father Giuseppi Piazzi observed an unknown light between Mars and Jupiter. At first he thought it was a comet, but he had actually discovered the first asteroid.

The next four planets, Jupiter, Saturn, Uranus, and Neptune, are called the gaseous planets or the jovian planets. They are also called the "outer planets" because they are distant from the Sun. Distant Pluto is a very small solid planet.

The Sun's gravity prevents the planets and other heavenly bodies from hurling into space.

The word "planet" comes from the Greek word *planetes,* meaning "wanderer."

While the planets are orbiting the Sun and revolving on their axis, the entire solar system is circling the Milky Way in a counterclockwise motion.

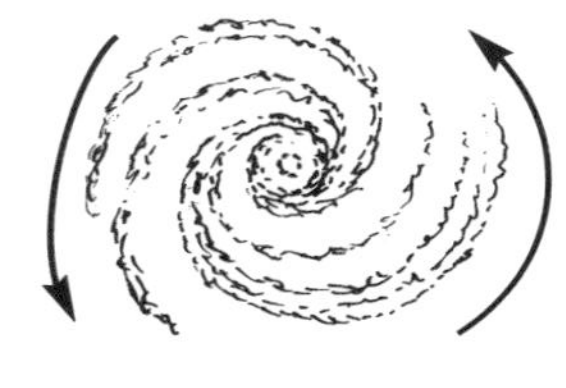

The Sun is at the center of our solar system. The first four planets, Mercury, Venus, Earth, and Mars, are called the rocky or solid planets. These terrestrial planets are also called "inner planets" because of their locations near the Sun.

Mars
Earth
Mercury
Venus

In ancient Greece, the circle was believed to be a perfect geometric form. Ptolemy believed the Universe was perfect; therefore, objects moved in perfect circular orbits. In the 16th century, Johannes Kepler determined that planets moved in elliptical or oval orbits.

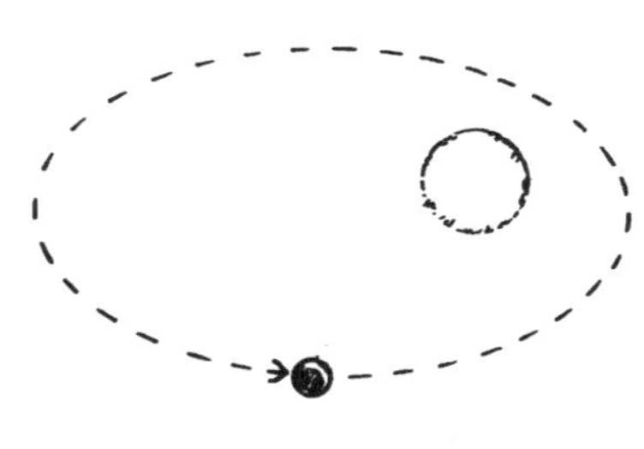

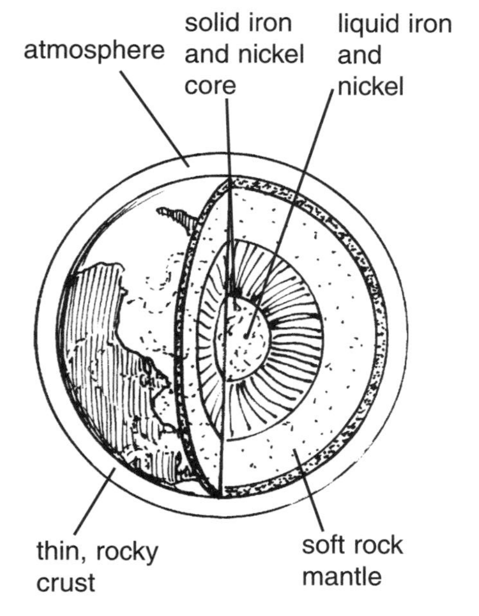

Earth is the planet we know the most about. Earth, the third planet, is about 93 million miles (150 billion km) from the Sun. Earth is not a perfect circular sphere. It is slightly flattened at the top and bottom - its poles - so that it bulges out at the middle.

An imaginary line around the middle of Earth divides it into two parts, the northern and southern hemispheres. This imaginary line is called the equator. Earth's climate is hottest at the equator because it is closest to the Sun. The North and South Poles are the coldest places on Earth.

North Pole

Equator

South Pole

The circumference at the equator is 24,902 miles (40,066 km). The circumference at the poles is 24,859 miles (40,000 km).

Earth is the only planet known to have both living and nonliving matter.

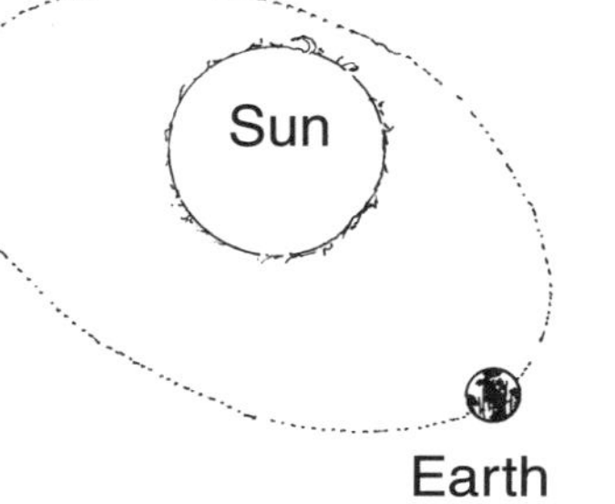

Living matter is called organic matter. Nonliving matter is called inorganic matter.

Earth's surface is about 79% water and 21% land. Earth's protective atmosphere allows water to exist in all three states of matter: solid ice, liquid water, and water vapor.

Earth spins eastward. When we say "the Sun rises in the east", we mean that it appears that way because of this eastward movement. As Earth rotates, different parts of it are exposed to the Sun.

Earth is "just right" in relationship to the Sun. If it were 2% closer or farther from the Sun, life as we know it could not exist. This is sometimes called the "Goldilocks Theory."

Earth's coldest air temperature is recorded at about –140° F. The hottest air temperature is recorded at about +140° F.

1) The center, or core, of Earth is solid iron and nickel, surrounded by a layer of liquid iron and nickel.
2) The next layer, or mantle, is made up of soft rock that is in motion.
3) All of this is covered by Earth's thin, rocky crust. Earth's crust is divided into plates that sit on top of the mantle. Often the mantle's movement results in earthquakes and volcanoes.

As the Earth spins on its axis, it also orbits the Sun in a counter-clockwise motion. The orbital movement around the Sun is called a revolution. It takes $365^1/_4$ days, or one year, to make one trip around the Sun. That is why every fourth year, (called leap year), a day is added to February.

Sun

Earth

Earth spins at about 500 MPH around an imaginary line called its axis. It is spinning on its axis at a tilt. The Earth spins at about 500 MPH. It takes 24 hours to spin around one time. One spin makes a complete day and night. The spinning motion of a planet is called rotation.

Earth measures about 24,902 miles (40,066 km) around at the equator. The diameter of Earth is 7,926 miles (12,753 km).
If you could drive a car at 60 MPH, day and night, without stopping, it would take about 17 days to drive around the Earth's equator.

If a full moon occurs on the first night of a month, there could be another full moon at the end of the month, since there are only 29.53 days between full moons. When there are two full moons in one month, the second full moon is called a "blue moon." Blue moons occur about every 2 $^1/_2$ to 3 years, so if someone says something happens "once in a blue moon" you will know how often they mean.

The Moon appears to be the largest object in the night sky.

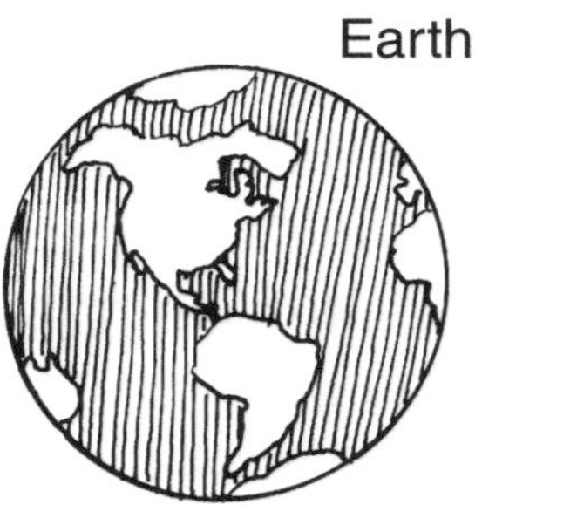

The surface of the Moon is covered with a layer of gray dust that smells like gunpowder. The Moon has no liquid water and it has thousands of small and large holes, called craters. Asteroids crashing into the Moon formed most of the craters.

A satellite is an object that orbits another, larger, object. The Moon is Earth's natural satellite. Earth's gravity keeps the Moon in its orbit. It takes the Moon about 27 days to complete one trip around Earth.

For years people wondered what was on the other side of the Moon. In 1959, the unmanned Russian space probe *Luna 3* revealed more craters and fewer plains on the far side of the Moon.

Earth looks beautiful and bright from the Moon because Earth's water reflects the light of the Sun.

The Moon is about 238,868 miles (384,338 km) away from Earth.

The Moon appears to change shape because we see sunlight reflected from it at different angles as it orbits Earth. The different shapes of the Moon are called phases.

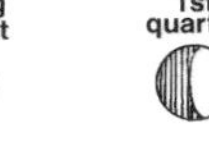

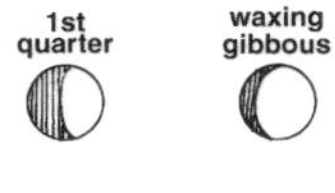

During a new Moon, the Moon appears invisible because you cannot see any of the sunlit side.

The Moon has $^1/_6$th the gravity of Earth. A rock weighing 100 lbs (45 kg) on Earth would only weigh about 17 lbs (7.7 kg) on the Moon.

100 lbs
on Earth

17 lbs
on the Moon

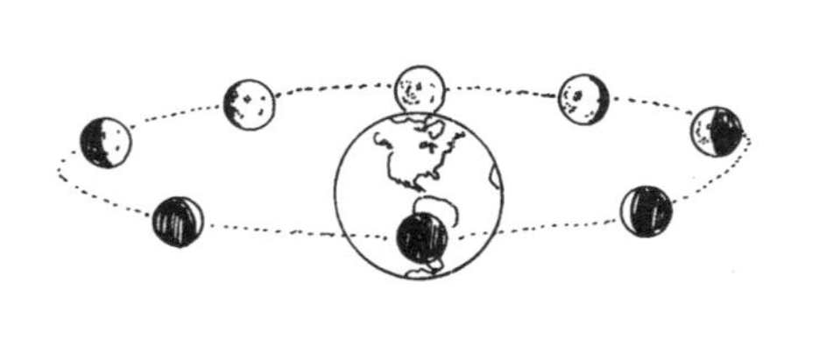

When a little of the Moon's sunlit side can be seen, it is called a crescent moon. When you can see all of the Moon's sunlit side, it is called a full moon. When the Moon goes from a full Moon to a new moon, it is waning. When the Moon goes from new moon to full moon, it is waxing.

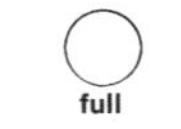
full

waxing gibbous

last quarter

waning crescent

From Earth the Moon appears to be about the size of the Sun, but it is much smaller. Since the Moon is closer to Earth, than the Sun, it appears large. The diameter of the Moon is about 2,160 miles (3,475 km), $^1/_4$ the diameter of Earth. It would take about 50 Moons to fill a ball the size of Earth.

A footprint will remain on the surface of the Moon for hundreds of years because there is no wind to blow it away.

The gravity of the Moon is too weak to hold atmospheric gases close to its surface.

As the Moon revolves around Earth, it also spins very slowly. It takes about 27 days for the Moon to rotate on its axis. Since this is the same amount of time it takes for the Moon to revovle around Earth, the same side of the Moon always faces the Earth.

When the time to complete one rotation is the same as the time to complete one revolution it is called synchronous rotation.

The Moon appears to shine brightly but it produces no light. It is not luminous; it mirrors, or reflects, the light of the Sun.

The term "albedo" refers to the amount of light from the Sun that is reflected off a planet or satellite. The Moon is dull gray and is not very reflective, so it has a low albedo of 17%.

From Earth, the smooth plains of the Moon look like dark patches. These dark areas sometimes give the appearance of a face. Have you ever seen "the man in the moon?"

The smooth plains are called maria, regions formed by cooled, hardened lava.

Benjamin Banneker (1731-1806), the first African-American astronomer, successfully predicted a solar eclipse, a very difficult task in his time. Today, eclipses are predicted precisely.

The Moon is Earth's natural satellite. It revovles around Earth. The Moon is a big space rock that has no light of its own.

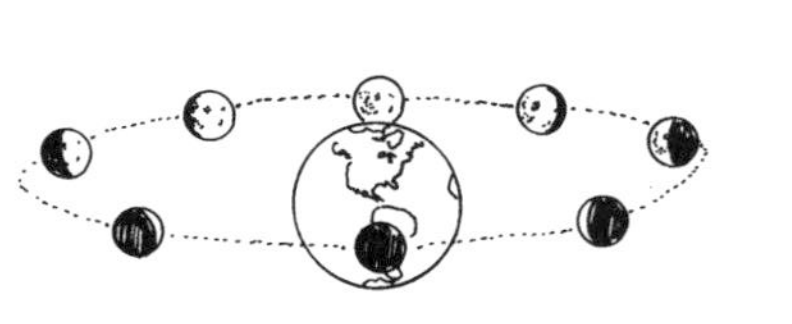

The part of Earth that is in the partial shadow of the Moon experiences a partial solar eclipse.

The Moon's partial shadow is called the penumbra.

umbra

Sun

Earth

Moon

penumbra

During a solar eclipse, astronomers can study the Sun's atmosphere because the Moon blocks the Sun's glare.

Sometimes the Sun, Earth, and Moon line up perfectly so that Earth's shadow falls on the Moon.

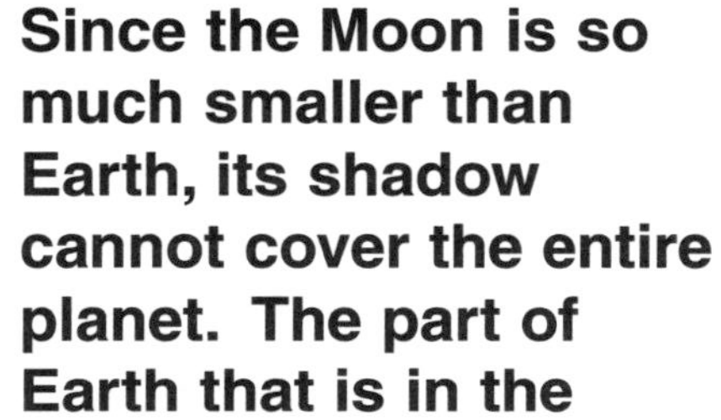

Since the Moon is so much smaller than Earth, its shadow cannot cover the entire planet. The part of Earth that is in the shadow experiences a total solar eclipse.

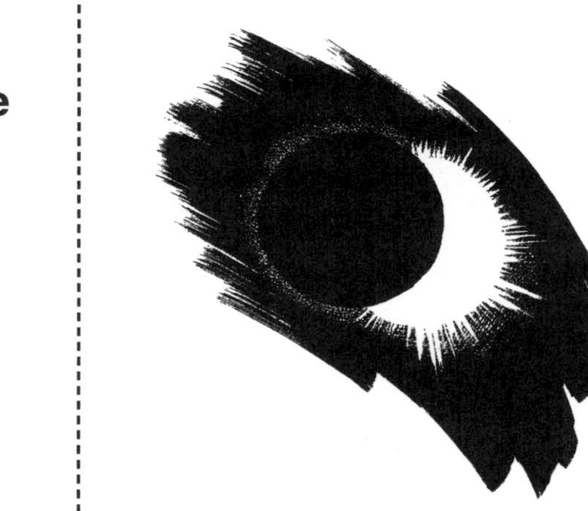

During a lunar eclipse, the Moon slowly becomes covered by the round, black shadow of Earth. This is because the Moon is moving into Earth's shadow.

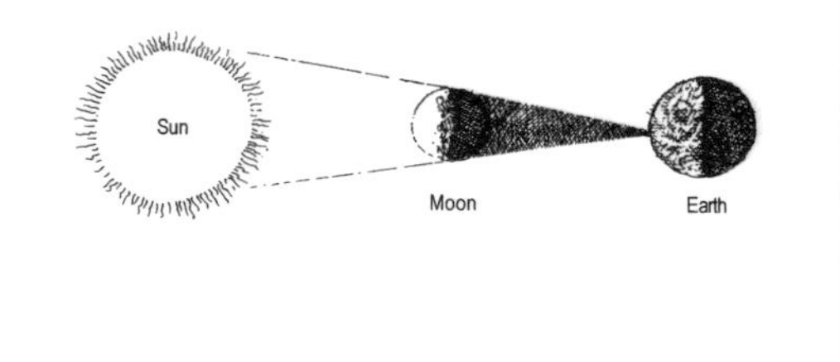

As the Moon revovles around Earth, Earth revovles around the Sun.

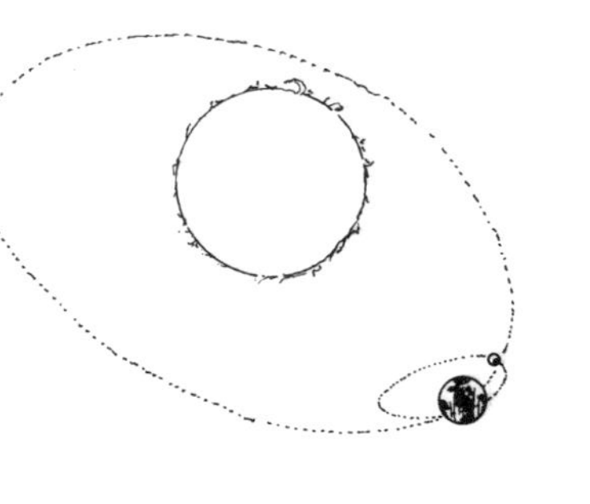

This poem will help you remember the names of eclipses.

Eclipsing means
what's eclipsing
can't be seen.
Solar eclipse:
Sun doesn't show.
Lunar eclipse:
The Moon will go.

Dinah Zike

The ancient Babylonians predicted lunar eclipses with great accuracy in 500 B.C.

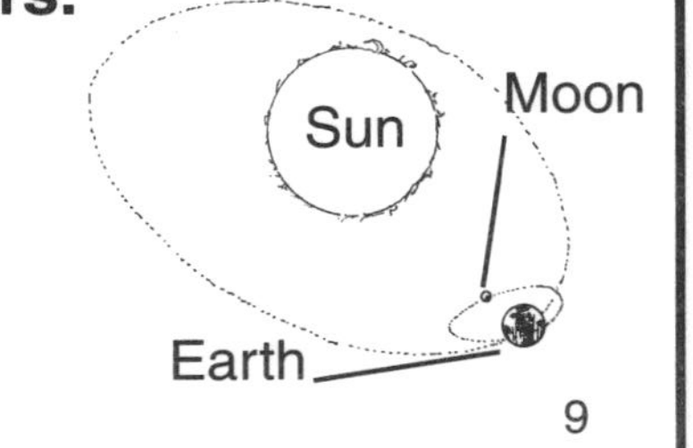

The Moon sometimes passes between Earth and the Sun in its orbit. When the Sun, Moon, and Earth line up so that the Moon's shadow is cast on Earth, a solar eclipse occurs.

Sun
Moon
Earth

When this happens, the Moon is blocked from view. This is called a lunar eclipse. A lunar eclipse is only seen at night and is visible to only half of Earth.

Sun
Moon
umbra
penumbra
Earth

Mercury was named after the mythological Roman messenger god because of its great speed. Mercury does not have a moon.

Our first stop as we travel through our solar system is Mercury, the closest planet to the Sun. It is about 36,000,000 miles (58,000,000 km) away from the Sun.

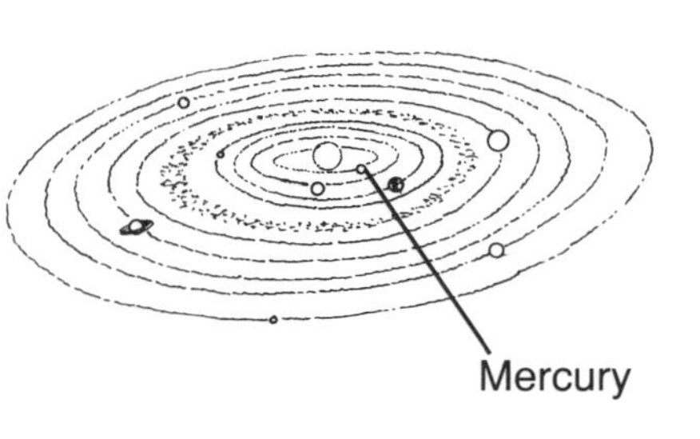

All the planets orbit the Sun in a rounded oval, or ellipse, except Mercury. Mercury's orbital path is very elongated.

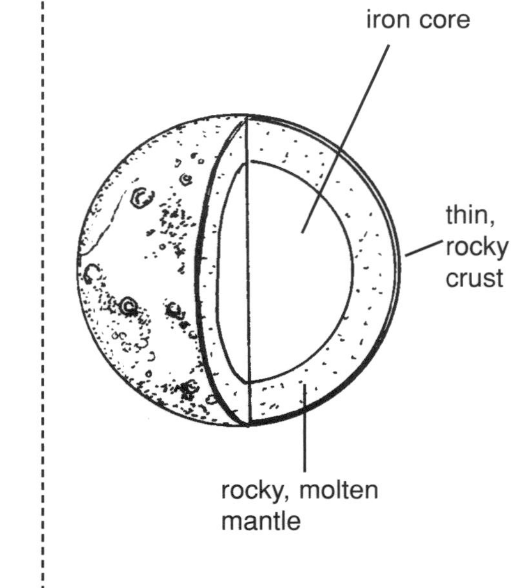

While Mercury orbits the Sun, it also rotates on its axis. Although it revolves around the Sun quickly, it rotates very slowly. One rotation takes about 59 Earth days.

In 1974, the unmanned spacecraft *Mariner 10* visited Mercury providing us with information about the planet. Mercury's surface is about 50% craters and about 50% plains. It is completely covered by dust.

Mercury can be seen from Earth without a telescope. However, it is difficult to see because it is very close to the horizon and appears sometimes at dusk and sometimes at dawn.

For eight weeks you can see Mercury in the morning sky, just before sunrise. For eight weeks you can see Mercury in the evening sky, just after sunset.

One of the largest craters in our solar system is on Mercury. This crater is called the Caloris Basin and measures about 800 miles across.

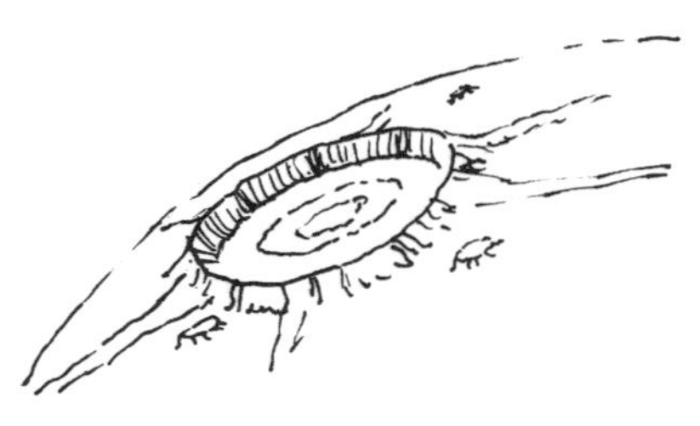

Its many large craters give Mercury an appearance like that of our Moon. Mercury has almost no atmosphere. Because of its thin atmosphere, its surface is unprotected from passing meteoroids, asteroids, and comets.

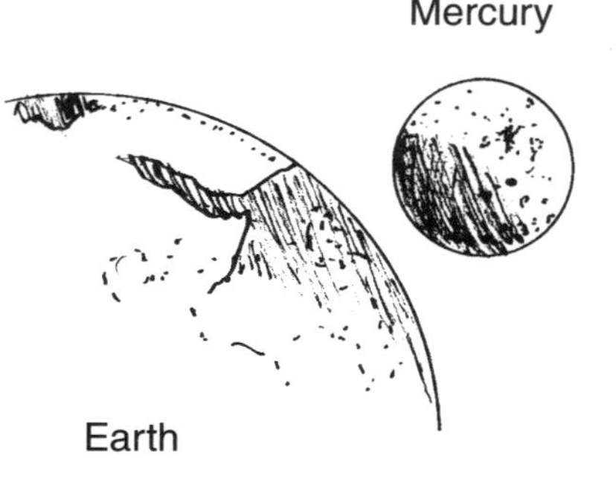

Since Mercury is the closest planet to the Sun, it experiences extremely hot temperatures on its sunlit side, about 800 F (400 C). This temperature is hot enough to melt lead. Mercury also experiences extrememly cold temperatures on its dark side, about -300˚ F (-180˚ C).

Although Mercury is the closest planet to the Sun, Venus is the hottest planet. Read more about it in Lots of Science Library Book #11.

axial tilt of 2°

Mercury's atmosphere is too thin to carry sound waves. Even if you yelled and screamed on Mercury, no sound could be heard. It is completely silent there. The thin atmosphere also prevents the scattering of light waves, making Mercury's sky always appear black.

Gravity on Mercury is less than half of what it is on Earth. A rock weighing 100 lbs (45 kg) on Earth would weigh only about 40 lbs (18.14 kg) on Mercury.

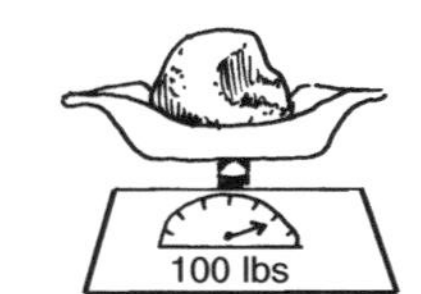

weight on Earth

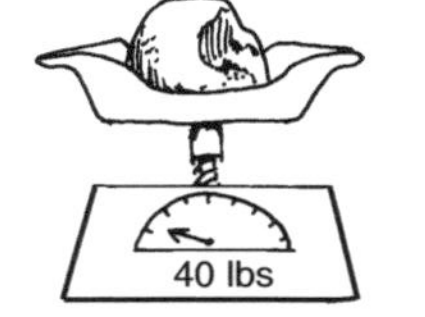

weight on Mercury

Mercury is less than half the size of Earth, with a diameter of 3,030 miles (4,875 km). It is the second-smallest planet in our solar system. The core of the planet is iron, creating a magnetic field. Covering the iron core is a layer of rocky, molten mantle. The surface of the planet is a thin, rocky crust.

The closer a planet is to the Sun, the shorter the time it takes to complete a revolution around the Sun. It takes only 88 Earth days for Mercury to complete one trip around the Sun.

Venus is a beautiful planet, appropriately named after the Roman goddess of love and beauty.

Venus is the second-closest planet to the Sun. It is about 67,200,000 miles (108,100,000 km) away. Venus is one of the solid planets.

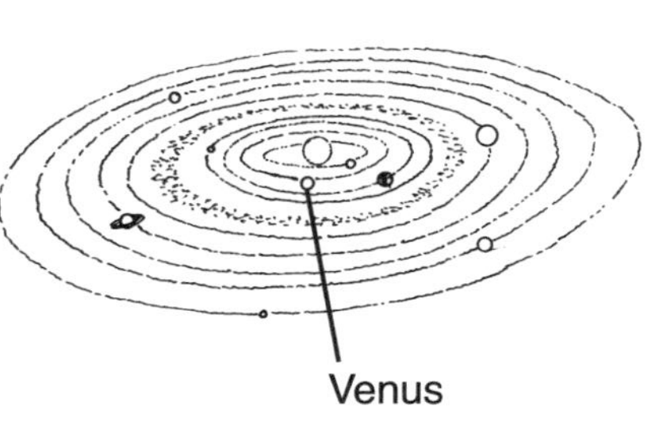

From Earth, Venus looks beautiful because it is so bright. Even with a telescope, Venus' surface cannot be seen due to thick layers of atmospheric clouds.

From Earth, we can see Venus three hours before sunrise and three hours after sunset.

These gases trap heat between Venus' atmosphere and its surface, resulting in a rise in temperature.

Venus is very reflective. It is the brightest planet in our sky.

thin, rocky crust

semisolid metal core

rocky mantle

Venus rotates on its axis in the opposite direction from the other planets. It takes Venus 243 Earth days to complete one rotation.

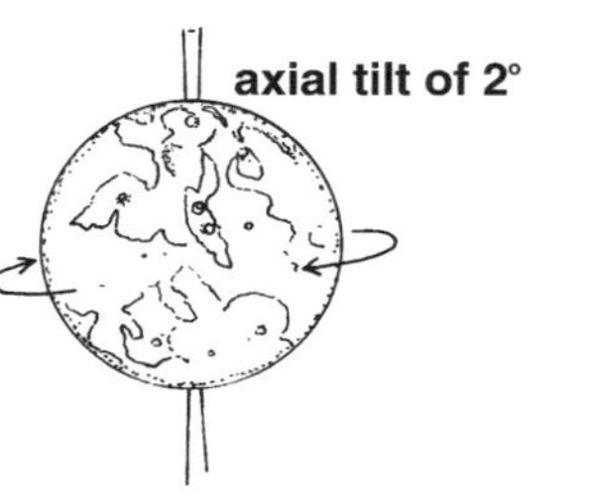

This is similar to what happens when the Sun's heat energy passes through glass in a greenhouse. The heat energy can enter but it cannot escape, and this raises the temperature in the greenhouse. For this reason Venus, although not the closest planet to the Sun, is the hottest planet.

It takes Venus 225 Earth days to complete one orbit around the Sun. That means that a day on Venus is longer than its year.

Venus is often called Earth's twin because they are similar in size and both have an atmosphere. Venus is just a little smaller than Earth, with a diameter of 7,500 miles (12,100 km). Like Earth, Venus' core is a semisolid metal. A rocky mantle and a thin, rocky crust surround this core.

The gravity on Venus is less than that on Earth. A rock weighing 100 lbs (45 kg) on Earth would weigh about 90 lbs (40.8 kg) on Venus.

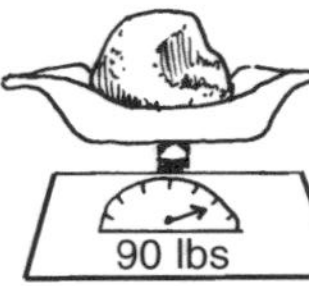

In 1982, the *Venera 14* landed on Venus and sent back photos and data. The spacecraft lasted less than an hour before it was destroyed by the extreme heat of the planet.

Most of the surface on Venus is flat with a few rolling plains. In one region, mountains higher than Mount Everest can be found. Venus has no moon.

These mountains are found in the Maxwell Montes Range.

In many ways Venus is different from Earth. Venus is a very hot planet with extremely high atmospheric pressure. Thick clouds made up mostly of carbon dioxide, other poisonous gases, and water vapor cover the surface of Venus.

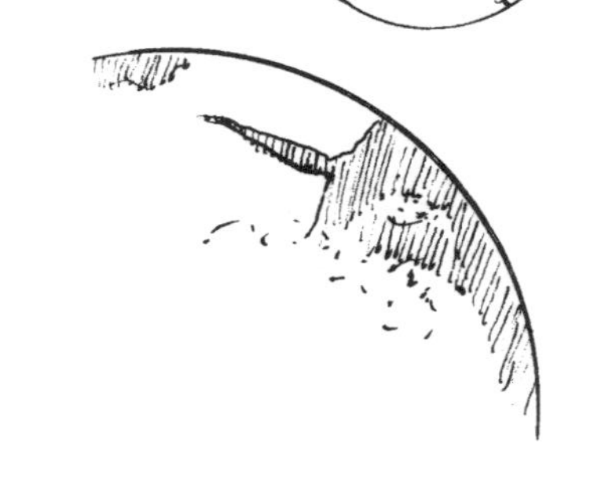

In December 1996, Americans launched *Pathfinder*. *Pathfinder* successfully landed on Mars in July 1997. It contained a rover, *Sojourner*, which gathered important data about the surface of Mars.

Mars is the fourth planet from the Sun at a distance of about 141,600,000 miles (227,830,000 km). It takes 687 Earth days for Mars to make one orbit around the Sun.

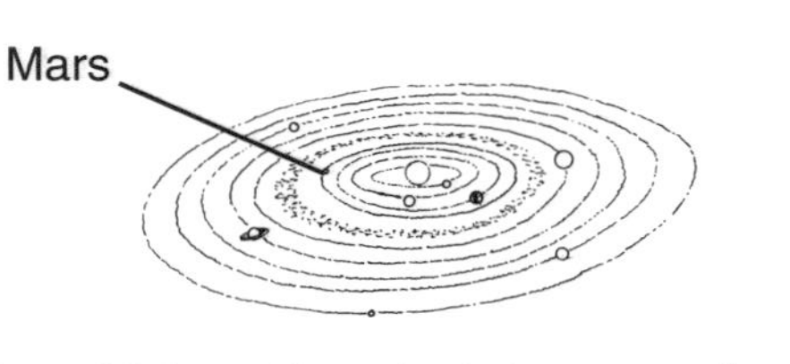

If we were standing on Mars, the sky would look pinkish–orange and the Sun would look about half the size that it does from Earth. Sunlight hitting the planet would feel comfortable to us, but after the Sun sets, the temperature would fall below freezing.

axial tilt of 2°

In 1877, an Italian astronomer, Giovanni Schiaparelli, observed a network of dark lines crisscrossing Mars. Some people believed that these were irrigation canals, possibly indicating intelligent life on Mars. However, the canals turned out to be optical illusions.

Mars was named after the Roman god of war because of its blood–red color.

Mars is one of the solid planets and has two small, potato–shaped moons. Due to the small size of the moons, astronomers believe they may have been asteroids trapped by Mars' gravity.

Delmos

Phobos

Unlike the Earth's crust, which is broken into plates that float on molten rock, Mars is covered with a solid, rocky crust that does not move. This structure causes enormous volcanoes to occur on Mars.

Similar to Earth, Mars has mountains, deserts, polar caps, volcanoes, and seasons. Mars also had rivers at one time, but they dried up.

Mars has a solid, rocky core covered with a thick, rocky mantle. This is covered with a solid, rocky crust that contains frozen subsoil.

solid, rocky crust

solid, rocky core

thick, rocky mantle

The atmosphere on Mars is very thin, consisting mostly of carbon dioxide, so humans cannot breathe on Mars. The planet looks like a giant, orange-colored desert with dark markings and white polar caps. Constant dust storms cover Mars with rusty dust.

Mars is visible from Earth without a telescope. Mars is often called the Red Planet because it has a red glow. Iron in its soil gives Mars this red color. Mars has a diameter of about 4,220 miles (6,790 km), approximately half the size of Earth.

In 1965, the American spacecraft *Mariner 4* revealed photographs of a barren planet. In 1976, two *Viking* space probes landed on Mars to search for any signs of life. Tests on Martian soil were conducted and observed, but no life was found.

Mars contains the largest volcano in our solar system, Olympus Mons. Olympus Mons is about three times taller than Mount Everest and is no longer active.

Olympus Mons

Mount Everest

Mars is sometimes called Earth's little brother because they share some similarities. Mars' rotation is about 24 $^{3}/_{4}$ hours, just a little longer than Earth's rotation.

Mars' rotation is 41 minutes longer than Earth's rotation.

The gravity on Mars is about the same as it is on Mercury. A rock weighing 100 lbs (45 kg) on Earth would weigh about 40 lbs (18.15 kg) on Mars.

100 lbs

weight on Earth

40 lbs

weight on Mars

The spacecraft *Galileo* photographed asteroids Ida and Gaspra on August 1993 on its way to Jupiter. It revealed that Ida, which is only 1 mile across, had an even smaller satellite orbiting it. That satellite was named Dactyl. It is thought that other asteroids may also have moons.

Before going on to the next planet, we must travel through the asteroid belt. This area between Mars and Jupiter contains most of the asteroids in our solar system.

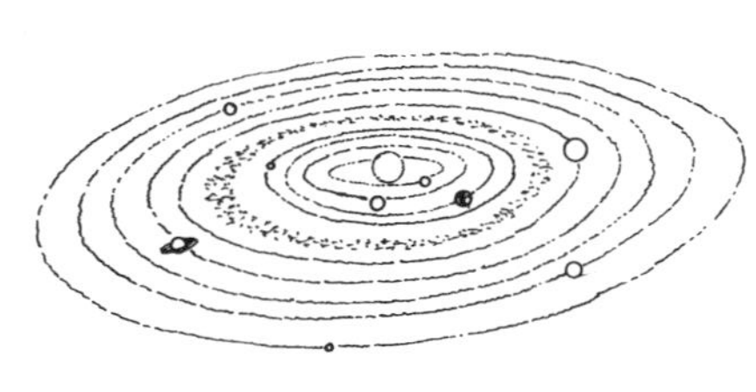

3) About 7% of asteroids are M Type. They are made of nickel and iron. They are silvery in color, so they reflect sunlight well. These asteroids are the brightest, with the highest albedo. Most of these asteroids are found in the middle region of the asteroid belt.

Over 20,000 asteroids have been discovered, and several thousand have been named.

Father Giuseppe Piazzi discovered Ceres in 1801. It was the first and largest asteroid discovered and it was named after the Sicilian goddess of grain. Ceres is about 623 miles (1002 km) in diameter.

Asteroid comes from a Greek word meaning "star-like."

2) About 17% of asteroids are S Type. They are made of nickel, iron, and a rocky material called silicate, which is made of sand. They are somewhat reddish in color with a high albedo. Most of these asteroids are found in the inner region of the asteroid belt.

Asteroids are made of metal, rock, or a combination of both. They have varying reflective qualities, or albedo. There are three main types of asteroids:

1) C Type
2) S Type
3) M Type

Asteroids often collide with one another as they orbit the Sun. Often, they break apart into smaller pieces. These smaller pieces are called meteoroids.

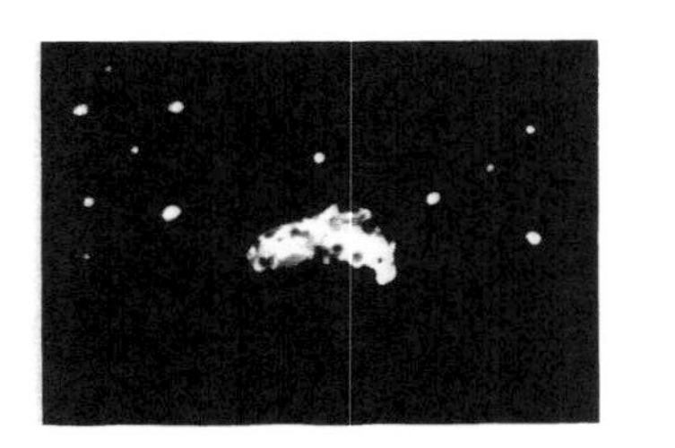

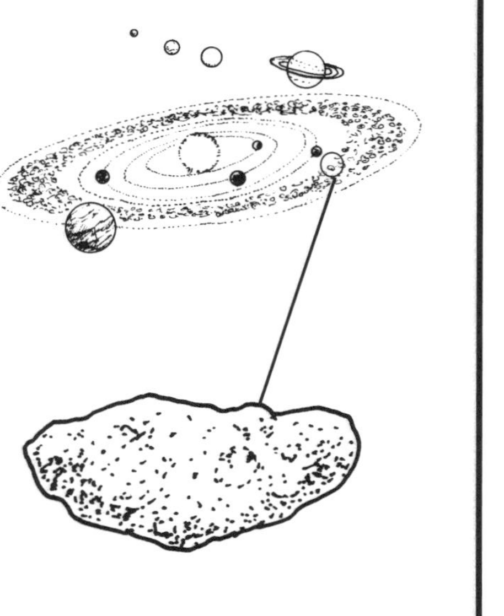

Like planets, asteroids orbit the Sun. They are sometimes called the minor planets. All the asteroids orbit the Sun in the same direction, taking from three to six Earth years to complete one orbit.

The next four asteroids discovered are:

1) Pallas, at about 378 miles (608 km) in diameter
2) Juno, at about 143 miles (230 km) in diameter
3) Vesta, at about 334 miles (537 km) in diameter
4) Astrea at about 73 miles (118 km) in diameter

1) About 75% of asteroids are C Type. They are made mostly of carbon. Their dark color causes them to have a low albedo, meaning that they do not reflect the Sun's light well. Most of these asteroids are found in the outer region of the asteroid belt.

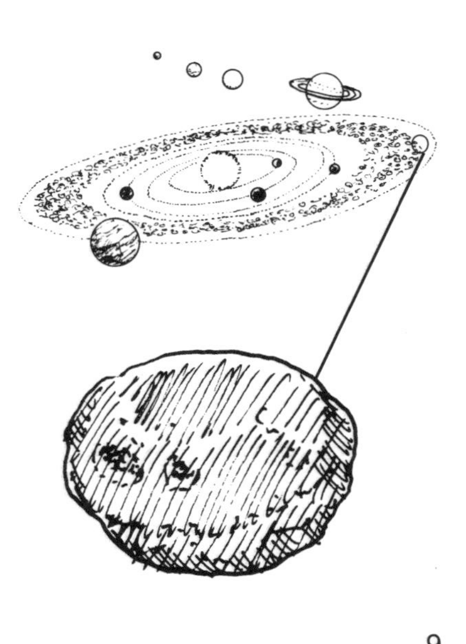

Most asteroids are pebble-sized, but some are about the size of small cars. Most asteroids are irregular in shape. Only the largest asteroids are round.

***Galileo* was launched in 1989 and arrived in Jupiter's orbit in 1995. *Galileo* launched a space probe through Jupiter's cloudy atmosphere and transmitted data to Earth until Jupiter's pressure caused the transmitter to malfunction. Scientists continue to study Jupiter.**

Now that we have passed the Asteroid Belt, let's head to the giant planet Jupiter. Jupiter is the fifth planet from the Sun. It is about 483,600,000 miles (778,112,400 km) away from the Sun.

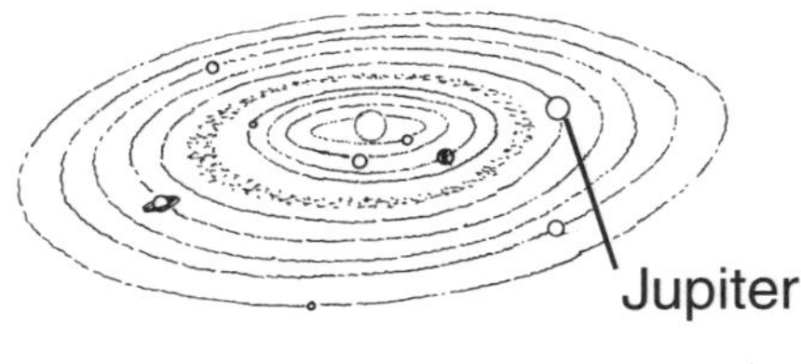

If you could stand on Jupiter, severe winds would pick you up and slam you through the clouds. A hailstorm of ice particles often whips through Jupiter's atmosphere.

Remember, the first four planets are solid. Jupiter is the first of the four gaseous planets.

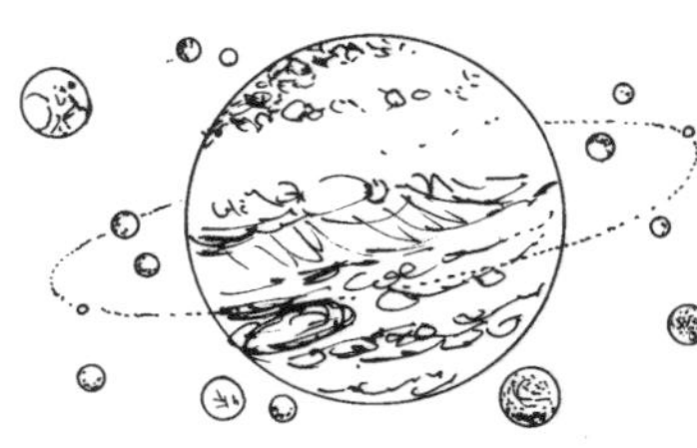

Ganymede

Calisto

In July 1992, the comet Shoemaker-Levy 9 broke into 21 pieces when it moved too close to Jupiter's gravitational field. Then in July 1994, fragments of the comet crashed into Jupiter. This was the first time that astronomers were able to view large objects hitting a planet.

Jupiter was named after the Roman king of the gods. Because of its great size, it was considered the king of the planets.

Jupiter rotates faster than any other planet. Due to Jupiter's speed, its outer atmosphere swirls into layers of clouds, forming bands, which bulge at its equator. In 1979, a ring system was discovered surrounding the planet.

Jupiter is usually the second–brightest planet, following Venus. Jupiter has 16 known moons.

Galileo discovered the four large moons of Jupiter in 1610. They are referred to as the Galilean moons.

Jupiter's gravity is 2 $^1/_2$ times greater than Earth's. A rock weighing 100 lb (45 kg) on Earth would weigh about 250 lbs (113.4 kg) on Jupiter.

Jupiter's atmosphere contains warm and cool areas that cause high and low pressure. This causes windy, stormy conditions across Jupiter's surface. These thick clouds form a swirling layer of winds blowing in opposite directions.

Jupiter is the largest planet in our solar system. In fact, Jupiter is larger than all the other planets and their moons combined. Its diameter is about 88,850 miles (142,960 km). It would take about 1,000 Earths to fill a ball the size of Jupiter.

Pioneer 10 was the first spacecraft to fly by Jupiter. Jupiter was also visited by *Pioneer 11* a year later, and then by *Voyager 1, Voyager 2, Ulysses,* and *Galileo.*

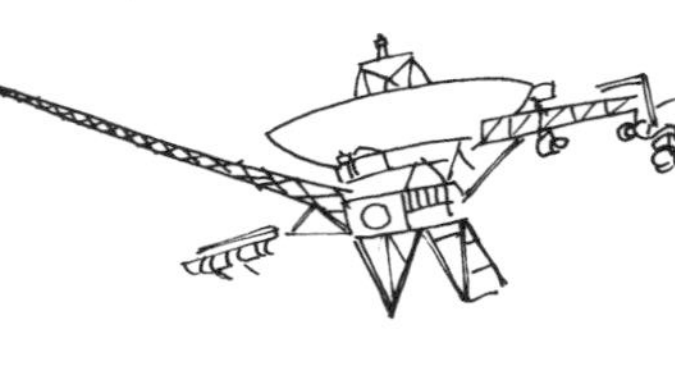

Jupiter's small, rocky core is very hot. The core is covered with an inner mantle of metallic hydrogen, covered by an outer mantle of liquid hydrogen and helium. Jupiter does not have a solid surface, but has an atmosphere of mostly hydrogen and helium.

outer mantle of liquid hydrogen and helium

rocky core

atmosphere of mostly hydrogen and helium

inner mantle of metallic hydrogen

It takes Jupiter only 10 Earth hours to complete one rotation. This means that one day on Jupiter is only 10 Earth hours. One orbit of Jupiter takes about 12 Earth years.

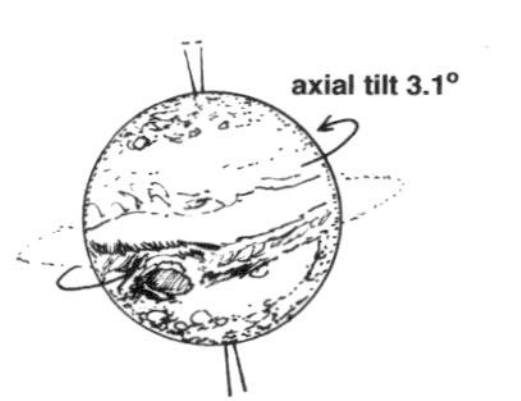

One region of Jupiter, called the Great Red Spot, is a huge storm system that has been observed for over 300 years. The Great Red Spot changes in size but is usually larger than Earth.

Great Red Spot

Saturn is the farthest planet we can see from Earth without a telescope. It was named after the Roman god of the harvest.

Saturn is the sixth planet. It is about 886,000,000 miles (1,426,000,000 km) from the Sun.

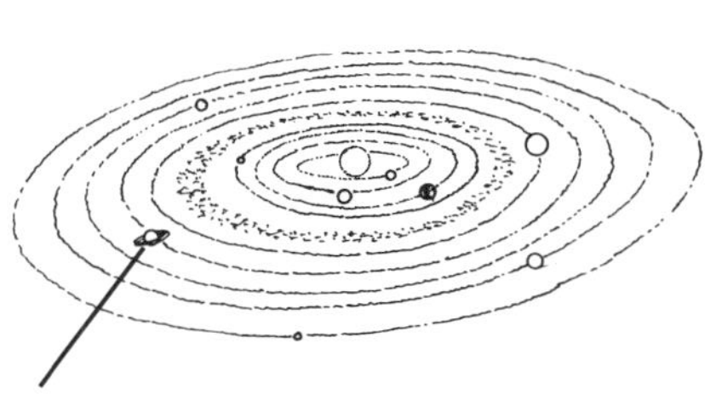

Like Jupiter, Saturn consists of a very hot, rocky, inner core. Surrounding the inner core is an inner mantle of liquid, metallic hydrogen. An outer mantle of liquid hydrogen merges into an atmosphere of mostly hydrogen and helium.

From Earth, we can see Saturn's rings with a simple telescope. In 1610, Galileo observed two rings around Saturn. However it was not until 1655 that Dutch astronomer Christiaan Huygens first viewed the rings clearly, using a powerful telescope.

Saturn is composed mostly of hydrogen and helium, both light gases. Although Saturn is one of the larger planets, it would float on water if there were an ocean large enough to hold it.

It takes about 10.7 Earth hours for Saturn to complete one rotation.

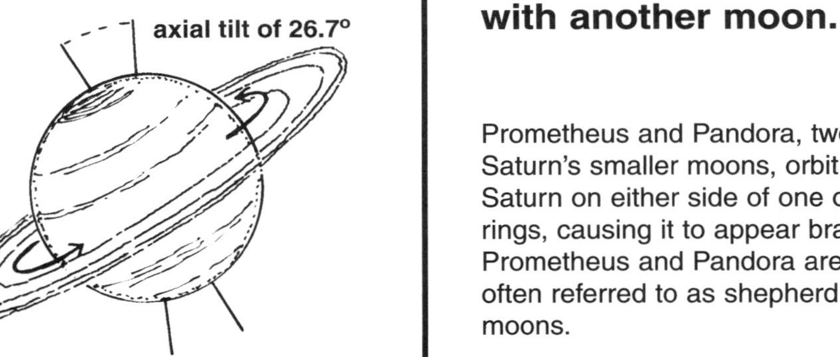

Astronomers have discovered 22 moons orbiting Saturn. Seven of Saturn's moons share an orbital path with another moon.

Prometheus and Pandora, two of Saturn's smaller moons, orbit Saturn on either side of one of the rings, causing it to appear braided. Prometheus and Pandora are often referred to as shepherd moons.

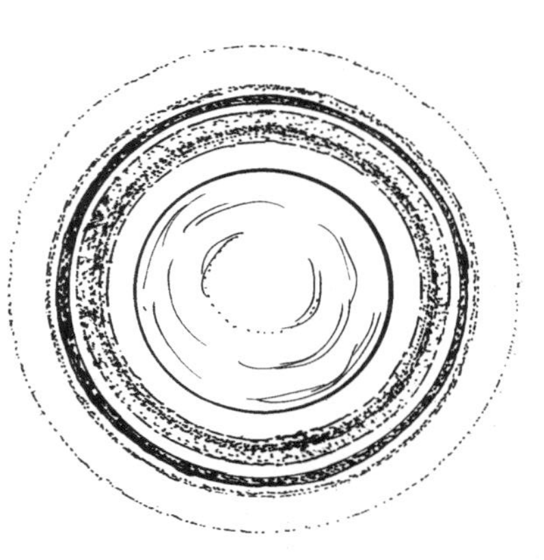

★

From Earth Saturn's rings look smooth and solid. They are actually made of frozen gas, rocks, and billions of fragmented ice particles. Most of the icy rocks are small, but some are as big as a house.

Saturn is the second–largest planet. Its diameter is about 74,900 miles (120,500 km). Saturn is one of the gaseous planets. It rotates quickly, causing a bulge at its equator.

Saturn's is just a little greater than Earth's. A rock weighing 100 lbs (45 kg) on Earth would weigh about 110 lbs (49.9 kg) on Saturn.

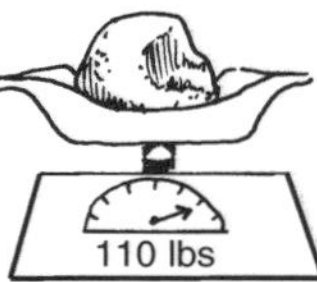

In 1675, French astronomer Giovanni Cassini observed a gap separating the two main rings. It is 3,000 miles (4,800 km) wide and is called the Cassini Division. In 1981, photographs from *Voyager 2* revealed five more rings.

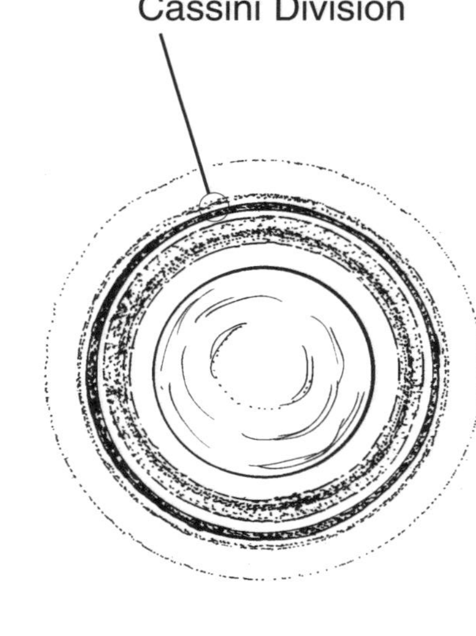

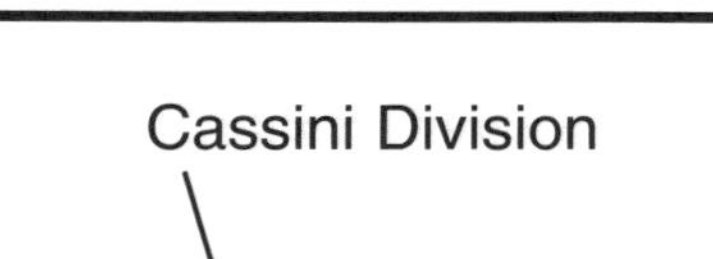

It takes Saturn about 29.5 Earth years to complete one orbit around the Sun. This is the length of one year on Saturn.

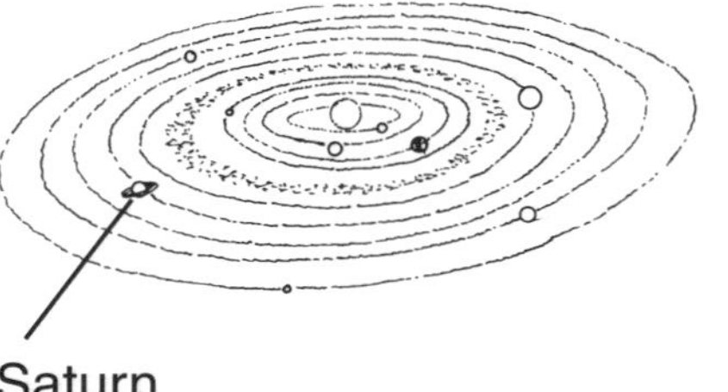

inner mantle of liquid, metallic hydrogen

rocky, inner core

outer mantle of liquid hydrogen

atmosphere of mostly hydrogen and helium

Uranus was named after the Roman god of the heavens.

Uranus is the seventh planet. It is about 1,786,000,000 miles (2,874,000,000 km) from the Sun. Uranus is so far away from the Sun that it is a dark and frozen world, barely visible without a telescope.

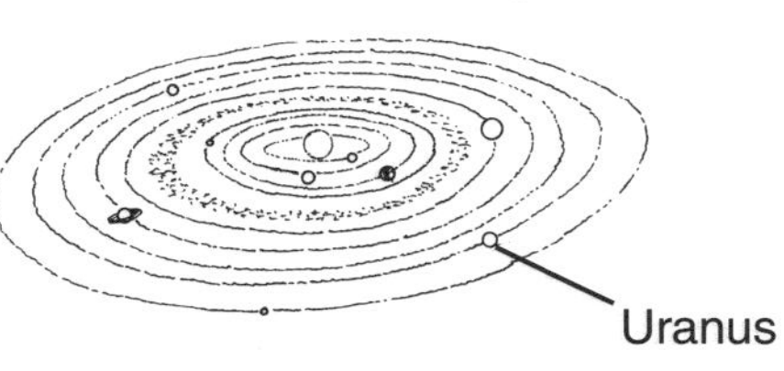

Uranus is the first planet discovered with a telescope. German composer and amateur astronomer William Herschel discovered it in 1781. He discovered Uranus by using his homemade telescope.

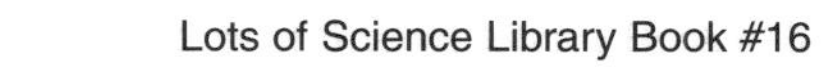

axial tilt of 97.9°

Miranda, one of Uranus' moons, has an unusual surface. The surface is icy and jagged with a towering cliff twice the size of Mount Everest.

The solid, rocky core of Uranus is covered with a dense mantle of water, methane, and ammonia. An atmosphere of hydrogen, helium, and methane gases covers Uranus. Methane gives the planet its distinctive aqua color.

It takes Uranus about 17 Earth hours to complete one rotation. This means that a complete day on Uranus is only 17 hours long.

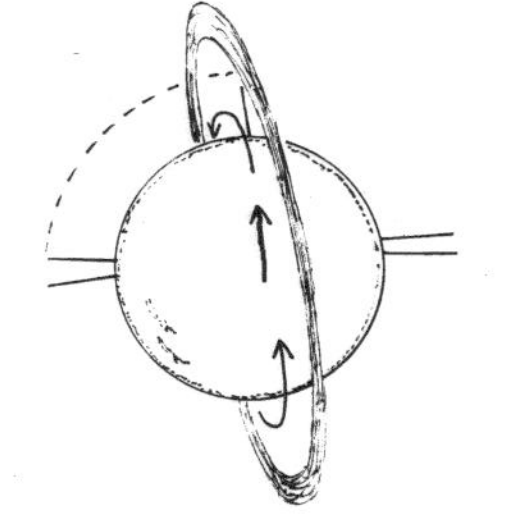

Uranus is so far away that even telescopes cannot give us much information about it. However, in 1977, nine rings were discovered around Uranus. These rings are most likely made of ice and rocks.

dense mantle of water, ammonia, and methane

solid, rocky core

atmosphere of hydrogen, helium, and methane

Uranus is the third largest planet in our solar system, with a diameter of about 31,750 miles (51,086 km). It is a gaseous planet.

Photographs from *Voyager 2* revealed that Uranus' rings look brighter when the Sun shines behind them. Ten narrow, dark rings surround Uranus.

However, one trip around the Sun takes Uranus 84 Earth years and 25 Earth days to complete.

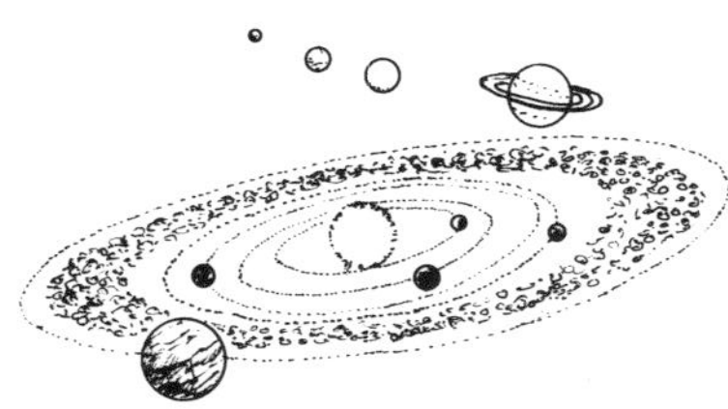

The gravity on Uranus is a little less than that of Earth. A rock weighing 100 lbs (45 kg) on Earth would weigh about 90 lbs (40.8 kg) on Uranus.

100 lbs
weight on Earth

90 lbs
weight on Uranus

Uranus' axis tilts at about 98°. This makes the planet look like it is moving through space sideways. The tilt of the axis causes the poles to point toward the Sun, making its poles warmer than its equator.

In 1986, *Voyager 2* space probe photographed some of Uranus' largest moons. Uranus has 21 known moons.

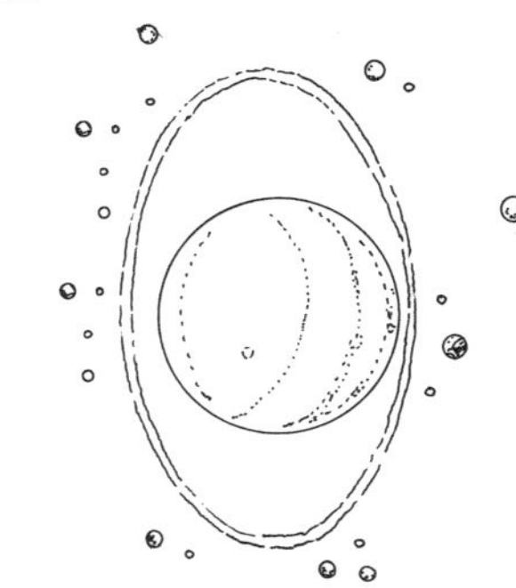

Because of its sea-blue color, Neptune was named after the Roman god of the sea.

Neptune is the eighth planet from the Sun. It is about 2,798,800,000 miles (4,503,300,000 km) from the Sun. A telescope is needed to see Neptune.

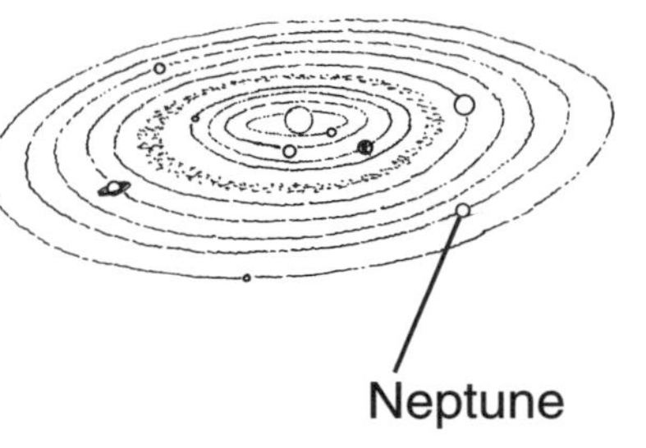

Neptune has eight known moons. One of Neptune's moons, Triton, has the coldest known surface in our solar system. The surface temperature of Triton is about –390˚ F (-235˚ C).

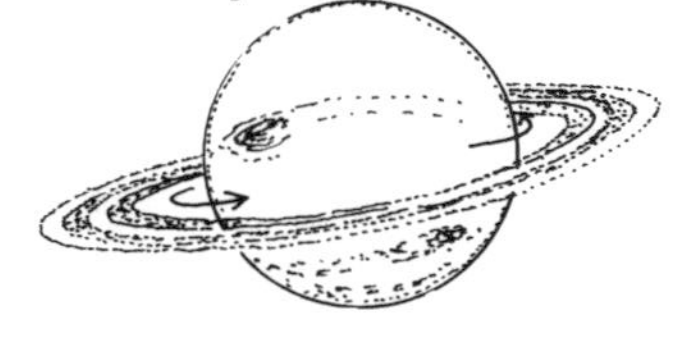

Neptune gives off heat that creates currents in the atmosphere. Strong winds are created due to the speed of Neptune's rotation and the warm currents.

In 1845, English astronomer John Couch Adams and French astronomer Urbain LeVerrier independently calculated the existence and position of another planet past Uranus. This led to the discovery of Neptune.

Neptune's gravity is the same as that of Saturn and a little more than that of Earth's. A rock weighing 100 lbs (45 kg) on Earth would weigh about 110 lbs (49.9 kg) on Neptune.

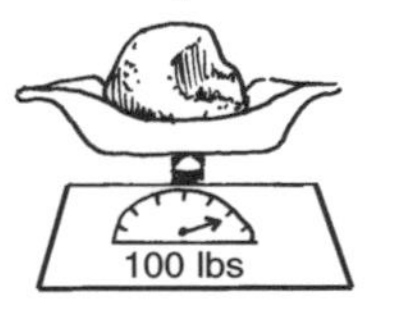

weight on Earth

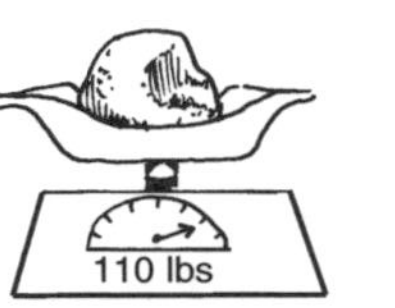

weight on Neptune

Neptune consists of a small, rocky core surrounded by a mantle of icy water and gases. An atmosphere of hydrogen, helium, and methane covers the surface. Frozen clouds and methane give Neptune a bluish appearance. Four dusty rings surround it.

***Voyager 2* reached Neptune in August 1989 after a long 12 year trip traveling at an average of 42,000 MPH (67,592 KPH). Winds blow faster on Neptune than on any other planet. It is sometimes called the windy planet because along its equator, winds move at 1,200 MPH (1,931 KPH).**

mantle of icy water and gases

rocky core

atmosphere of hydrogen, helium, and methane gases

Neptune's diameter is about 30,800 miles (49,500 km). It is the fourth largest planet in our solar system. Although Neptune is the smallest of the gaseous planets, it has the greatest density.

Density is the amount of matter squeezed into a given amount of space.

***Voyager 2* space probe photographed several large storms. The largest storm, called the Great Dark Spot, is bigger than Earth.**

In 1994, the Hubble Space Telescope revealed that the Great Dark Spot had either vanished or moved. Astronomers conclude that Neptune's atmosphere changes rapidly.

Neptune's rotation takes about 16 Earth hours to complete. One orbit around the Sun takes about 164 Earth years.

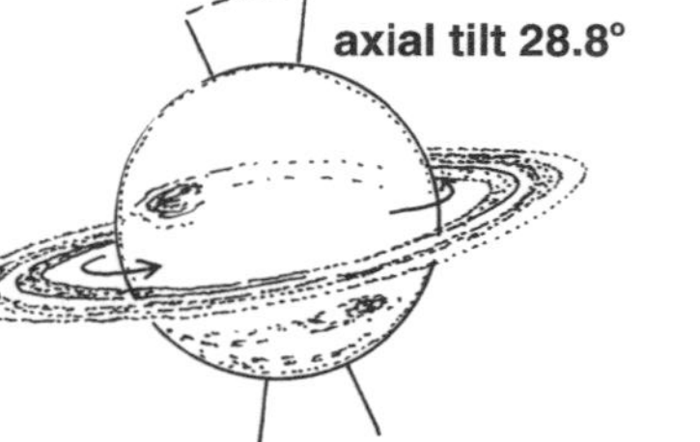

Triton orbits backward and spirals inward.

Astronomers predict that this movement will eventually cause it to crash into Neptune. An orbit that is opposite to the rotation of the planet is said to be retrograde.

For many years, astronomers thought that there might be another planet in our solar system beyond Pluto. Finally, in 1992, the search for the new Planet X was called off and it was determined that a tenth planet did not exist.

Pluto is the ninth and last planet in our solar system. It is about 3,670,000,000 miles (5,905,000,000 km) away from the Sun. From Pluto, the Sun looks like a very tiny, distant star.

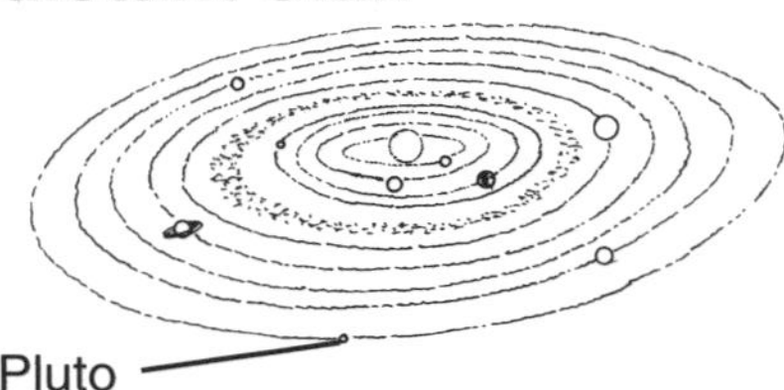

James Christy discovered Pluto's moon, Charon, in 1978. Pluto and Charon are sometimes referred to as double planets. Charon is about half the size of Pluto and similar to it in many ways.

They are similar in mass and share a common center of gravity. A common center of gravity is called barycenter.

Compared to Earth, there is very little gravity on Pluto. A rock weighing 100 lbs (45 kg) on Earth would weigh only about 7 lbs (3.18 kg) on Pluto.

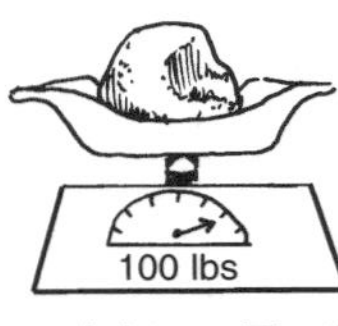

weight on Earth

weight on Pluto

Pluto is so far away that it is difficult to study, even with telescopes. All the planets have been visited by space probes except Pluto. In 1990, the Hubble Space Telescope took the first clear photographs of Pluto and its moon.

It was named Pluto, after the Roman god of the underworld.

Pluto travels inside of Neptune's orbit, during 20 of its 248 Earth years of orbiting. Pluto's orbit is very steep and is higher than Neptune's orbit. Although it might seem that Pluto's orbit would cross Neptune's, it does not. Neptune and Pluto will never collide.

surface of icy water and methane

core of rock and possibly ice

icy mantle

It is thought that Pluto's core is made of rock and ice, covered with an icy mantle. The surface is made of icy water and methane. The atmosphere is thought to consist mostly of nitrogen and some carbon monoxide and methane.

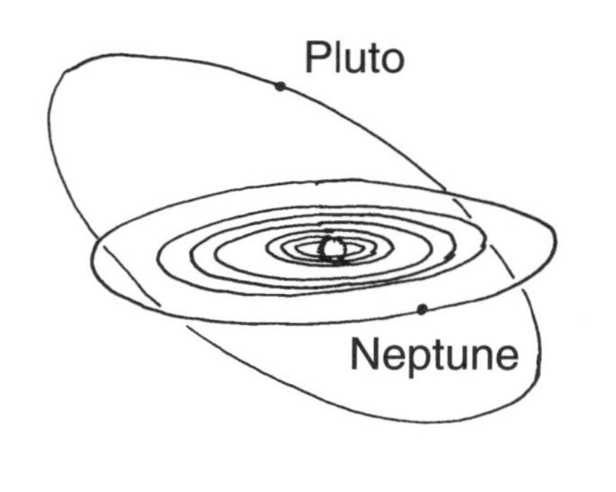

Before Pluto was discovered, American astronomer Percival Lowell believed that a ninth planet existed in our solar system. He believed in the existence of Planet X. In 1930, at the Lowell Observatory, Clyde Tombaugh found the distant planet.

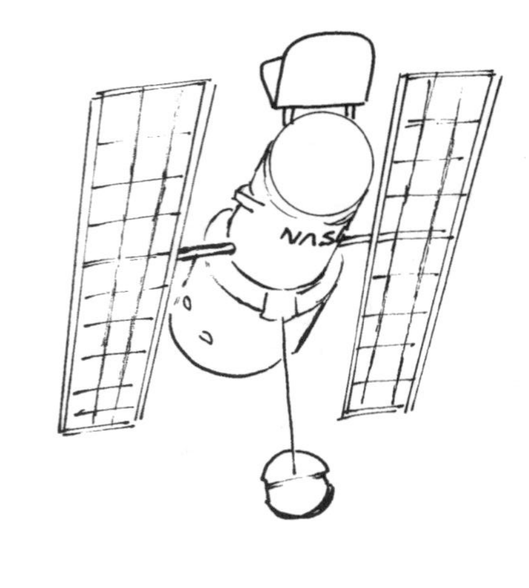

Pluto, like Uranus, has a large, tilted axis. It takes about 6 Earth days to complete a rotation. That means that one day on Pluto is 6 Earth days long.

axial tilt
of 28.8°

Pluto is so distant from the Sun that it takes about 248 Earth years for one orbit around the Sun.

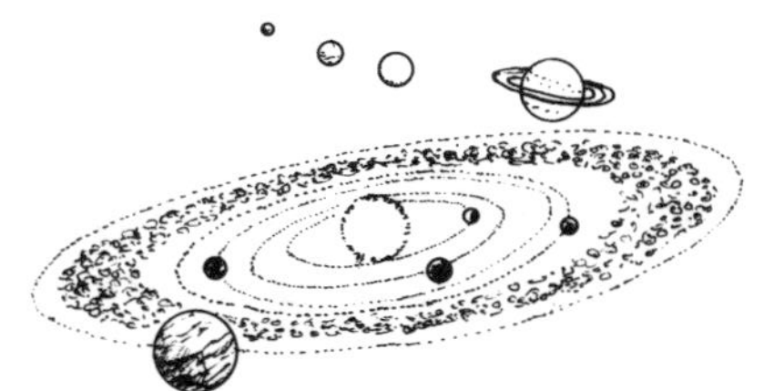

Pluto's orbit is off center, or eccentric.

Pluto is the smallest planet in our solar system, with a diameter of about 1,430 miles (2,300 km).

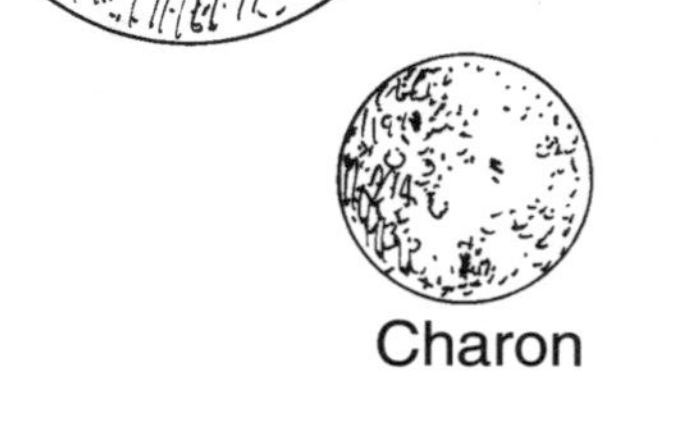

In 1992, the comet Shoemaker-Levy 9 moved so close to Jupiter's gravitational field that it broke into 21 pieces, allowing astronomers to view large objects hitting a planet for the first time. As with all comets, this comet was named after its discoverers, Carolyn and Eugene Shoemaker and David Levy.

On July 23, 1995, an unusually bright comet beyond Jupiter's orbit was observed independently by American amateur astronomers Alan Hale and Thomas Bopp. The Hale-Bopp comet was seen for several months in 1997.

Comets look spectacular with their long, glowing tails streaking across the sky.

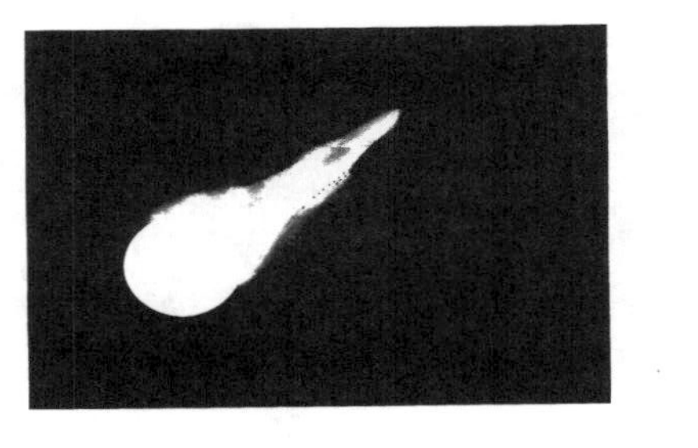

The tail of a comet always points away from the Sun because of solar winds. As a comet nears the Sun, the gravitational pull increases, causing the comet to move quickly.

Comets usually travel near the Sun and then begin a return trip into the outer solar system. As a comet travels away from the Sun, its tail points away from the Sun, giving it the appearance of traveling backwards.

Comets do not have light of their own so they are difficult to see until they get closer to the Sun. As they approach the Sun, they reflect its light, making them easier to observe.

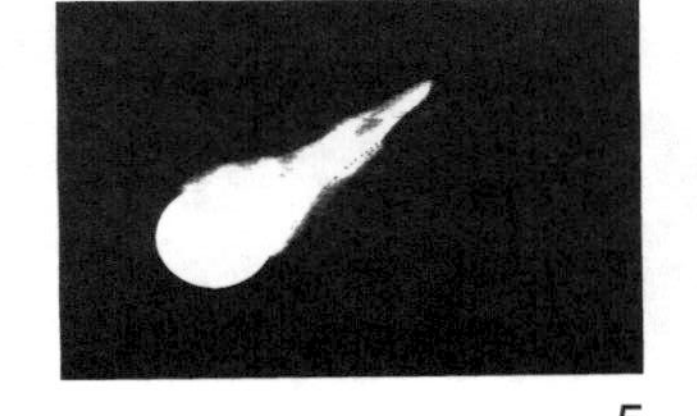

English astronomer Edmund Halley (1656-1742) calculated that the comet he saw in 1682 would reappear in 1758. The comet did appear as Halley had predicted and was later named for him. The orbital period of Halley's comet is about every 76 years, but it varies due to the gravitational pull of the planets.

Comets travel a long distance before they are seen by us on Earth. Some begin their trips in an area just beyond Neptune. Most come from the Oort Cloud, an icy region at the edge of the solar system.

A comet may have one or two tails. If two tails are visible, the jagged one is a gas tail and the smooth one, a dust tail.

2) As a comet nears the Sun, part of its nucleus melts. Gas and dust form a glowing, cloudy sphere around the nucleus. This is called the coma. Comas can extend for more than 100,000 miles (160,900 km).

Comets consist of three parts:

1) The head of a comet is called the nucleus. It can be one to fifteen miles wide. The head of a comet appears black until it reflects sunlight. Then it looks very bright because ice is highly reflective, or has a high albedo.

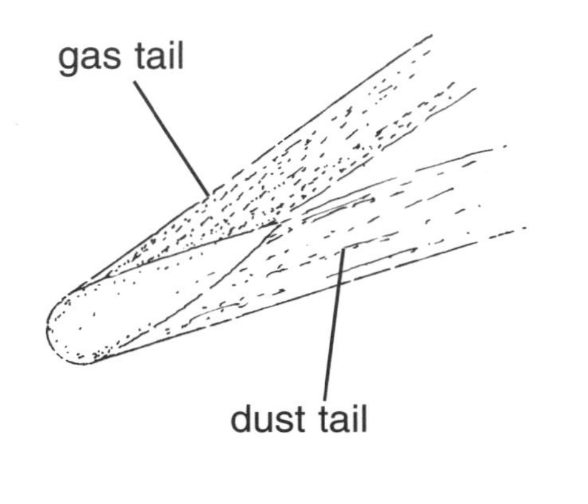

Comets are really nothing more than huge pieces of ice and dust. That is why in 1949, American astronomer Fred Whipple described comets as "dirty snowballs."

Halley's Comet is due to appear next in 2062.

3) As the comet nears the Sun, gas and dust are released, creating a long stretch of glowing light called a tail. The closer a comet gets to the Sun, the longer the tail. A tail of a comet can stretch for millions of miles.

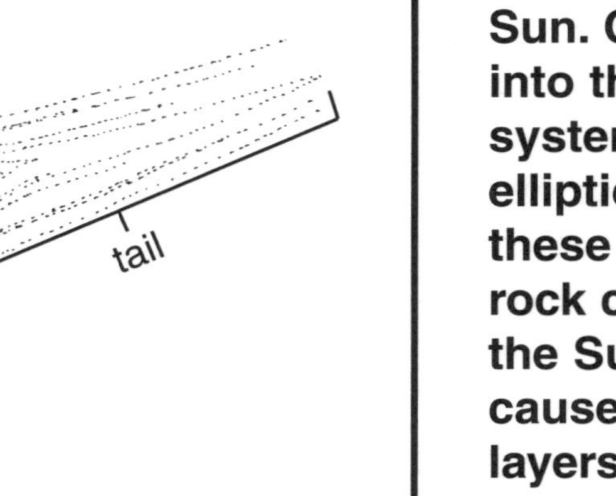

Collisions and the gravitational pull of the planets bring some comets toward the Sun. Comets that come into the inner solar system orbit the Sun in elliptical orbits. As these lumps of ice and rock come closer to the Sun, the heat causes their outer layers to evaporate.

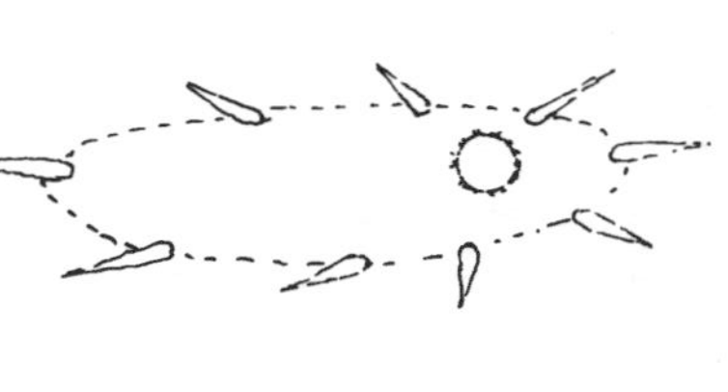

Although a meteorite may look like an ordinary Earth rock, scientists analyze meteorites to gain a better understanding of the universe.

Meteoroids are small pieces of comets, asteroids, or space dust moving through space.

The largest known meteorite was found in Africa in 1920. It was about 9 feet by 8 feet (2.74 m x 2.4 m) weighing over 60 tons (59 tonnes). This meteorite was named Hoba. The hole created by a meteorite when it lands is called a crater.

Friction between a meteor and the Earth's atmosphere causes the meteor to burn up, producing the effect of a bright fireball with a trail of light.

Scientists believe that about 100 giant craters around the world were created by huge meteorites. The Great Barringer Meteor Crater is located in Arizona. It is about 560 ft deep and about 4,150 ft wide (171 m deep and about 1,265 m wide).

When a meteoroid moves into Earth's atmosphere, it is called a meteor.

Sometimes meteorites break apart when they land. Admiral Robert Peary discovered the Ahnighito meteorite in Greenland in 1894. Within seven miles of this location, two smaller meteorites were found.

During a meteor shower or storm, meteors travel in parallel paths. From Earth, the meteors appear to spread out from one point in the sky.

On average, 10 meteors can be seen every hour in the night sky. When several dozens of meteors are seen in an hour, it is called a meteor shower. If thousands of meteors are seen in an hour, it is called a meteor storm.

The composition of all three meteorites was the same, indicating they were once part of a larger piece. Eskimos used parts of the meteorite for making spears, knives, and needles.

On a clear night, sometimes we see what looks like a star falling down. This is commonly called a "shooting star" or a "falling star." Actually, it is not a star. It is a meteoroid being pulled into the Earth's atmosphere by gravity.

Most meteors burn up completely before reaching the ground. However, if one is big enough to reach the Earth before it burns up, it is called a meteorite.

There are three main types of meteorites: iron meteorites, stony meteorites, and stony iron meteorites.

Rub your hands together quickly. The movement of your hands rubbing against each other creates heat. This is called friction.

By the time the *Apollo* program ended in 1972, ten more American astronauts explored the Moon's surface in a total of six manned moon landings.

There have been many highlights in space exploration, accomplished through successes and failures. Some of the men and women who lost their lives for the sake of knowledge are Virgil I. Grissom, Edward H. White II, Roger B. Chaffee, Francis R. Scobee, Michael J. Smith, Judith A. Resnik, Ellison S. Onizuka, Ronald E. McNair, Gregory B. Jarvis, and Christa McAuliffe.

For people to be able to to travel into space, the problem of escaping Earth's gravity had to be solved. Rockets were invented in the 1940's. Only rockets are powerful enough to escape the pull of Earth's gravity.

Neil Armstrong was the mission commander and the first man to set foot on the moon. As Neil Armstrong stepped on the Moon, he said, "That's one small step for man –one giant leap for mankind."

In January 1958, Americans successfully launched their first satellite, *Explorer 1*. This was the beginning of NASA, the National Aeronautics and Space Administration.

In January 1961, Americans sent Ham, a chimpanzee, into space to test the *Mercury* spacecraft. Ham returned safely to Earth.

Departing the Moon, the Lunar Module separated from the launch pad and joined the Command Service Module.

Lunar Module

launch pad

fuel tanks fall away when empty

Then in July 1969, as millions of people watched on television, the first man walked on the moon. It took three days for the American spacecraft *Apollo 11*, powered by *Saturn V* rocket, to reach the moon.

The three astronauts who made this historic journey were Neil Armstrong, Edwin (Buzz) Aldrin, and Michael Collins. The lunar module *Eagle* landed on the Sea of Tranquility. Neil Armstrong spoke: "Tranquility Base here. The *Eagle* has landed."

In February 1962, John Glenn became the first American to orbit Earth in *Friendship 7*. He made three complete orbits in about 5 hours.

In March 1965, the USSR marked another first in space history when Alexei Leonov aboard the *Voskhod 2*, became the first person to make a space walk. During a space walk, an astronaut goes outside the spacecraft but is connected to it by a tether line.

In April 1961, 27-year-old Yuri Gagarin of the Soviet Union boarded the *Vostok I* and became the first man to orbit Earth.

In May 1961, Alan Shepherd became the first American in space. His *Mercury* capsule was fired into space for 15 minutes 22 seconds, and then dropped into the ocean.

The *Apollo II* spacecraft consisted of:

1) The lunar module, which was designed to land on the moon.

2) The command module, which was the control and living quarters. It was designed to return the astronauts to Earth.

3) The service module, which was designed to carry fuel and oxygen.

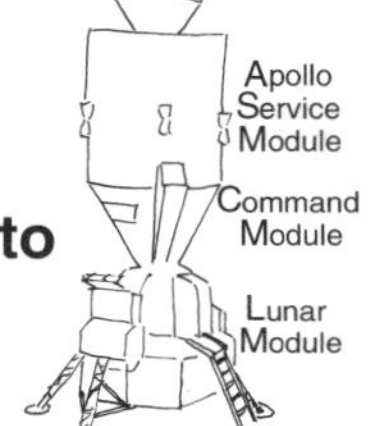

A rocket consists of stages, or parts, that carry fuel. As the fuel is used up, a stage falls away, decreasing the weight of the vehicle.

Konstantin Tsiolkovsky (1857-1935), a Russian scientist, was the first person to design a multistage rocket with fuel tanks that would fall away as their fuel was used up. This important discovery allowed spacecraft to travel far into space.

The Command Module separated from the Service Module. As the Command Module headed for Earth, it glowed brightly. Parachutes opened as it splashed into the Pacific Ocean. An eager ship waited for the returning astronauts. The three astronauts remained in a Module Quarantine Facility for 18 days before they were released.

In June 1965, Edward H. White, aboard *Gemini 4,* became the first American to walk in space while tethered to a spacecraft.

By February 1966, the Soviets sent the unmanned *Luna 9* to the Moon. *Luna 9* collected data and photographs of the Moon.

In June 1966, the Americans sent their first unmanned spacecraft, *Surveyor 1* to the Moon. It took thousands of photographs; but eventually, as the signals weakened, the project ended.

A major milestone in space exploration occurred when the USSR launched *Sputnik 1* in October, 1957. *Sputnik 1* was about the size of a beach ball but weighed 184 lbs. It transmitted data to Earth until January 1958 when it began to malfunction and eventually fell to Earth.

In November 1957, Soviets sent the first living animal into space. On board *Sputnik 2,* a dog named Laika was monitored for 7 days as it orbited Earth.

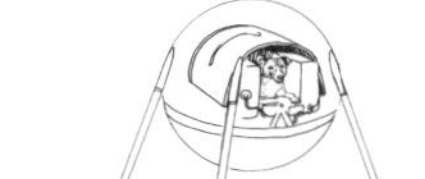

The astronauts planted the American flag on the Moon. Because there is no wind on the Moon, the flag was held open by wires.

The space shuttles in use today are *Columbia, Discovery, Atlantis,* and *Endeavor.* The USSR developed a similar spacecraft in the 1980's, but it has only made one flight. *Challenger* was destroyed in 1986, and replaced by *Endeavor.*

The space age began with rockets. This type of spacecraft could only be used one time. Scientists realized that using these crafts only once was a waste of hard work and money. If space travel was to be successful, they had to design reusable spacecraft.

The payload bay inside the orbiter is about 15 ft x 60 ft (4.6 m x 18.3 m), large enough to fit a bus. It is designed to carry out scientific experiments, repair orbiting satellites, and serve as a storage area for satellites retrieved from space.

The orbiter is the main part of the space shuttle. It has wings and is fueled by two rocket boosters and a giant external fuel tank.

orbiter

Attached to the payload bay is the Remote Manipulator System (RMS). The RMS is a 50-ft (15.2-m) robotic arm used by the mission specialist and operated from the flight deck. One of the uses of the RMS is to service and retrieve satellites.

The orbiter enters Earth's atmosphere and lands on a runway, similar to an airplane landing.

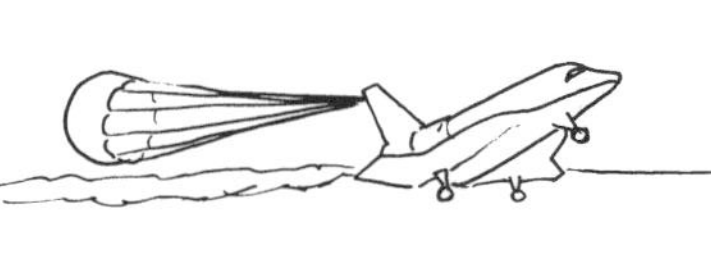

As the orbiter re-enters the Earth's atmosphere, it glows due to the friction.

The space shuttle soars into space and about two minutes later has reached a height of about 28 miles (45.1 km). When the fuel in the two solid rocket boosters is emptied, they fall away. They parachute into the ocean at a predetermined spot and are retrieved to be used again.

In April 1981, John Young and Robert Crippen boarded the first American space shuttle, *Columbia.* Its design allowed it to take off like a rocket, complete its space mission, return to Earth and land on a runway, similar to the way an airplane lands.

The space shuttle is a manned spacecraft designed to transport humans and cargo to and from space. The space shuttle revolutionized space travel as the world's first reusable spacecraft.

Today's space shuttle can transport a crew of ten people. The commander and pilot are astronauts; mission specialists and payload specialists are not always astronauts.

The giant external fuel tank (ET) is attached to the orbiter and helps to carry it into space. When it is empty, it separates from the orbiter.

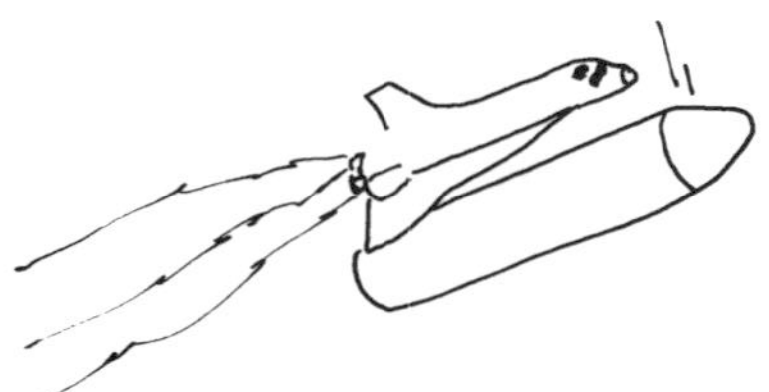

The orbiter is now ready to accomplish its mission. When the mission is completed, the orbiter's rocket engines fire, beginning its journey back to Earth.

Three main engines are supplied with liquid hydrogen fuel and liquid oxygen during the launch of the space shuttle.

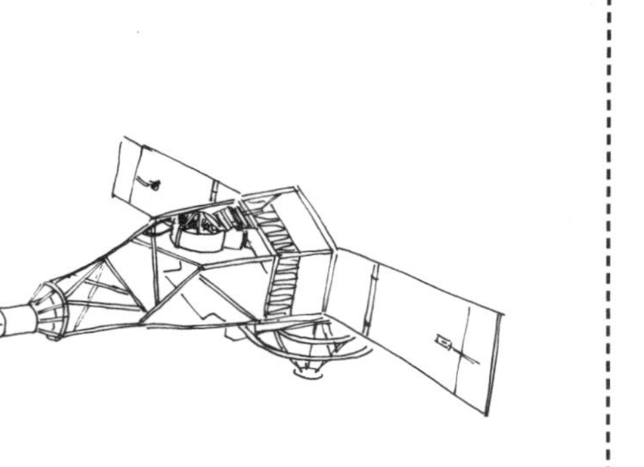

The Moon orbits Earth and is often referred to as Earth's satellite. A satellite is a smaller object orbiting a larger object. There are natural satellites and artificial satellites. In 1957, the Russians sent the first spacecraft into space, the satellite *Sputnik 1.*

In 1971, the Soviet space probe *Mars 3* took photographs of Mars. In 1976, US *Viking* space probes landed on Mars and tested its soil, took pictures, and gathered important data.

In July 1962, a communications satellite named *Telstar I* was launched. This satellite made it possible to view live television broadcasts across the Atlantic Ocean for the first time.

***Voyager 1* holds a time capsule containing videodisks that show the sights and sounds of Earth.**

If a satellite moves at a different pace than the rotating Earth, it has to be tracked by moving dishes.

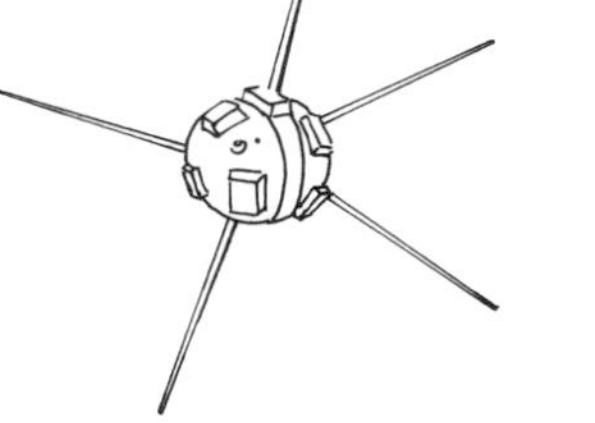

Weather satellites can determine temperature, wind speed, waves, and more. They provide very accurate weather forecasts.

The Hubble Space Telescope has two large, flat solar panels that make electricity from sunlight. When it was discovered that a mirror was faulty, the space shuttle *Endeavor* was sent to repair it in 1993. Since then, it has sent clear images.

Weather satellites and communications satellites orbit Earth at the same speed at which Earth rotates.

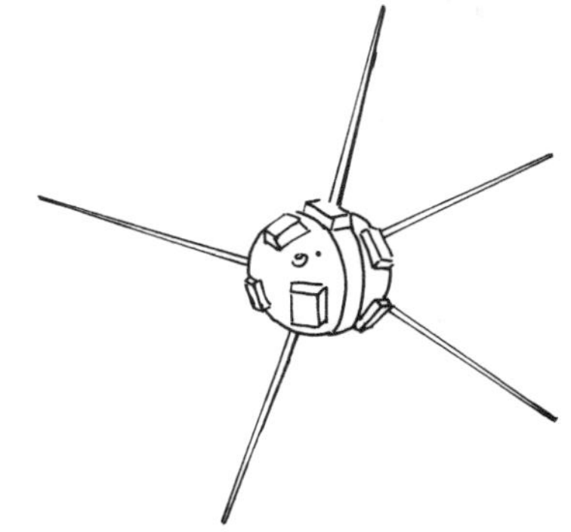

In July 1991, a weather satellite called *ERS-1* was launched. This satellite made it possible to receive radar images of the Earth's surface and information on winds and ocean activities. Our lives are greatly affected by the use of satellites.

ERS-1 is a shortened name for the European Earth Resources Satellite.

Space probes are unmanned spacecraft that help astronomers gain more information about space. Space probes can go farther than humans can travel.

Mariner 2 was the first space probe to visit another planet. In 1962, it sent back information about Venus.

Today, there are hundreds of artificial satellites orbiting Earth. A satellite may appear to stay in one place in space because it moves with the rotating Earth. That is why a radio dish on the ground can be aimed at a satellite and never move.

All the planets in our solar system have been visited by a space probe except Pluto.

In April 1990, the Hubble Space Telescope, named after Edwin Hubble, was launched from a space shuttle. The Hubble Telescope is a type of orbiting observatory that produces clear images of space that are not distorted by Earth's atmosphere.

Satellites help sailors and pilots to navigate. Communications satellites allow us to send and receive signals by using large dish antennae.

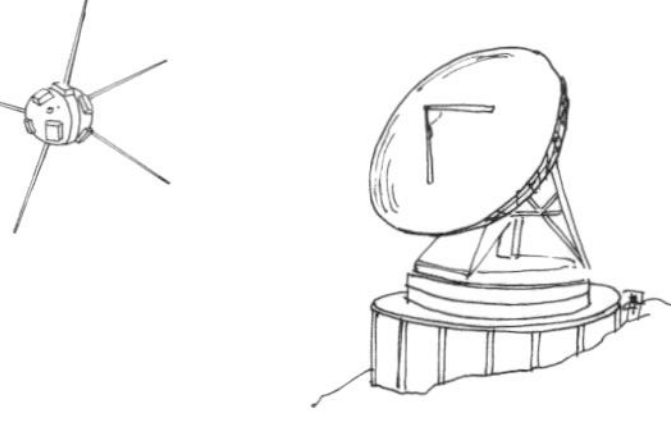

The *Voyager 1* was launched in 1977 and today is traveling around the edge of our solar system.

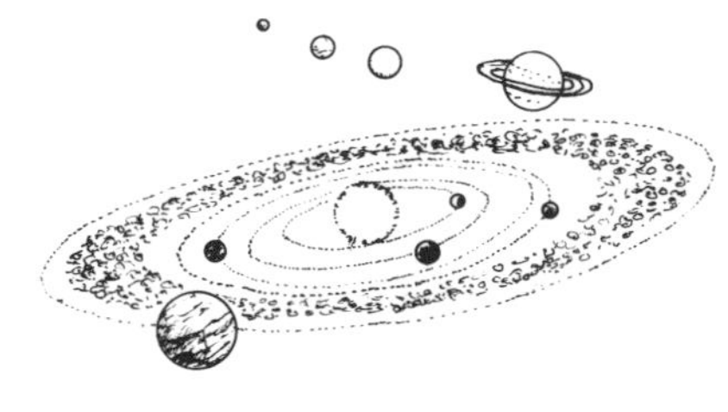

It is estimated to take approximately 800 hours to assemble the 70-ton (63.5 tonnes), 143-ft (43.6 m) long space station.

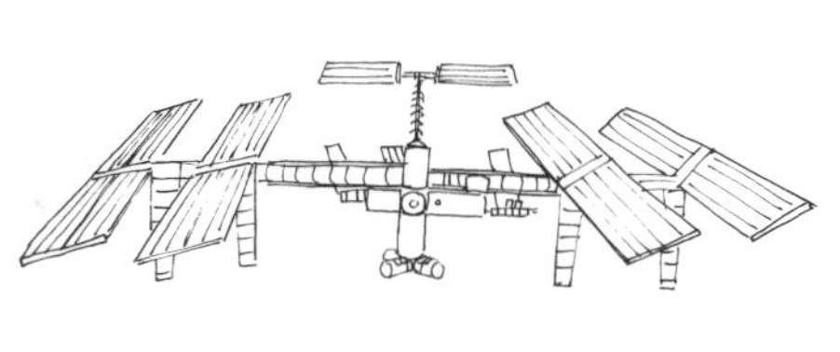

Space exploration is difficult because there is no air to breathe, very little gravity, and extreme temperatures. Astronauts need special accommodations when traveling in space.

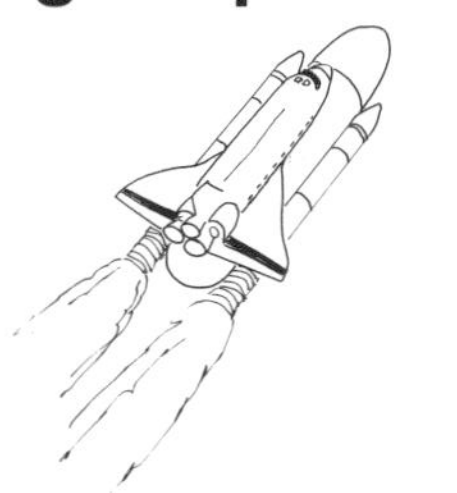

To complete more extensive space studies, scientists build space stations. The USSR launched the first space station, *Salyut 1*, in 1971. The first American space station was *Skylab*, launched in 1973. Many difficulties befell *Skylab*, and crews ceased working there in 1974.

The Soviet space station *Mir* was launched in 1986 and had sections added to it over the years. Many astronauts from several countries worked in *Mir*.

An astronaut's spacesuit is called the EMU, short for Extravehicular Mobility Unit. It contains a special backpack with an air tank that continually provides the astronaut with fresh air. The EMU locks together so the air inside cannot escape.

Astronauts are zipped in a sleeping bag attached to the walls so they will not float away.

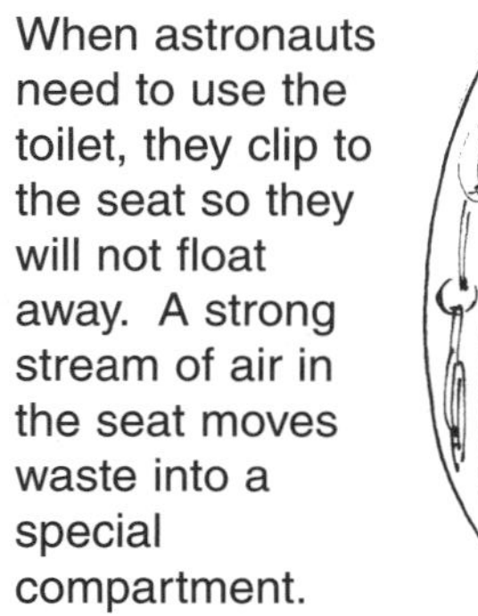

When astronauts need to use the toilet, they clip to the seat so they will not float away. A strong stream of air in the seat moves waste into a special compartment.

A radio headset goes on the astronaut's head and then a helmet is locked in place. Gloves are locked at the wrists.

Spacecraft are designed to support human life in space. When astronauts leave the spacecraft, they must wear a special spacesuit to stay alive.

When putting on an EMU, an astronaut first puts on long underwear that is covered with a network of plastic tubes. Water is pumped through the tubes to keep the astronaut's body at the correct temperature.

Next, the astronaut puts on pants, boots, and top and locks them together.

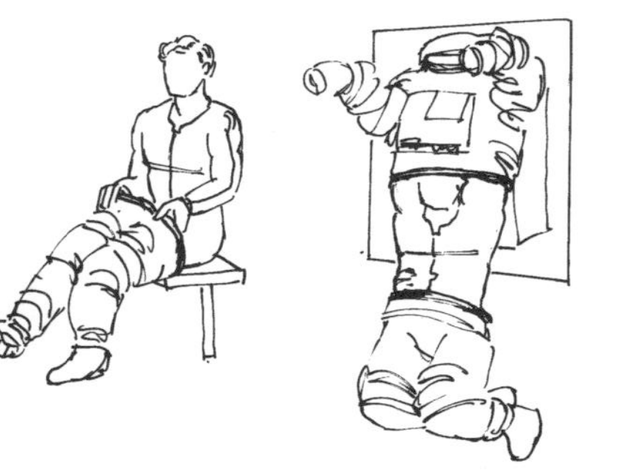

Astronauts wear the EMU when working outside the spacecraft, launching a satellite or conducting a scientific experiment.

When working outside the spacecraft, an astronaut is attached to lifelines to keep from floating away.

Most of the food an astronaut eats in space is dehydrated, or dried. Liquids must be consumed through tubes because drops of liquid would float around in the weightless environment.

There is no friction in a weightless environment. Without friction, human muscles do not get the workout needed to stay strong. To keep fit, astronauts use special exercise equipment on board the shuttle.

***Skylab* is no longer in space; it burned up during its re-entry into Earth's atmosphere.**

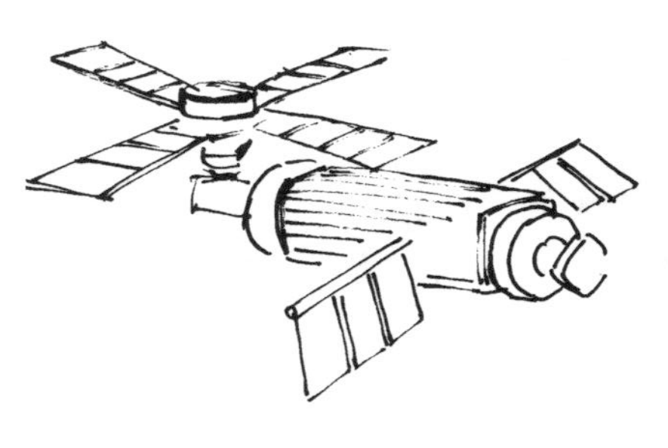

Currently, the International Space Station (ISS), a joint project of the USA, USSR, Europe, Japan, and other countries, is underway. The station is under construction and when finished it will be the size of 14 tennis courts.

Graphics Pages

Note: The owner of this book has permission to photocopy the *Graphics Pages* for classroom use only.

Investigative Loop™

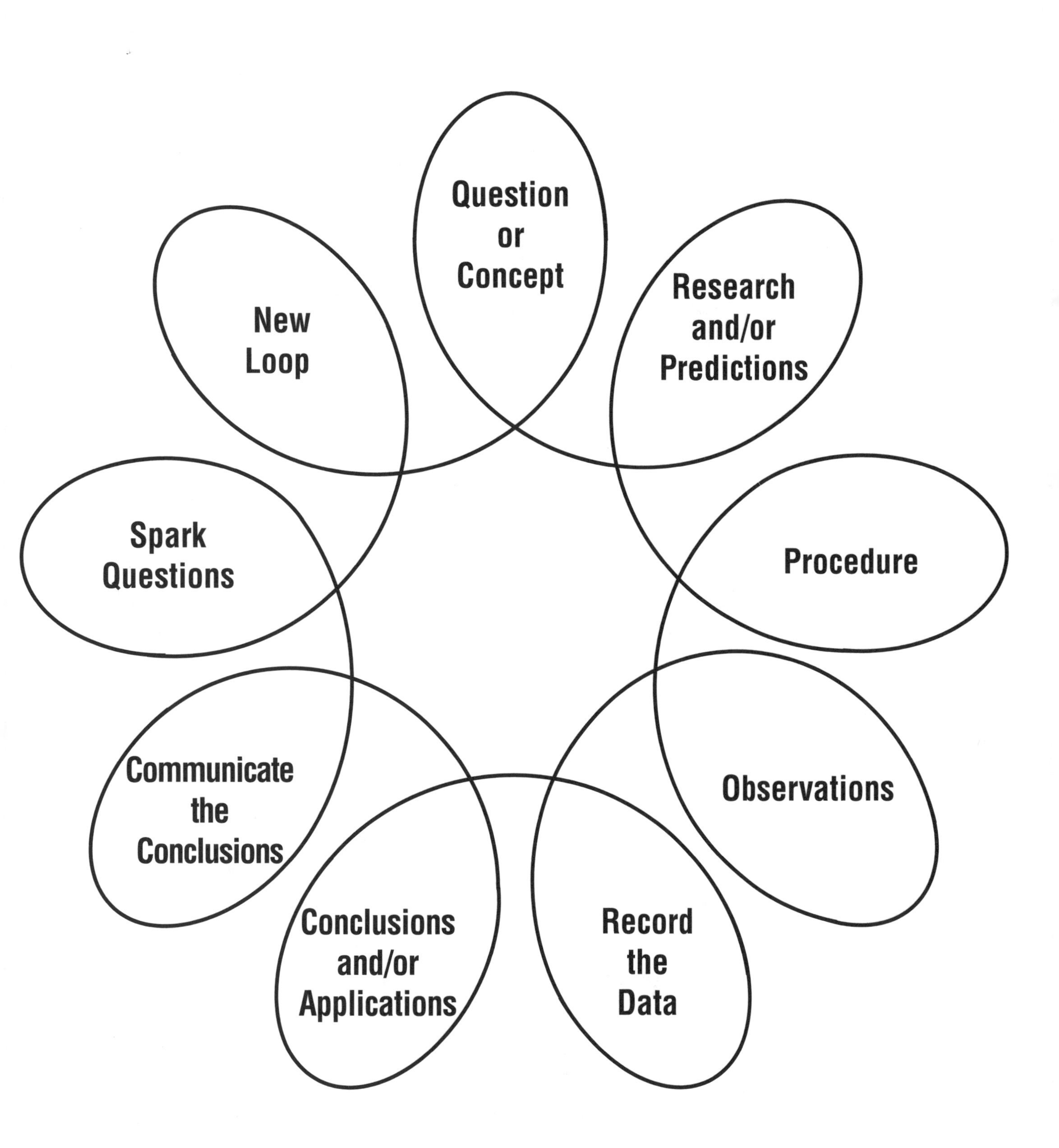

Space Scenarios

Problem: Space Survival Movie

You are writing a futuristic movie about space colonization. The movie opens showing a group of Earthlings evacuating planet Earth because of life threatening events. They have prepared for this evacuation for years, and as the movie opens, they are in the process of mobilizing the evacuation. Finish outlining the movie. Where are they planning to go? What do they need for this journey? How are they traveling to their destination? Design their space ship and explain design purposes. What is their destination like? What are they taking to help them develop a self-sustaining colony? Make your movie as scientifically accurate as possible, based upon current technology.

Problem: Asteroid Shower

The projected orbit of a giant asteroid indicates that it has a 1 in a billion chance of colliding with planet Earth in the year 2011. While the chance of impact is slim, as a specialist in Potentially Hazardous Asteroids it is your job to develop a plan to avoid the collision. What recommendations would you make? If the collision is not avoided, how could life on Earth be affected?

Problem: It is the 15th century in Europe, as an adventurer and explorer you wish to find a new trade route to the East. No one has ever sailed due west in hopes of circumnavigating the Earth to reach the Eastern trade countries. Many people believe that it is impossible to do so because the Earth is flat and not round. Using the science and technology available to a science minded explorer in the 15th century, explain ways in which to prove that the Earth is round.

Problem: Expanding or Shrinking Universe

As a college professor, you are preparing to teach your students about the Universe. The textbooks that you studied as a student in high school said that the universe was contracting; however, articles in current journals say the universe is expanding. What discoveries have been made to change the popular opinion so drastically? What will you teach your class?

Problem: In your World History class you are learning about events that took place in ancient Egypt and ancient Greece. While the dates in your textbook are based on our current calendar, you know that the Egyptians developed a calendar based on the sun and the Greeks developed a calendar based on the moon. What difficulties could arise between civilizations using different calendar systems? Investigate the history of our modern calendar.

Problem: You are an archeologist researching the Mayan Palace of the Governor at Uxmal in the Yucatan. The building was completed around 900 A.D. and believed to have been built in alignment with the planet Venus. How can you determine if this is true? What significance could the stars and planets have had in early civilizations?

Problem: Earth was hit by a giant asteroid which broke off a section of the planet, reducing its mass. It was also knocked out of its current orbit and into orbit as a satellite of Mars. What changes have and will occur on Earth?

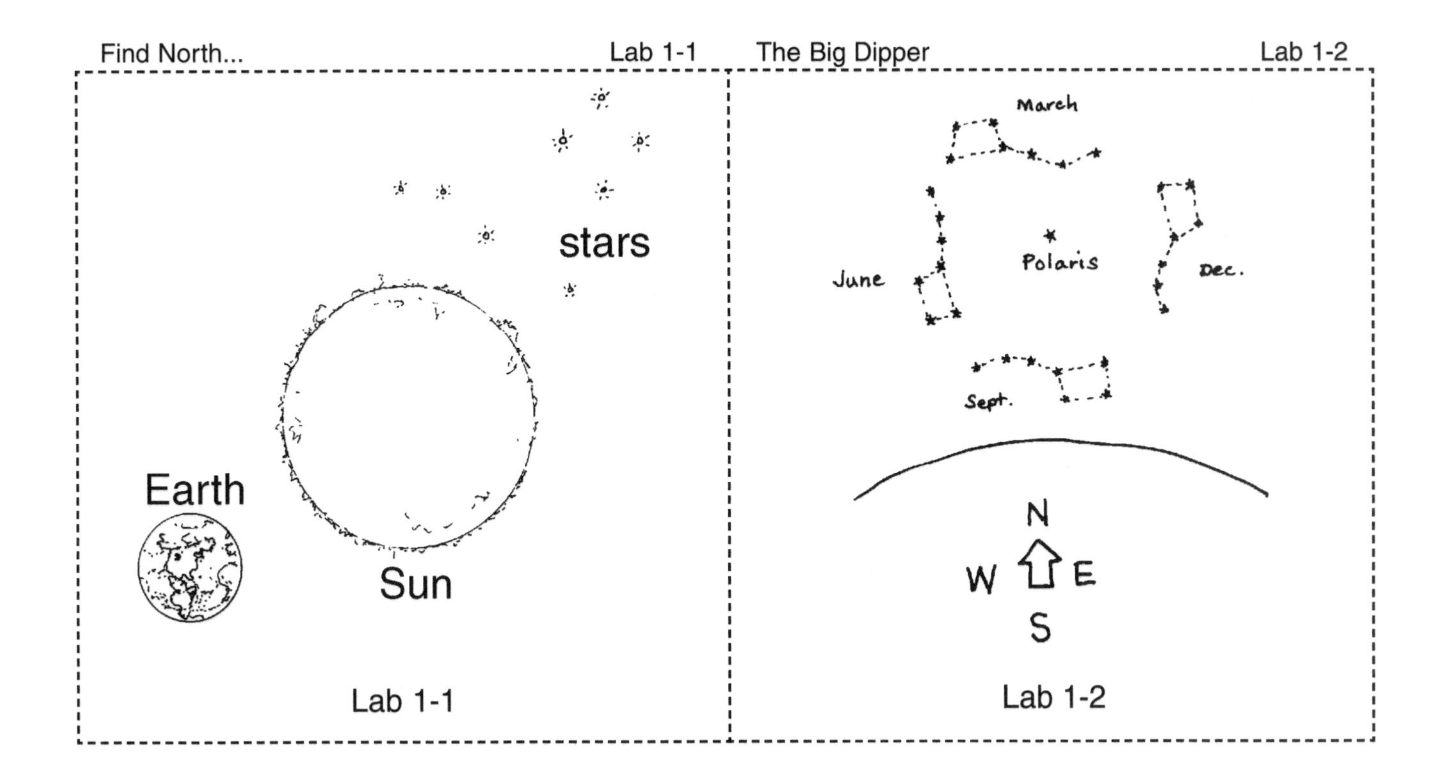

Cut on the dotted lines

1 A-D

Ancient Times

2000 B.C. 1 B.C.

1 A.D. 1600 A.D.

1601 A.D. 1700 A.D.

1701 A.D. 1800 A.D.

1801 A.D. 1900 A.D.

1901 A.D.

1950 A.D.

1960 A.D.

1970 A.D.

1980 A.D.

2000 A.D.

1-M

Ancient people marked the passing of time with the stars.

1-N

Babylonians used movements of stars and planets to know when to plant and harvest.

1-O

Ancient sailors used stars to navigate.

1-P

Ancient Egyptians marked one month as the time between one full moon and another.

1-Q

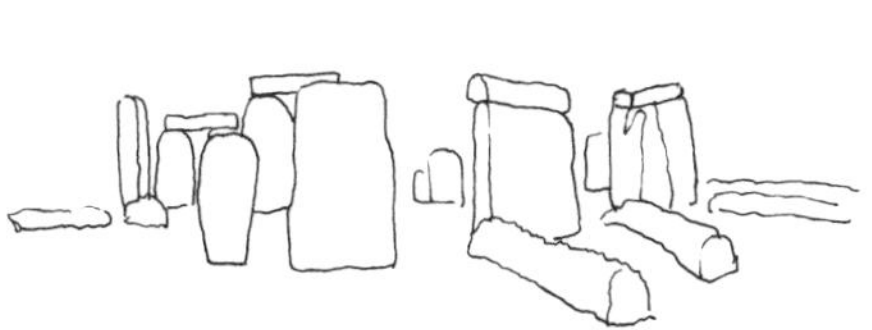

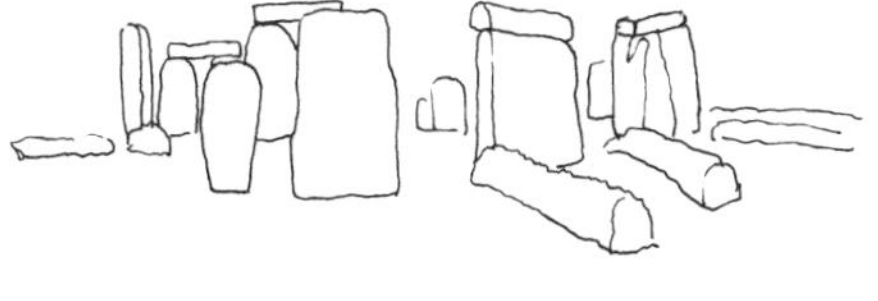

Stonehenge, built about 2000 B.C., may have been a type of clock or calendar.

1-R

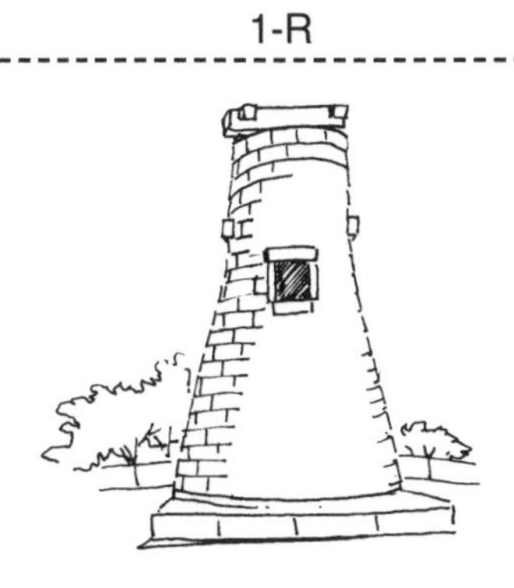

The Chomsungdae Observatory was built in South Korea about 632 A.D.

Round Earth Lab 2-1

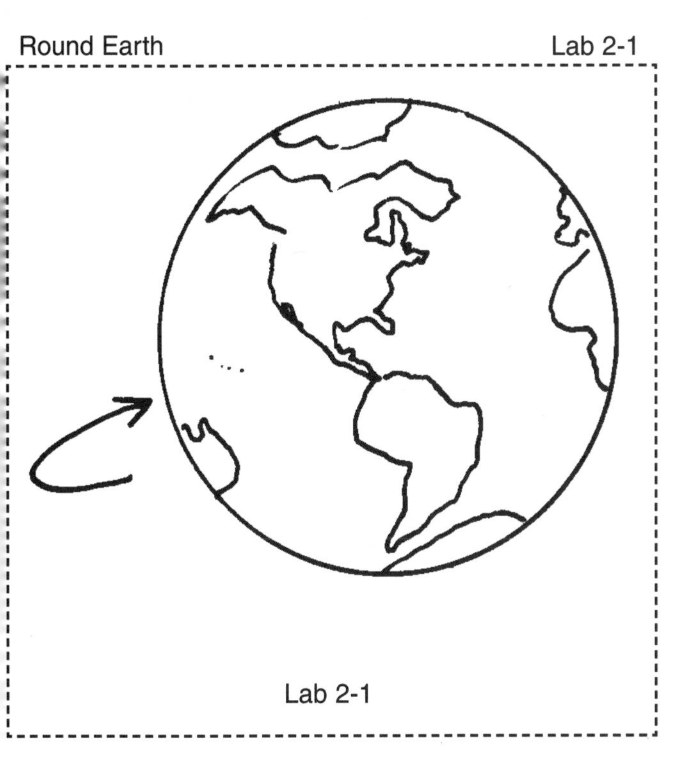

Lab 2-1

Timeline 2A

In 350 B.C., the Greek philosopher Aristotle argued that Earth was round, not flat.

Timeline 2B

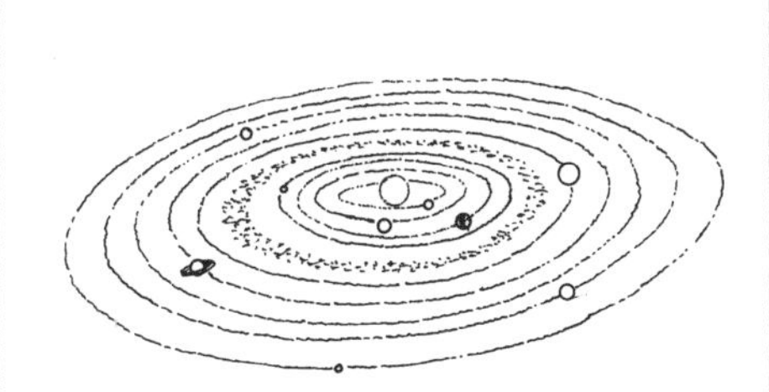

In 1543, Nicolaus Copernicus claimed Earth and all other plants circled a still sun.

Timeline 2C

About 1613, Galileo Galilei confirmed Copernicus' theory after inventing the first telescope.

Timeline 2D

Johannes Kepler (1571-1630) discovered three laws of planetary motion.

Timeline 2E

Sir Isaac Newton (1642-1727) invented the reflecting telescope and built upon Kepler's discoveries.

Hot Stars 3A

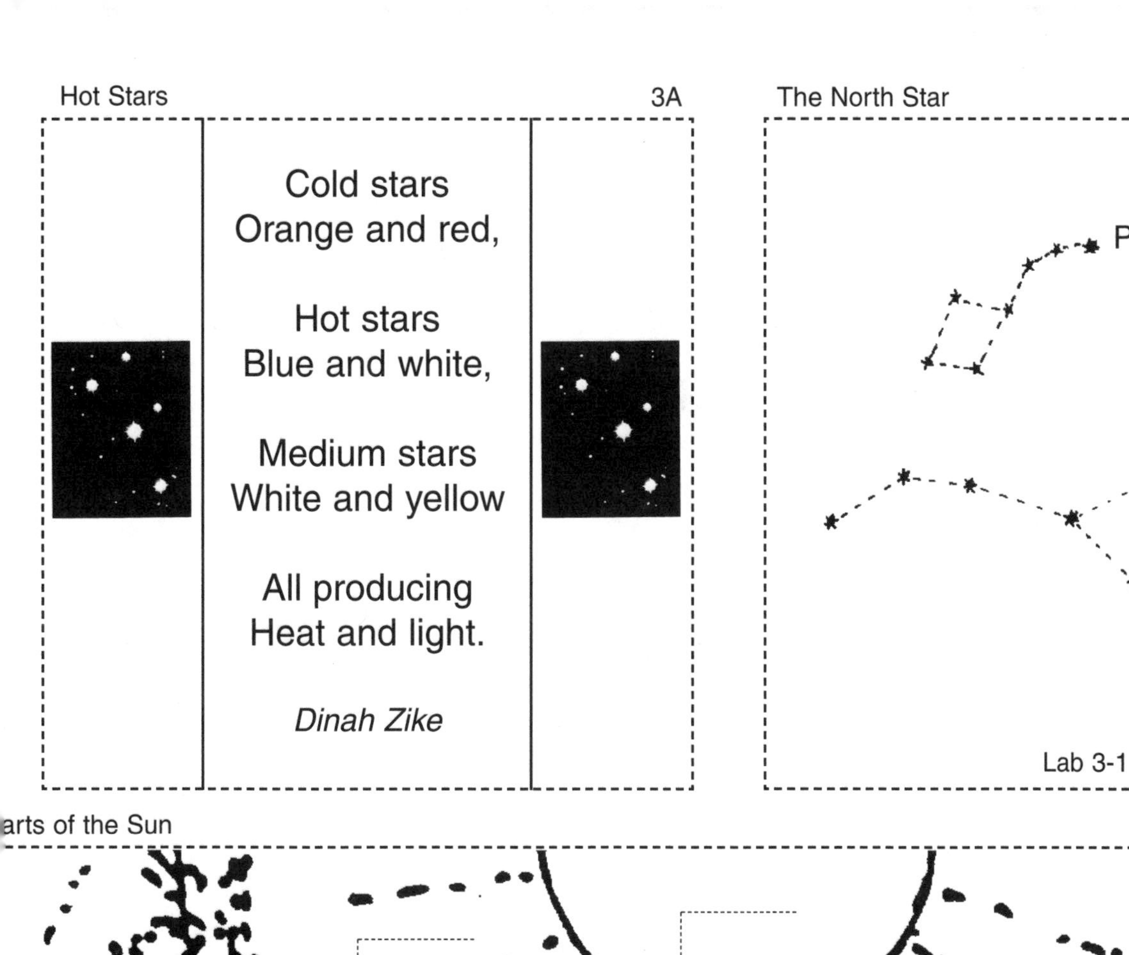

The North Star Lab 3-1

Polaris

Dubhe

Merak

Lab 3-1

arts of the Sun 4A

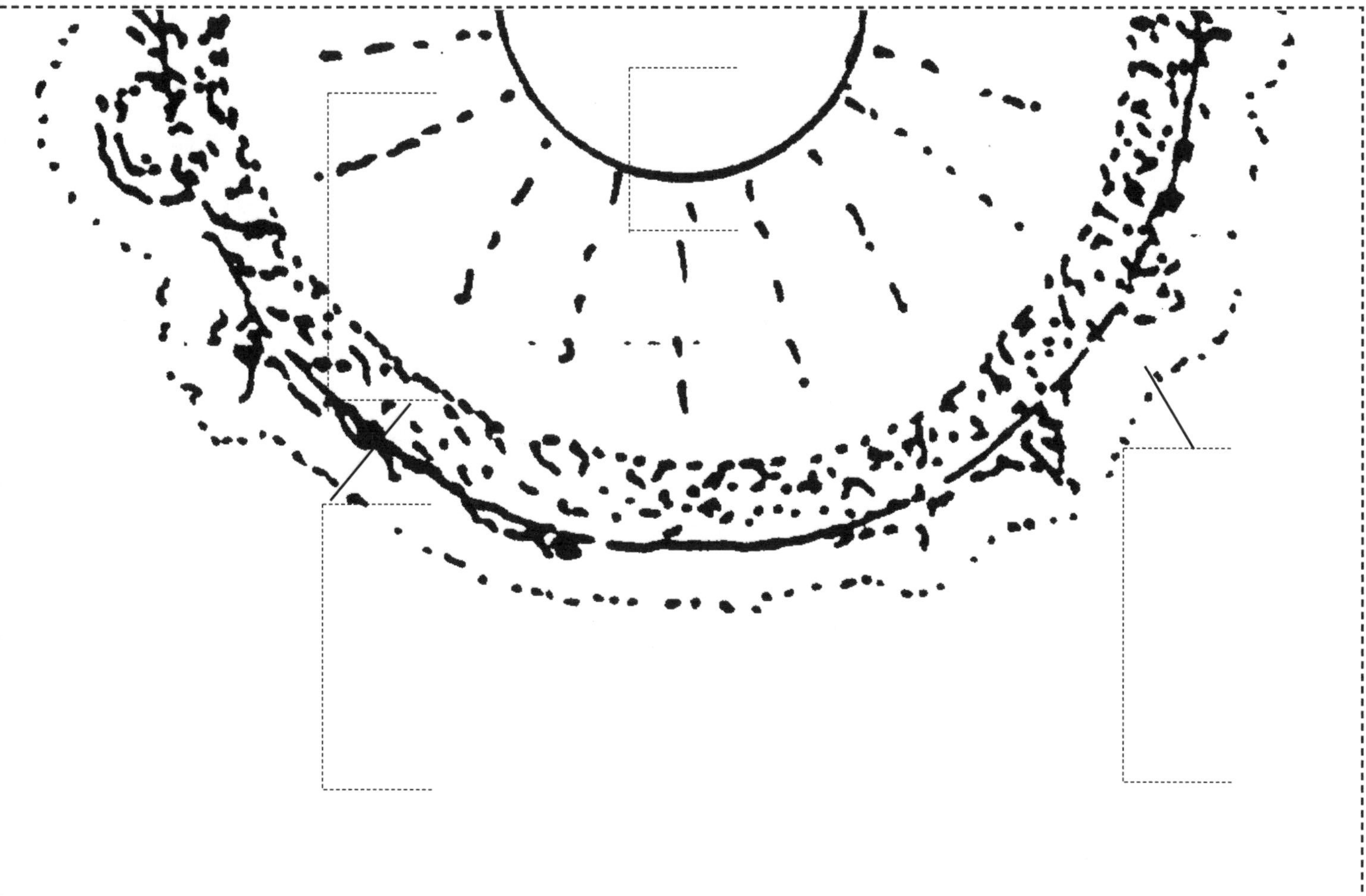

arts of the Sun 4B

Inside the sun
There is a core,
A giant energy
Production store.

The photosphere is
What we see,
Distributing
The Sun's energy.

Above this
Is the atmosphere,
Corona down to
Chromosphere.

Dinah Zike

arts of the Sun 4C

Core	Photosphere	Chromosphere	Corona

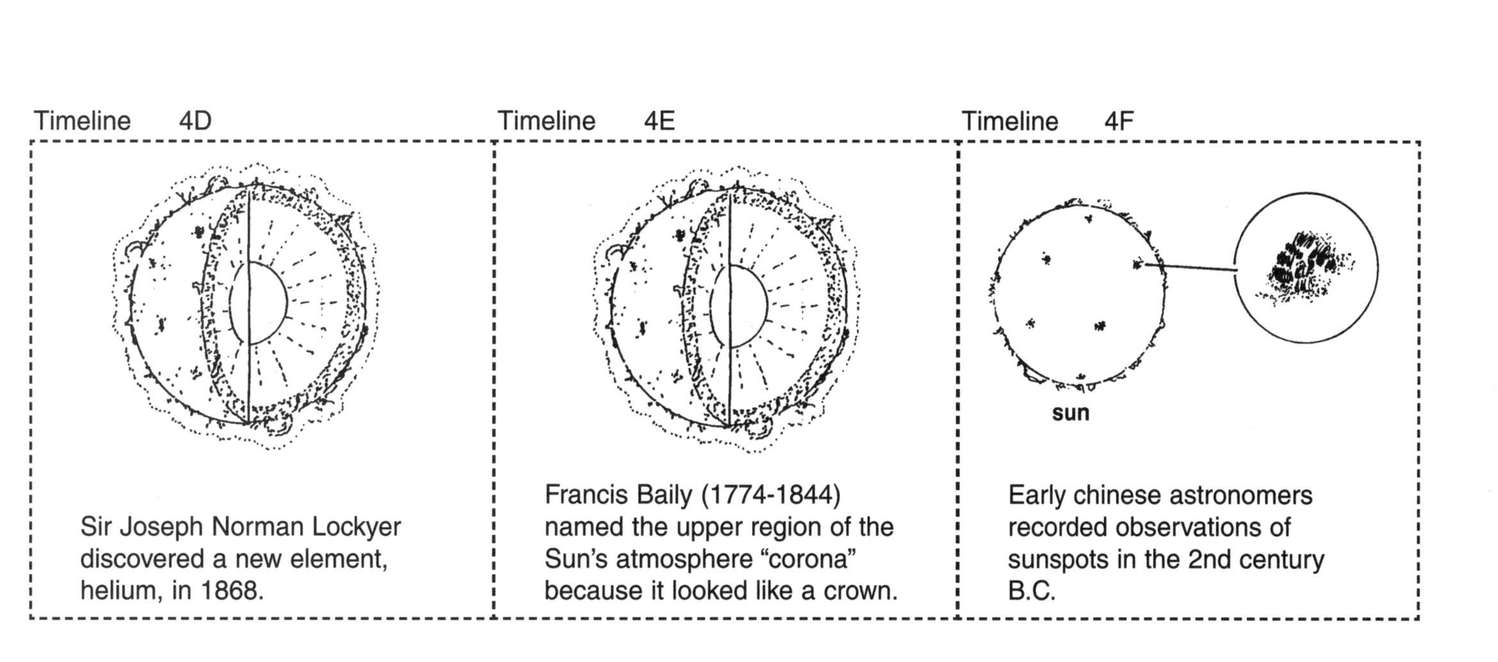

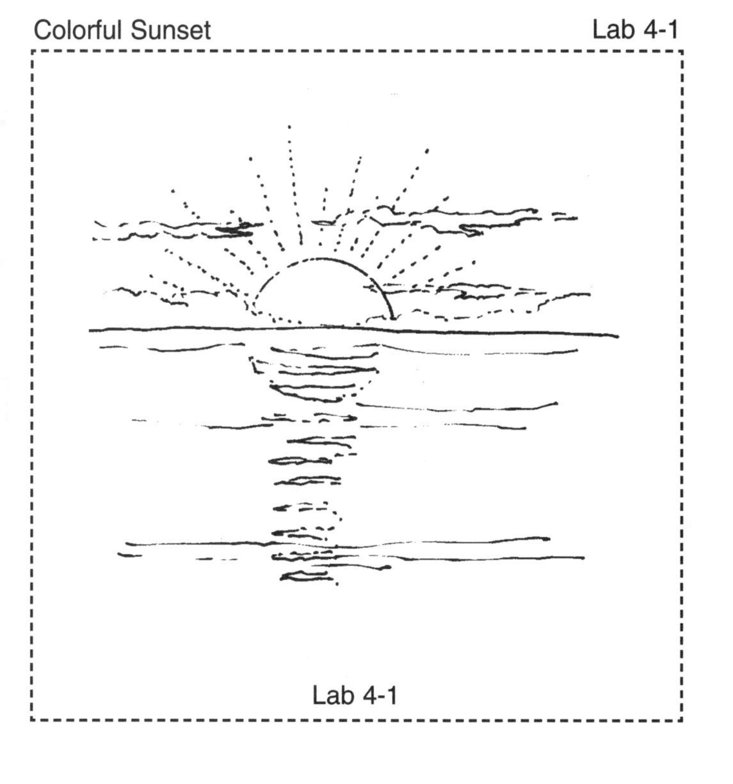

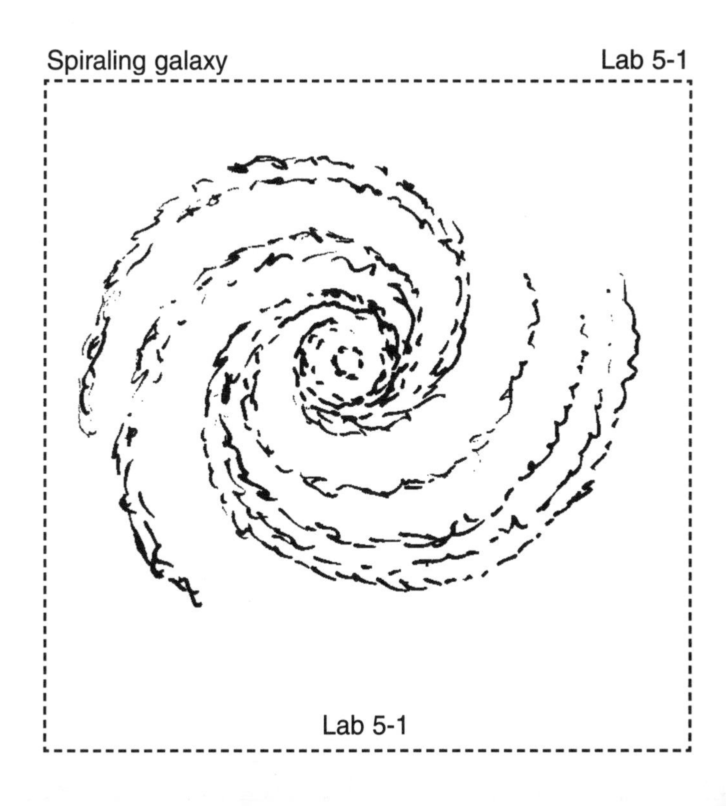

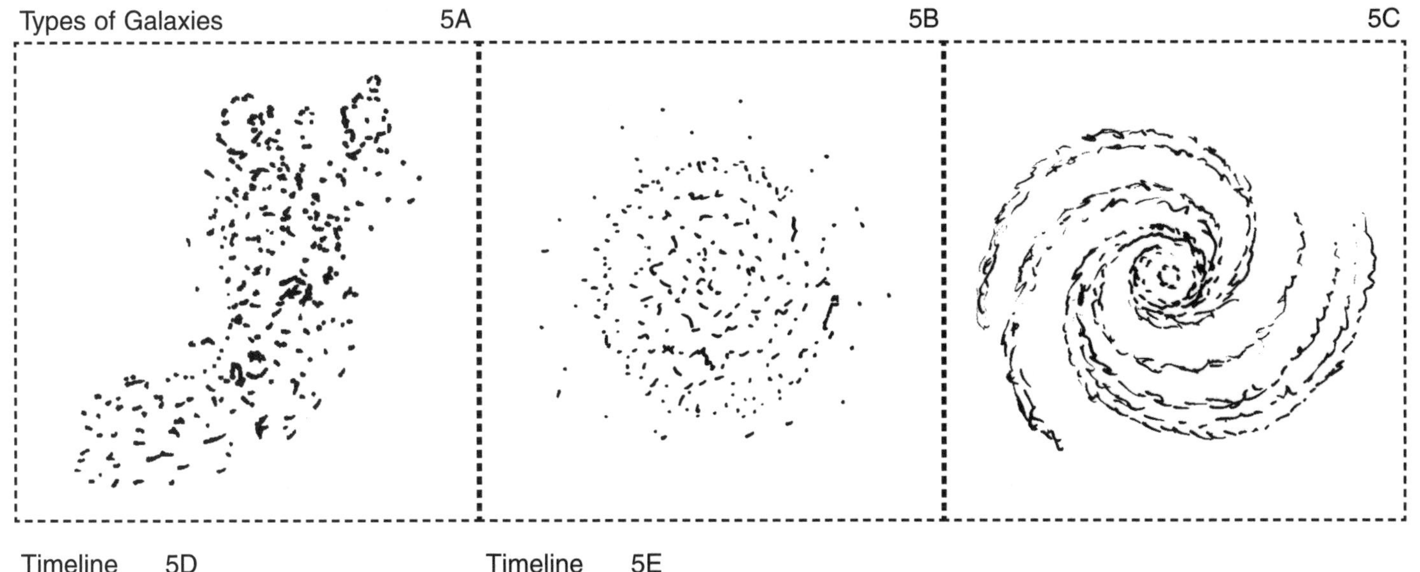

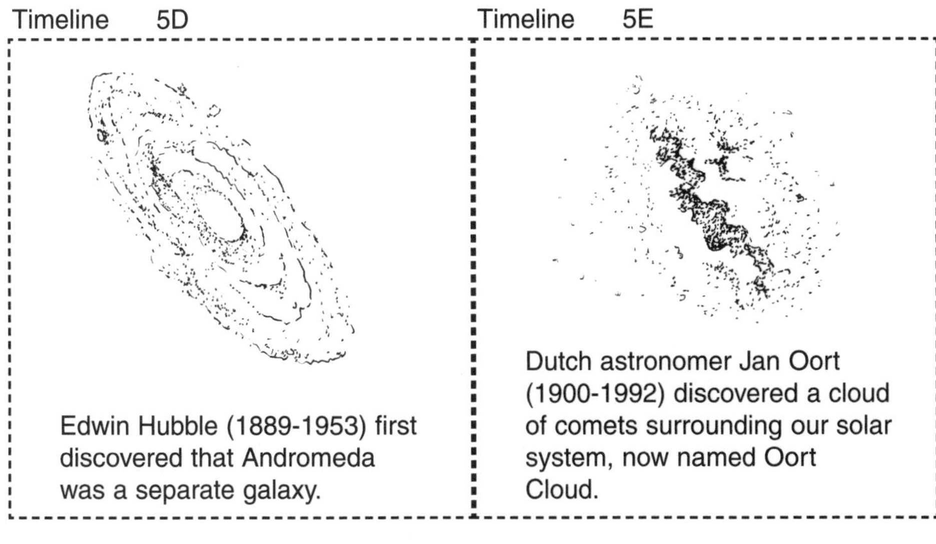

Edwin Hubble (1889-1953) first discovered that Andromeda was a separate galaxy.

Dutch astronomer Jan Oort (1900-1992) discovered a cloud of comets surrounding our solar system, now named Oort Cloud.

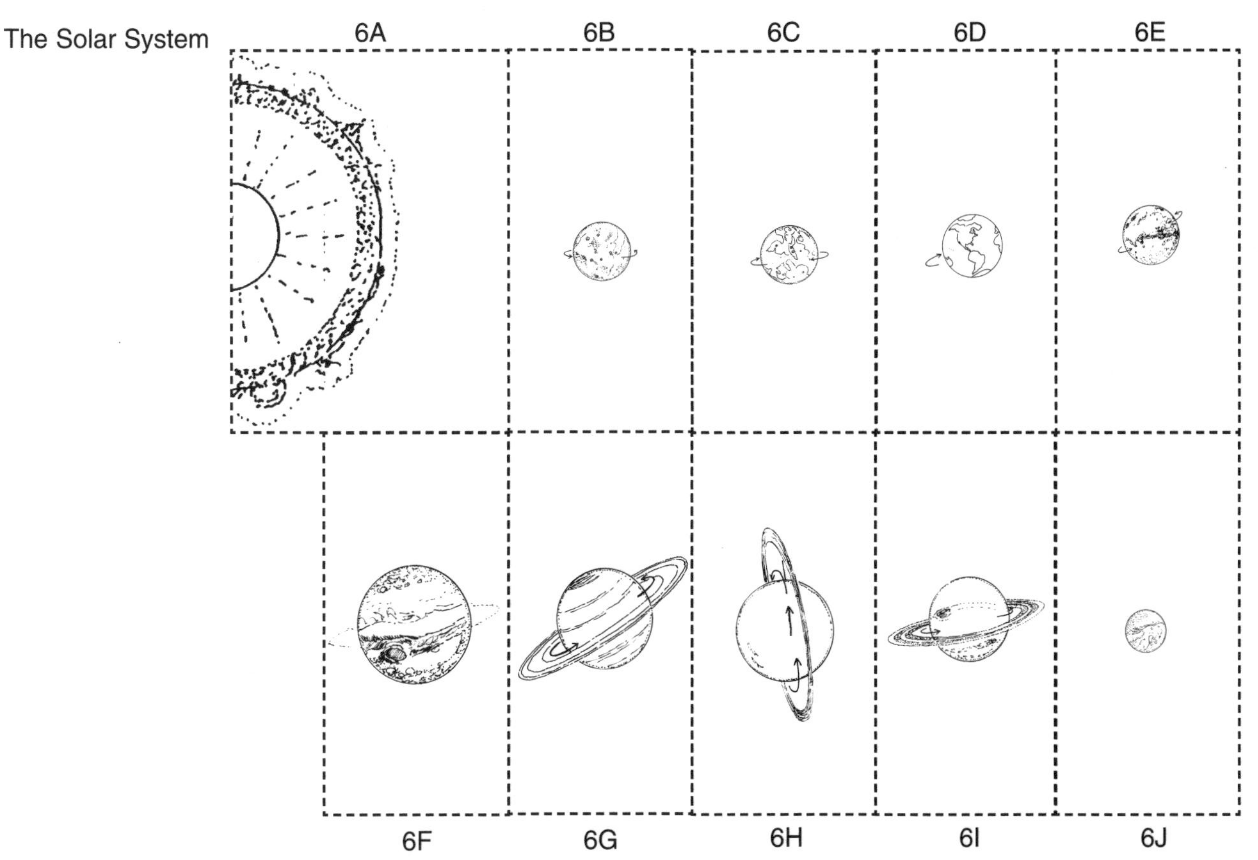

The Sun 6K

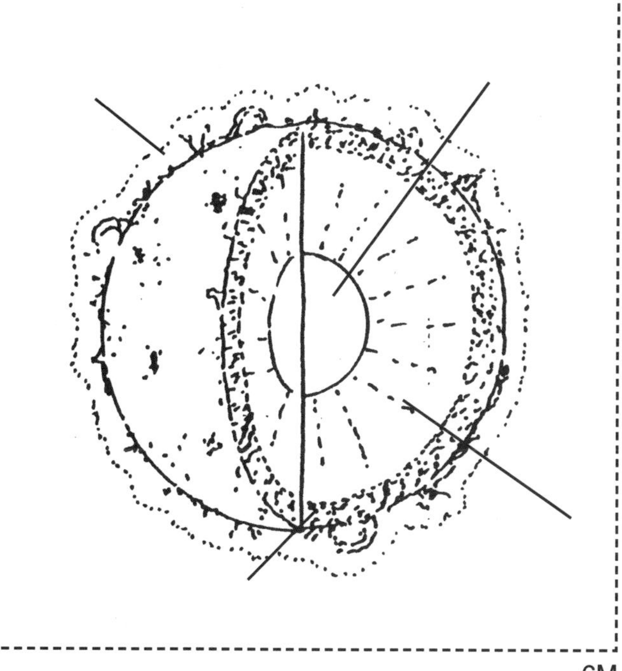

The Sun 6L

Diameter: ______________________________

Core Temperature: ______________________

How heat and light are produced: ____________

____

____

How long it takes light to travel to Earth: ________

____

6M

Fruity, Seedy Planet	Distance from the basketball Sun
Peppercorn – Mercury	5 inches (12 cm)
Pea – Venus	9 inches (22 cm)
Pea – Earth	12 inches (30 cm)
Peppercorn – Mars	18 inches (46 cm)
Grapefruit – Jupiter	61 inches (156 cm)
Large orange – Saturn	112 inches (286 cm)
Plum – Uranus	226 inches (574 cm)
Plum – Neptune	354 inches (900 cm)
Peppercorn – Pluto	465 inches (1180 cm)

My Monster Named Zanet 6N

Solar System - Earth 7A

Solar System - Earth 7B

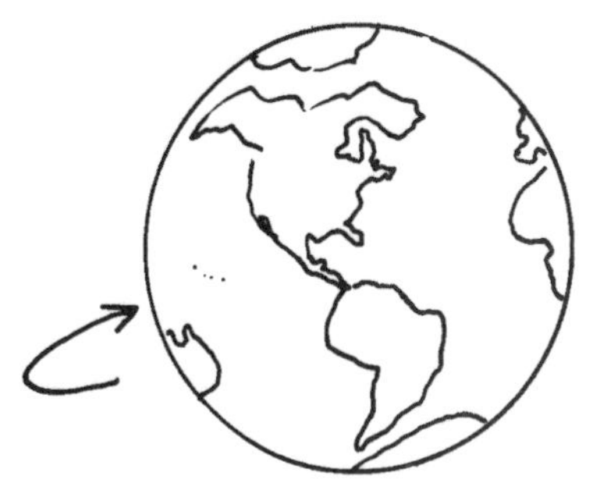

Distance from Sun: ____________________

Diameter: ____________________

Rotation: ____________________

Revolution: ____________________

Surface: ____________________

Known Moons: ____________________

Interesting Information: ____________________

____

____

Day and Night Lab 7-1

Lab 7-1

Solar System 8A

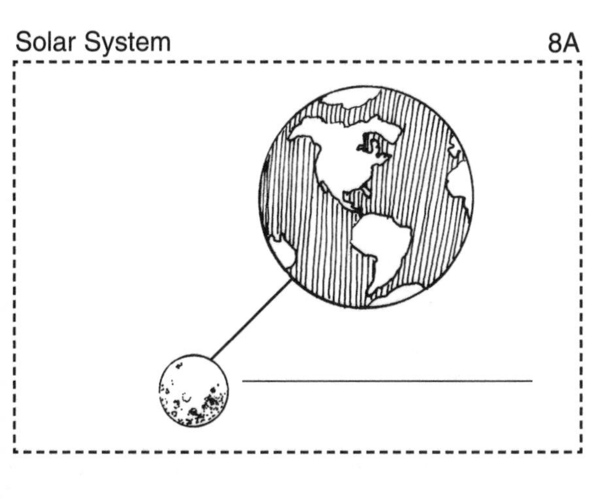

Timeline 8B

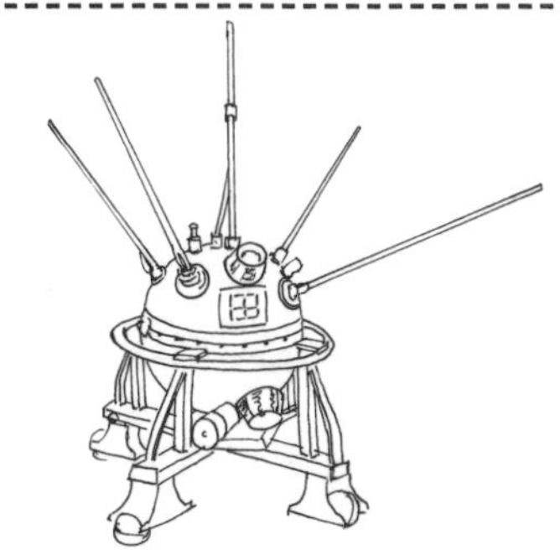

In 1959, the unmanned Russian space probe, *Luna 3*, revealed more craters on the far side of the Moon.

The Moon is not Luminous — Lab 8-1

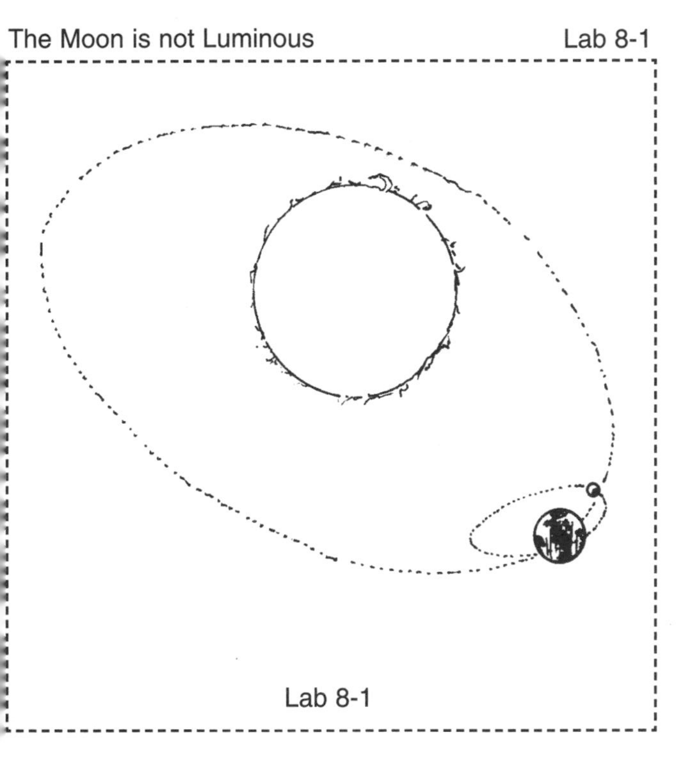

Craters on the Moon — Lab 8-2

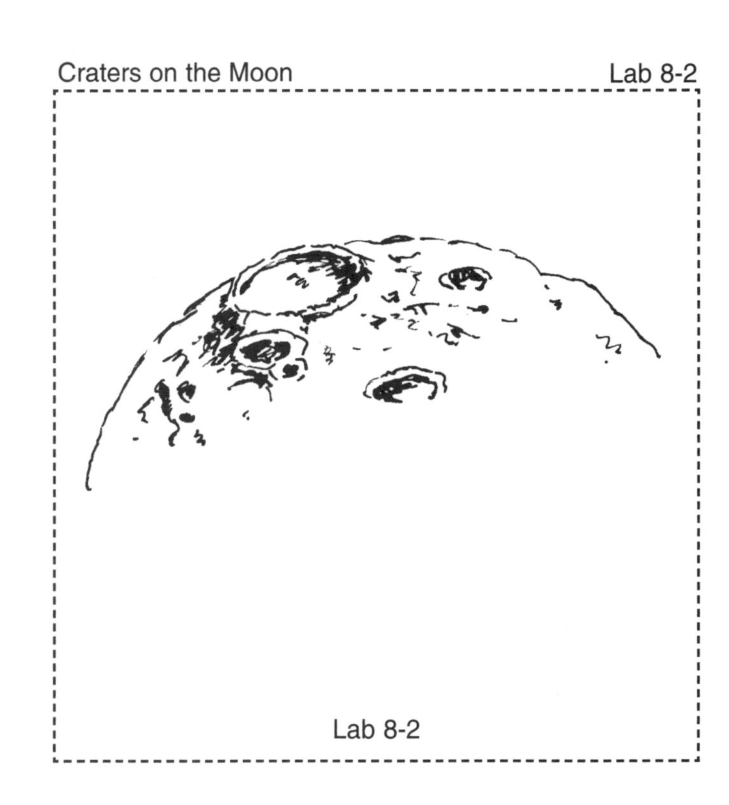

Solar and Lunar Eclipse — 9 A-B

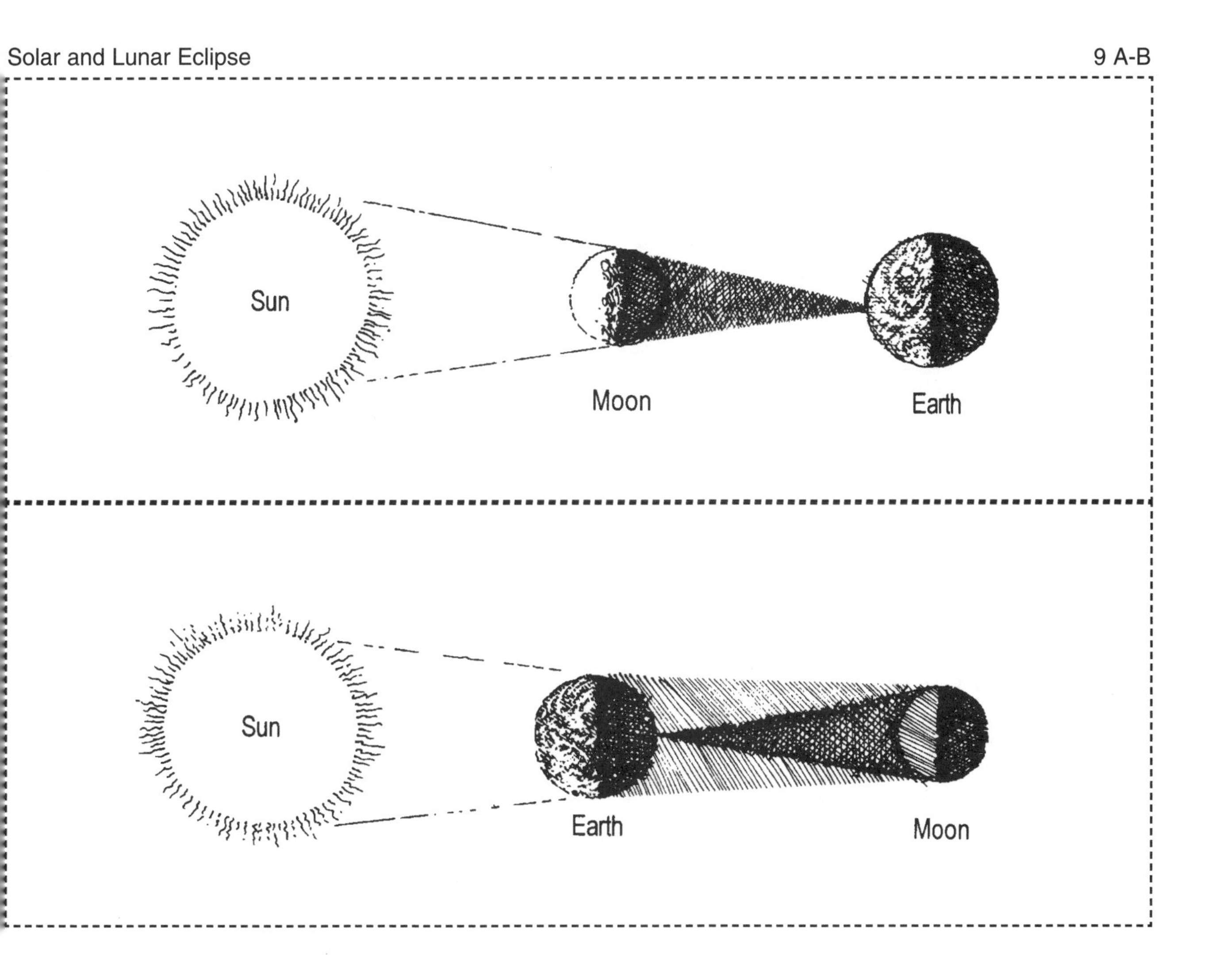

9C

Lunar Eclipse

Sun and Moon stand in line but Earth cuts in between. Earth casts a long shadow and Moon cannot be seen.
Dinah Zike

9D Timeline

Solar Eclipse

Sun and Earth stand in line, then Moon cuts between. The Sun is blocked by Moon so a black disc is seen.
Dinah Zike

9E

Benjamin Banneker (1731-1806) successfully predicted a solar eclipse.

Lunar Eclipse

Lab 9-1

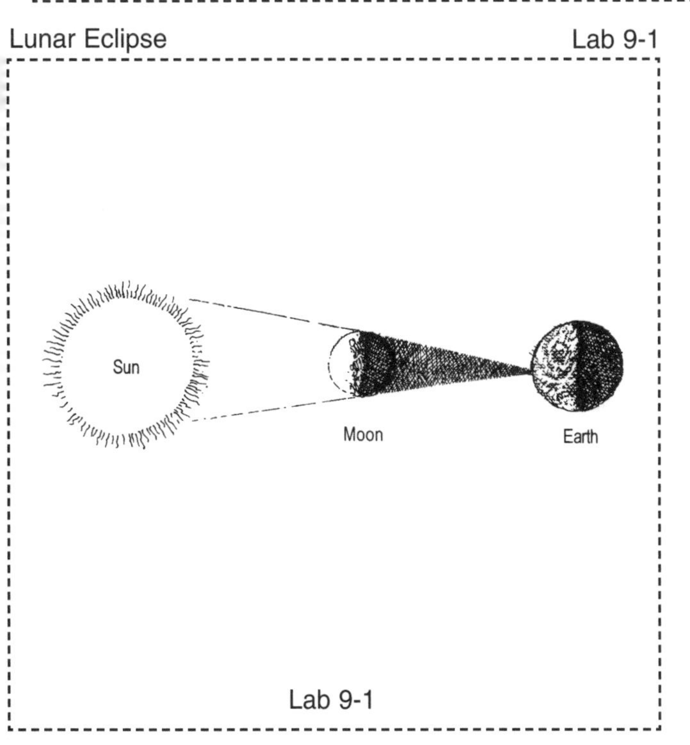

Lab 9-1

Solar System - Mercury

10A

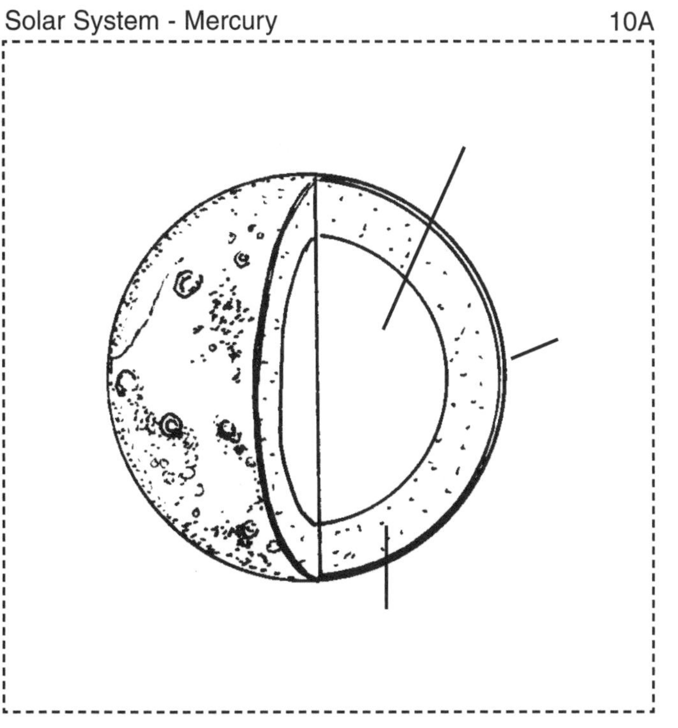

Solar System - Mercury

10B

Distance from Sun: ____________________

Diameter: ____________________

Rotation: ____________________

Revolution: ____________________

Surface: ____________________

Known Moons: ____________________

Interesting Information: ____________________

____

Timeline 10C

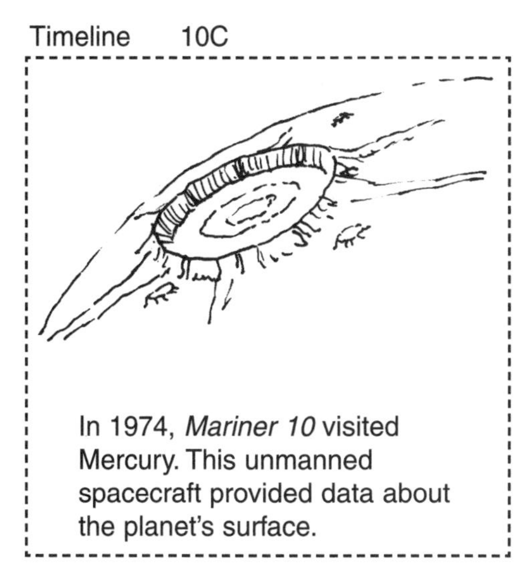

In 1974, *Mariner 10* visited Mercury. This unmanned spacecraft provided data about the planet's surface.

Hot Venus Lab 11-1

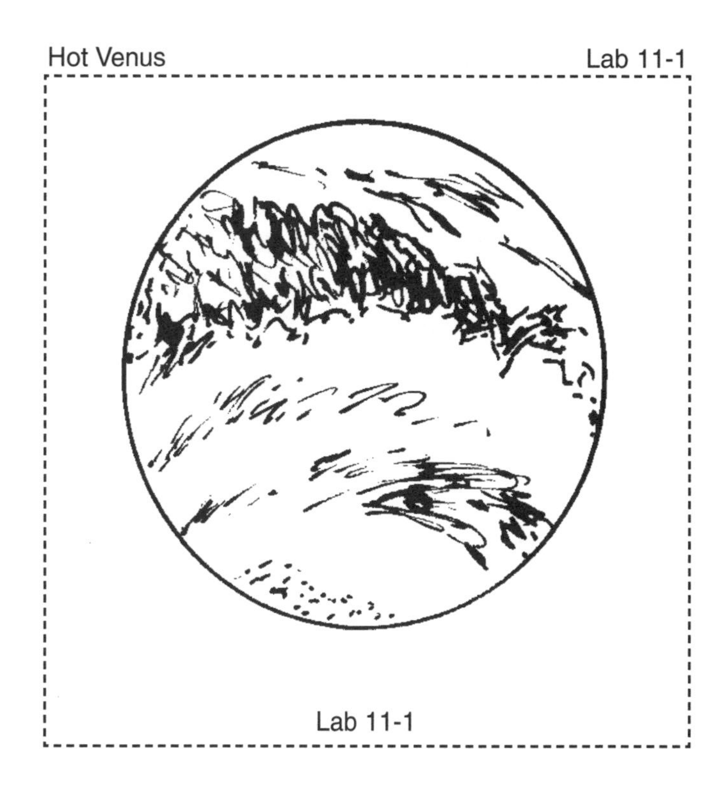

Lab 11-1

Solar System - Venus 11A

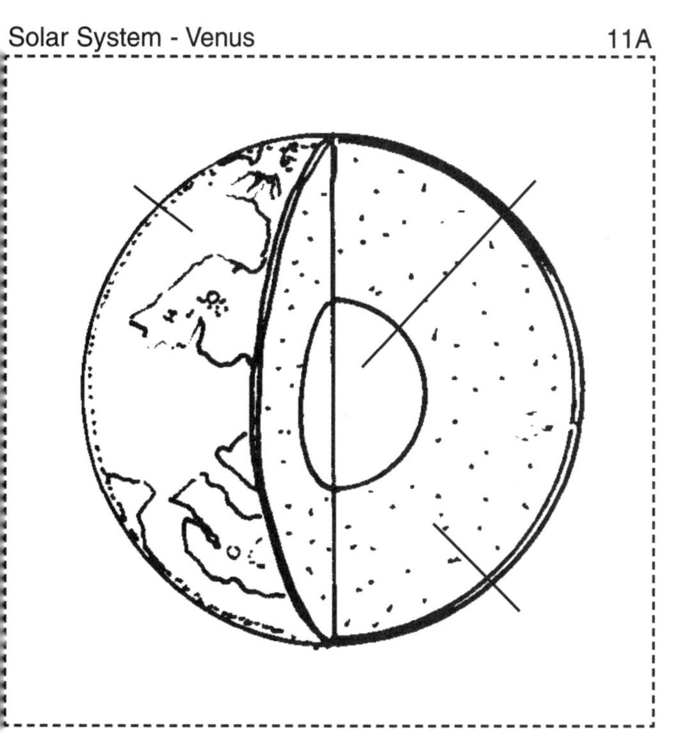

Solar System - Venus 11B

Distance from Sun: ______________________________

Diameter: ______________________________

Rotation: ______________________________

Revolution: ______________________________

Surface: ______________________________

Known Moons: ______________________________

Interesting Information: ______________________________

____

____

Compare Venus and Earth 11C

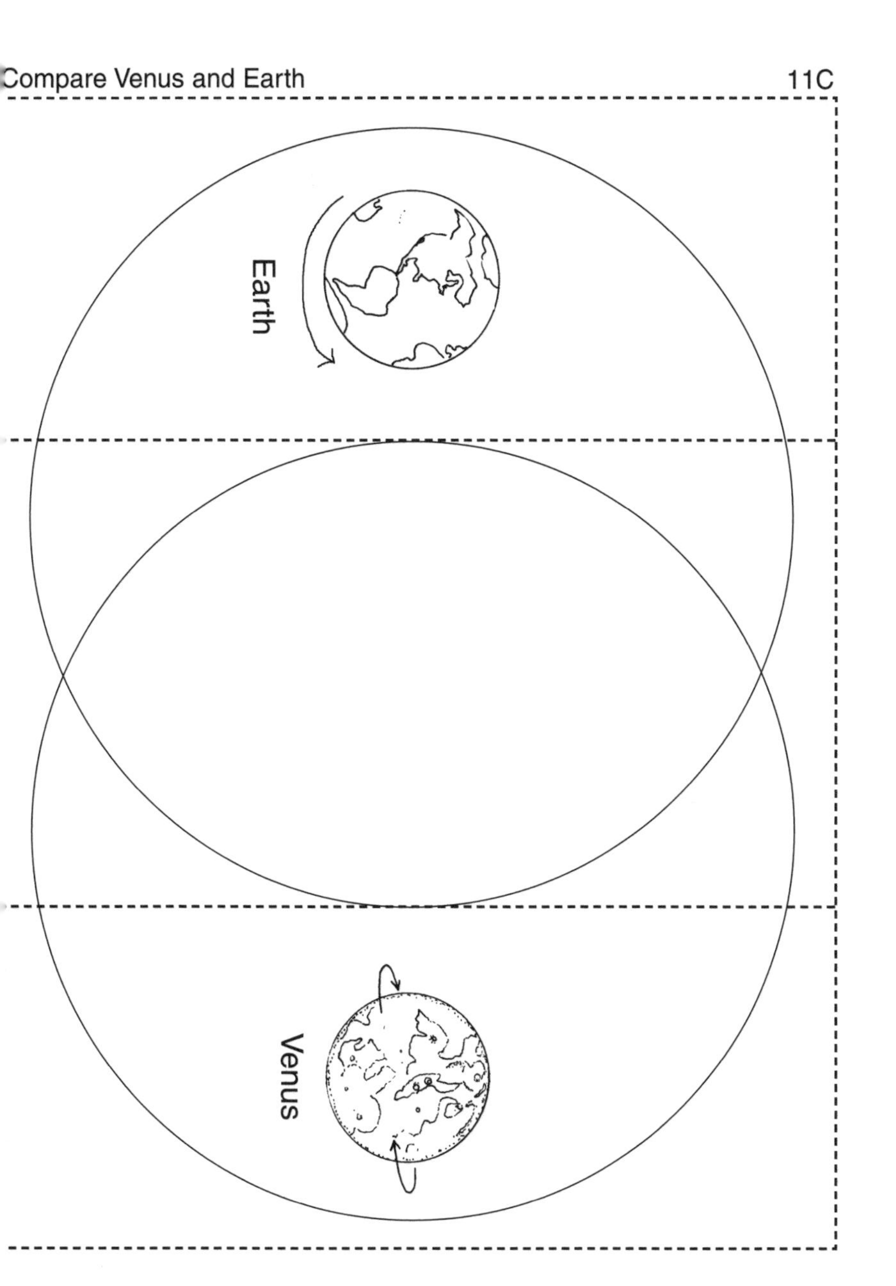

Timeline 11D

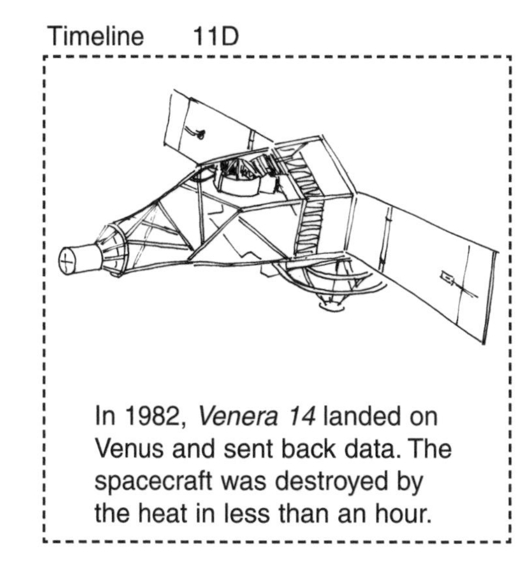

In 1982, *Venera 14* landed on Venus and sent back data. The spacecraft was destroyed by the heat in less than an hour.

The Red Planet Lab 12-1

Lab 12-1

Solar System - Mars 12A

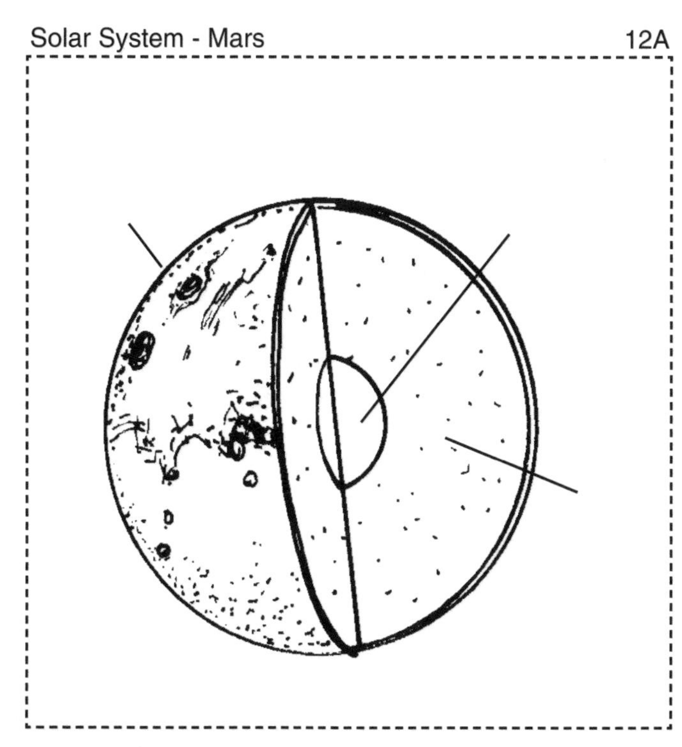

Solar System - Mars 12B

Distance from Sun: ______________________

Diameter: ______________________

Rotation: ______________________

Revolution: ______________________

Surface: ______________________

Known Moons: ______________________

Interesting Information: ______________________

____

Olympus Mons 12C

Olympus Mons

12D

Mount Everest

12E

Martian Giants

Impressive giants
Have been found on Mars,
Extinct volcano
And rock canyon stars.

Olympus Mons
Three times as high
As Earth's Mt. Everest
In the Martian sky.

Valley Mariners,
A deep canyon wide,
Could hold much of the
U.S.A. inside.

Dinah Zike

Timeline 12G

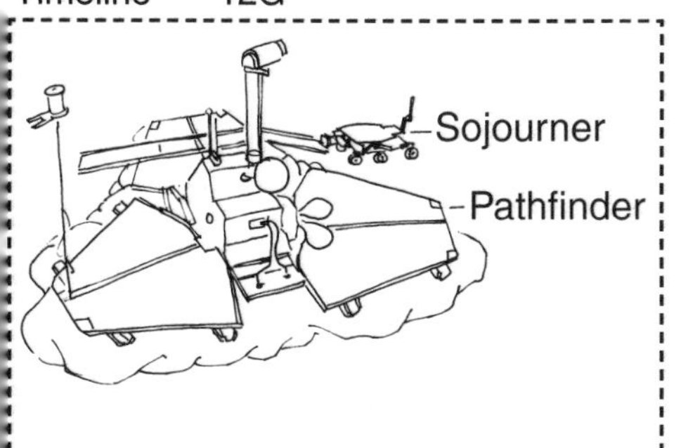

In July 1997, *Pathfinder* landed on Mars. A rover, *Sojourner,* gathered data from the surface.

Solar System 13A

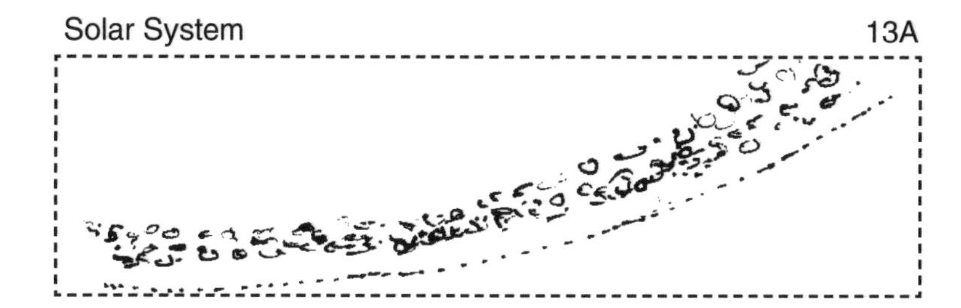

Asteroid Riddle 13B

Mystery Riddle

We are made of rock or metal,
Or combinations of the two.

We are planetary matter
That never formed and grew.

Travel from Mars to Jupiter
and there's a chance we'll hit you.

What are we?

Dinah Zike

Asteroid Riddle 13C

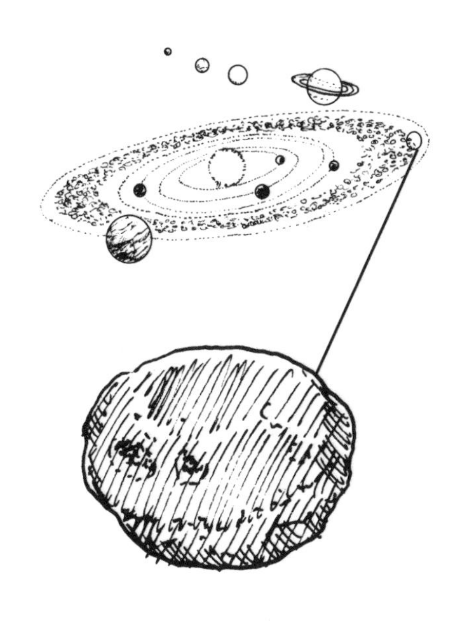

13D

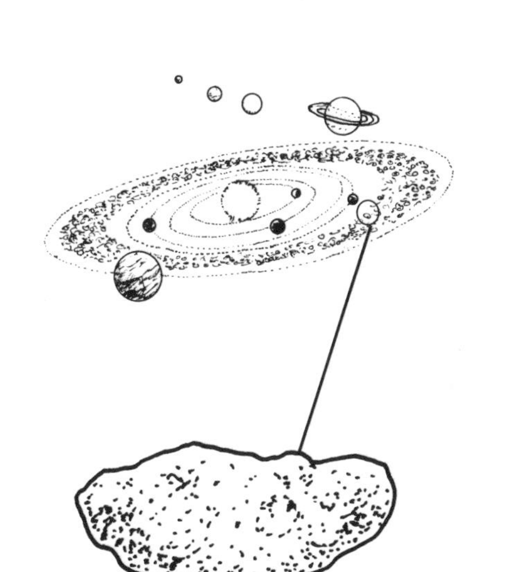

13E

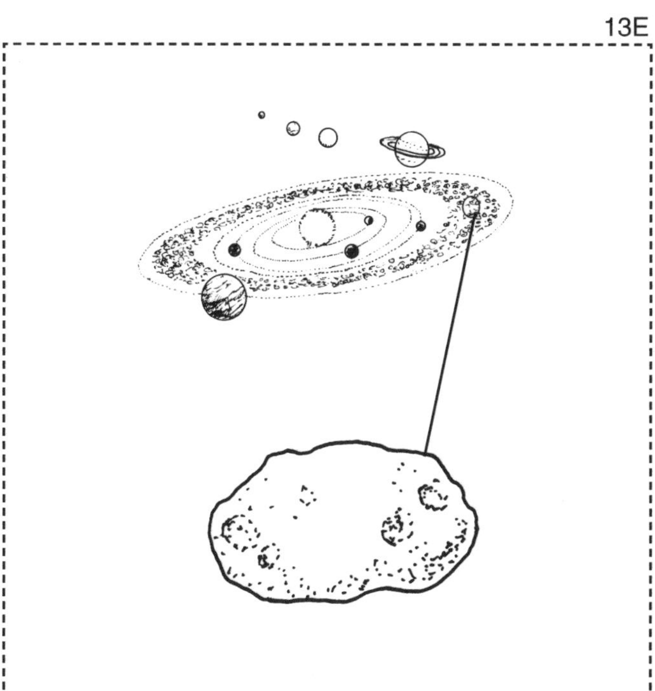

Solar System - Jupiter 14A

Stormy Jupiter Lab 14-1

Lab 14-1

Solar System - Jupiter 14B

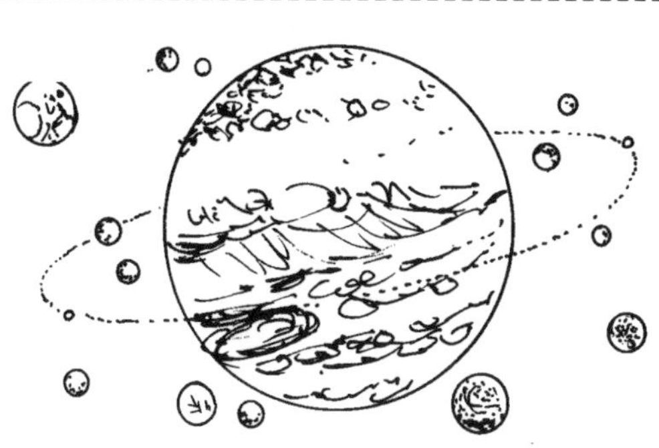

Distance from Sun: ______________________

Diameter: ______________________

Rotation: ______________________

Revolution: ______________________

Surface: ______________________

Known Moons: ______________________

Interesting Information: ______________________

____

Timeline 14H

Great Red Spot

In the late 1600's, a huge storm on Jupiter was discovered, later named the Great Red Spot.

Timeline 15C

In 1610, Galileo observed rings around Saturn.

Timeline 15D

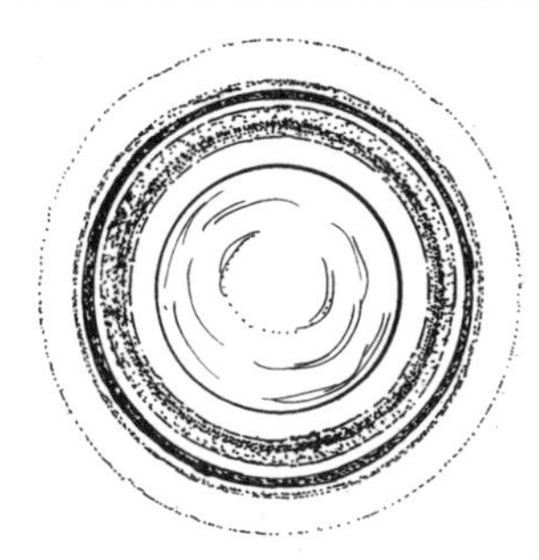

In 1675, Giovanni Cassini observed a gap separating the rings.

Solar System - Saturn 15A

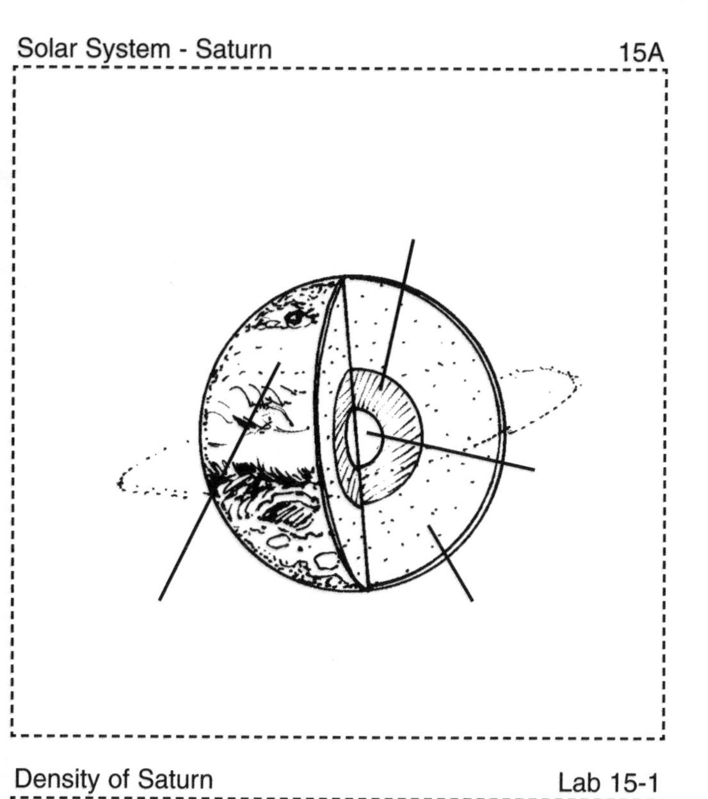

Density of Saturn Lab 15-1

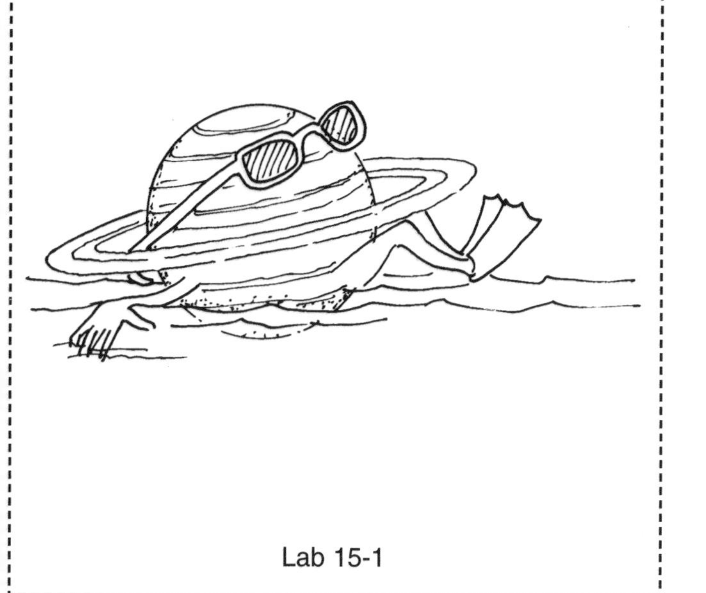

Lab 15-1

15B

Distance from Sun: ____________________

Diameter: ____________________

Rotation: ____________________

Revolution: ____________________

Surface: ____________________

Known Moons: ____________________

Interesting Information: ____________________

____

Rings of Uranus Lab 16-1

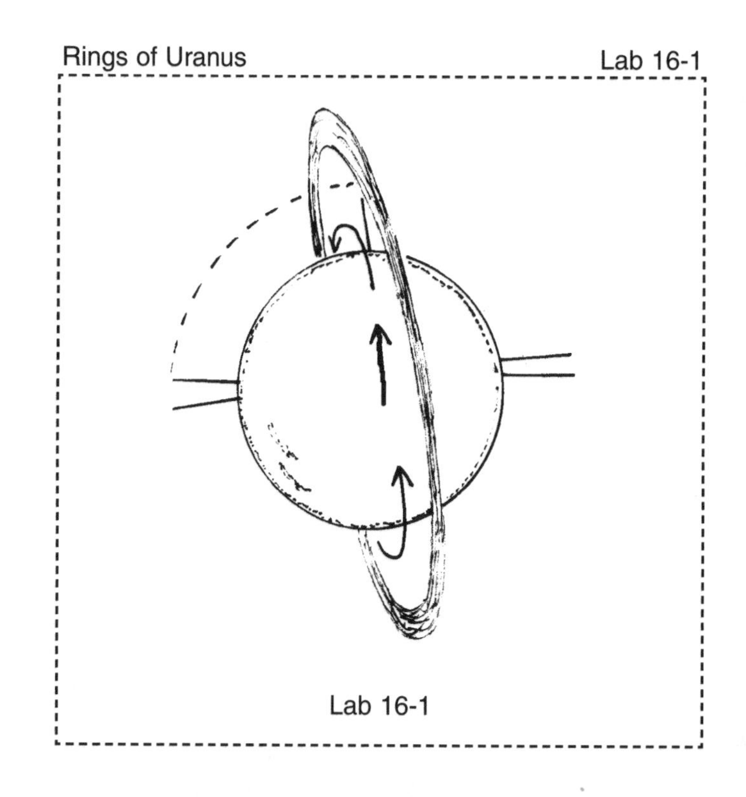

Lab 16-1

Solar System - Uranus 16A

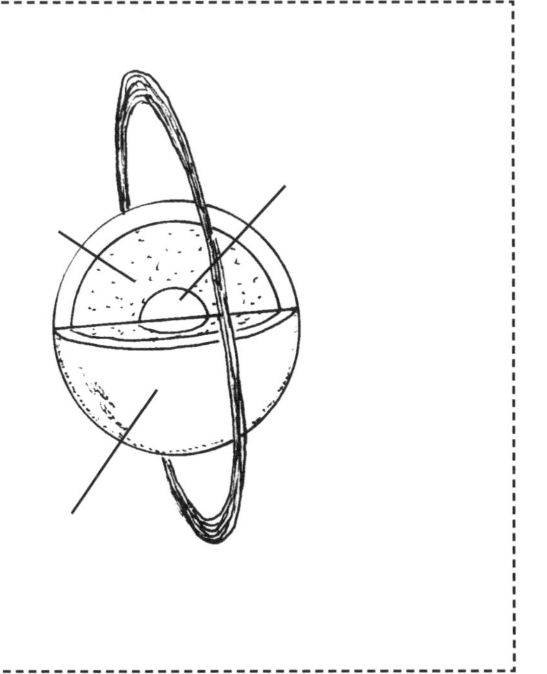

Solar System - Uranus 16B

Distance from Sun: ______________________

Diameter: ______________________

Rotation: ______________________

Revolution: ______________________

Surface: ______________________

Known Moons: ______________________

Interesting Information: ______________________

____

Timeline 16C

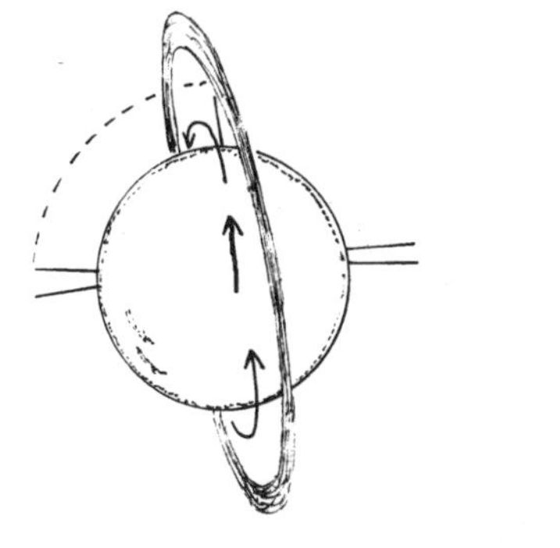

Uranus was the first planet discovered with a telescope in 1781 by William Herschel.

Timeline 16D

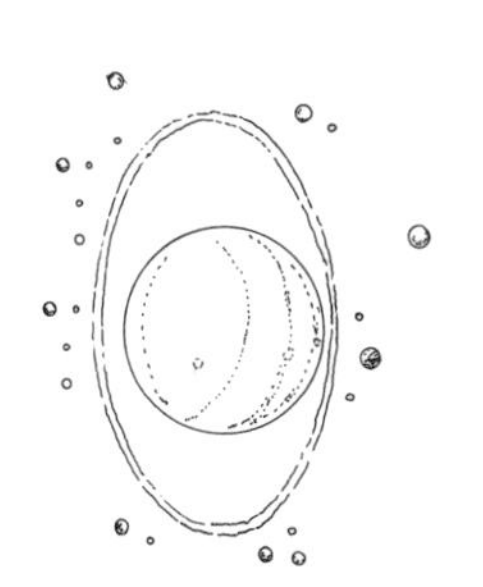

In 1986, *Voyager 2* space probe photographed some of Uranus' largest moons.

Solar System - Neptune 17A

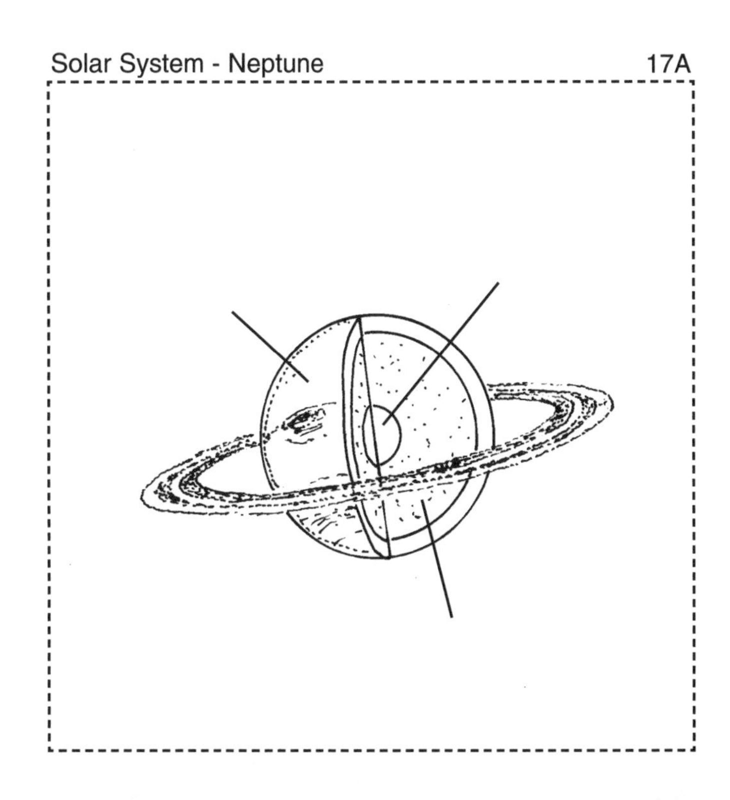

Solar System - Neptune 17B

Distance from Sun: ______________________________

Diameter: ______________________________

Rotation: ______________________________

Revolution: ______________________________

Surface: ______________________________

Known Moons: ______________________________

Interesting Information: ______________________________

____

Icy Triton Lab 17-1

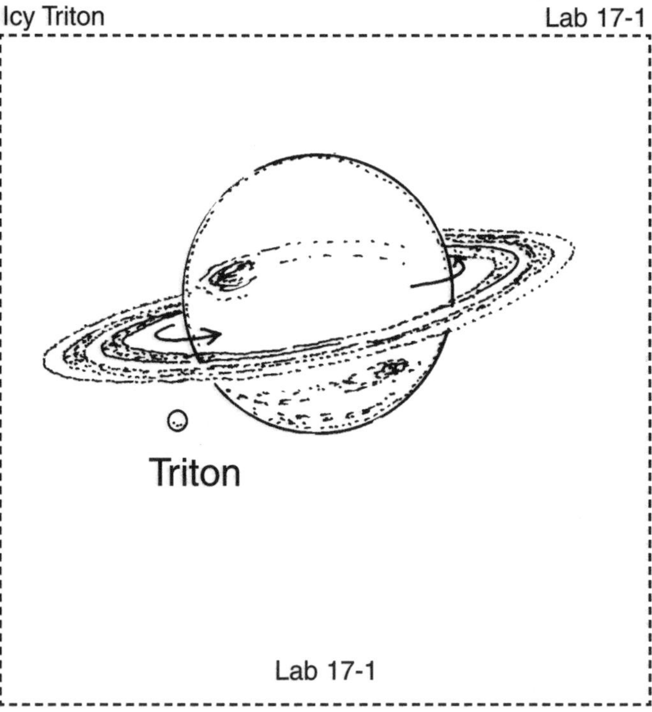

Lab 17-1

Timeline 17C

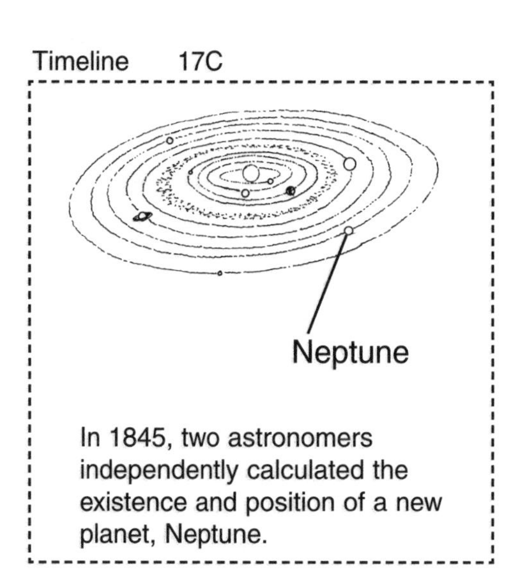

In 1845, two astronomers independently calculated the existence and position of a new planet, Neptune.

Solar System - Pluto 18A

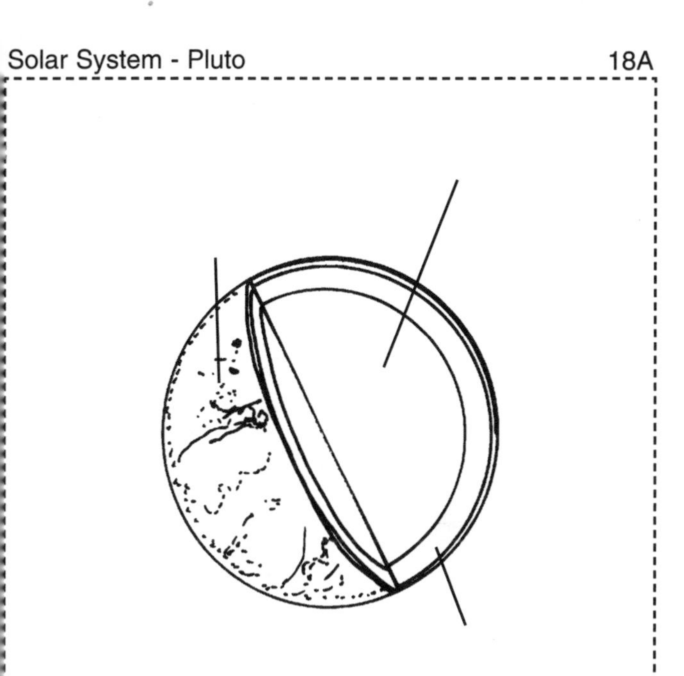

Solar System - Pluto 18B

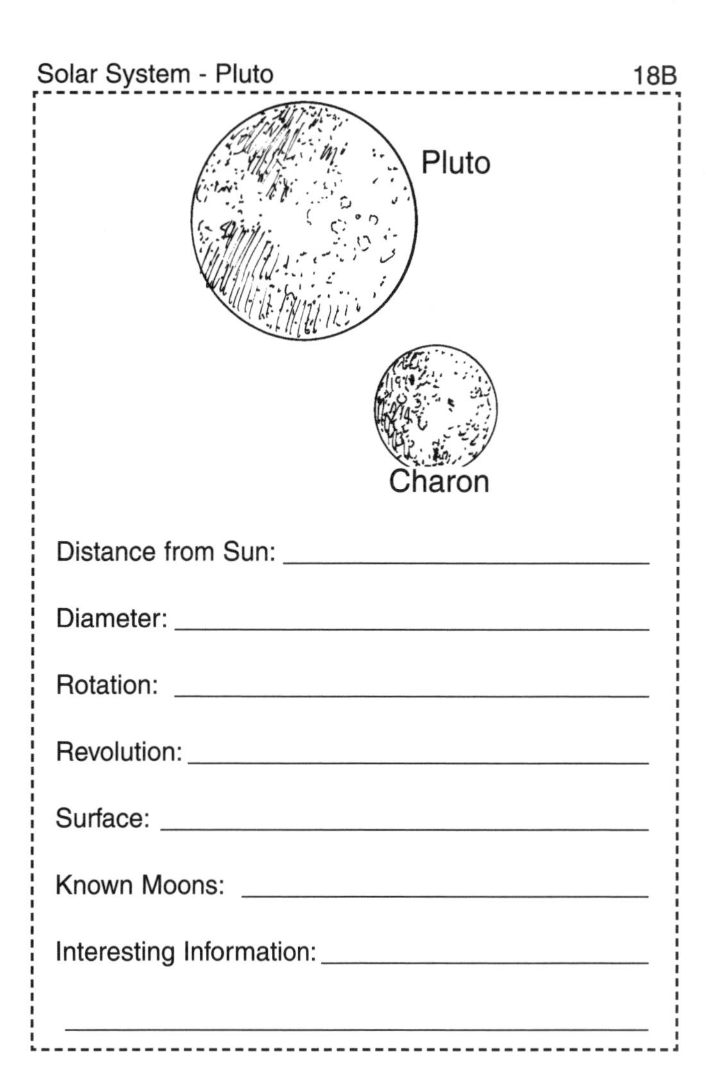

Distance from Sun: ______________________

Diameter: ______________________

Rotation: ______________________

Revolution: ______________________

Surface: ______________________

Known Moons: ______________________

Interesting Information: ______________________

____

Timeline 18C

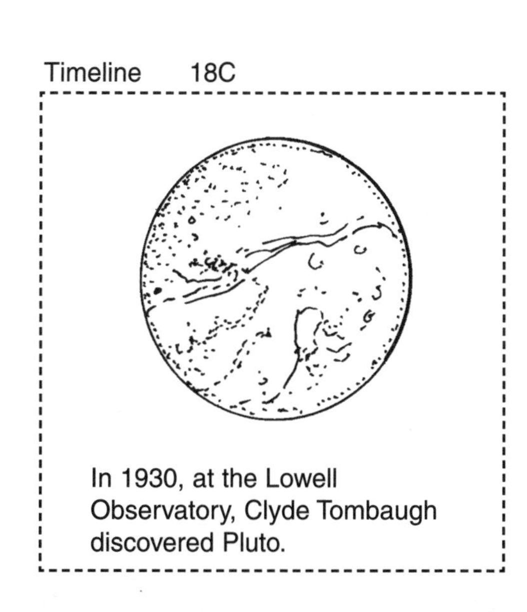

In 1930, at the Lowell Observatory, Clyde Tombaugh discovered Pluto.

Timeline 18D

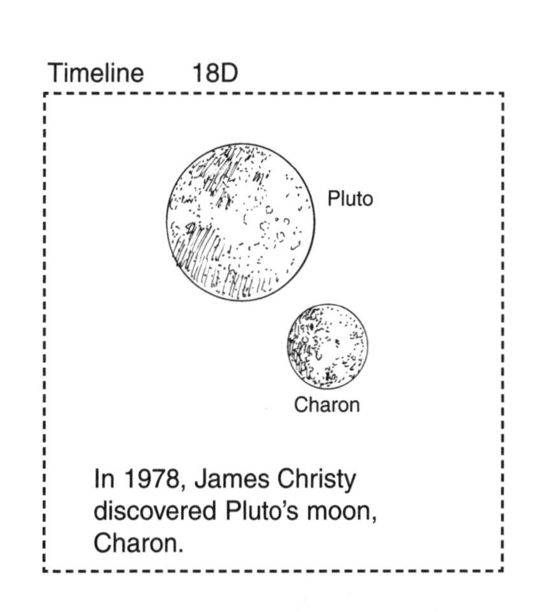

In 1978, James Christy discovered Pluto's moon, Charon.

Earth

Mercury

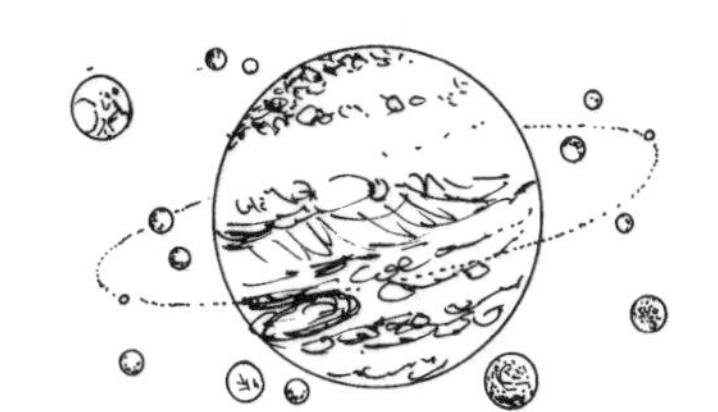

Jupiter

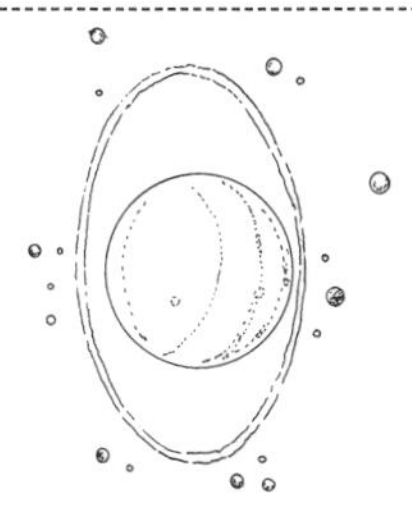

Uranus

Venus

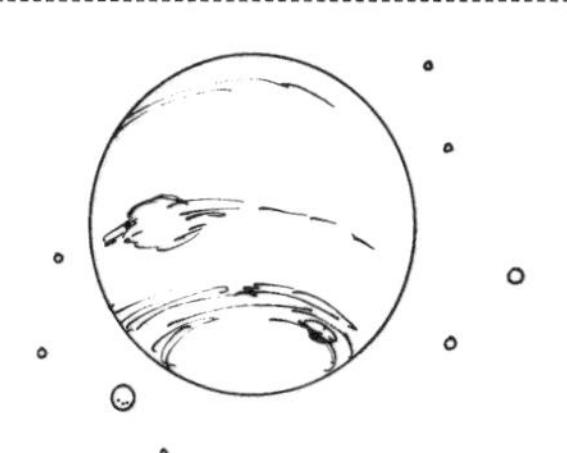

Neptune

Saturn

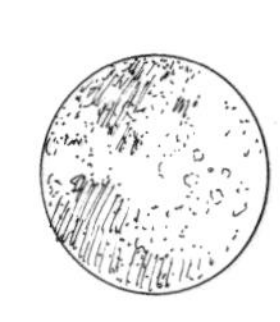

Pluto

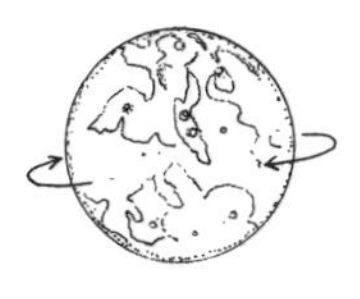

Mars

Which planet am I?

For centuries it has been said.
That this planet appears bright red.
But *Viking I* recently found
A rusty-brown, dark colored ground.
It's cold at night and days are hot
With a sky thats, colored apricot.

Which planet am I?

The gaseous planets
All have rings,
But none of them has
More than I.
Scientists learned
interesting things
when *Voyager* made a fly by.

Which planet am I?

I have a circular orbit
And a thick, cloudy atmosphere.
From my surface Earth can't be seen,
And no planets appear.

Which planet am I?

I appear to be aquamarine;
eleven thin rings can be seen.
My axis is tilted in a way
that points my poles sunward everyday.

Which planet am I?

I'm invisible
I'm so close to the Sun;
View me when it's
Below the horizon.

Which planet am I?

The fastest winds
in the Solar System whip around me.
I'm a gaseous planet,
but look like a turquoise sea.

Which planet am I?

78% nitrogen, 21% oxygen
in my atmosphere;
lots of liquid water
and life forms everywhere.

Which planet am I?

I am the most recent planet discovery.
I'd been predicted for a century.
A famous dog that's cartoon-y
has the same name as little 'ol me.

Which planet am I?

I am a gas giant,
As big as a planet can be.
I have lots of weather.
But no geography!

Parts of a Comet 19A

Timeline 19B

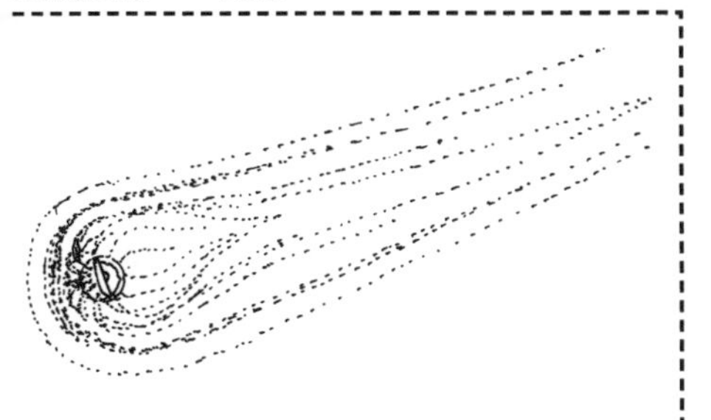

In 1949, American astronomer Fred Whipple described comets as "dirty snowballs."

Timeline 19C

English astronomer, Edmund Halley (1656-1742) correctly calculated that the comet he saw in 1682 would reappear in 1758.

Meteor, Meteoroid, Meteorite 20 A

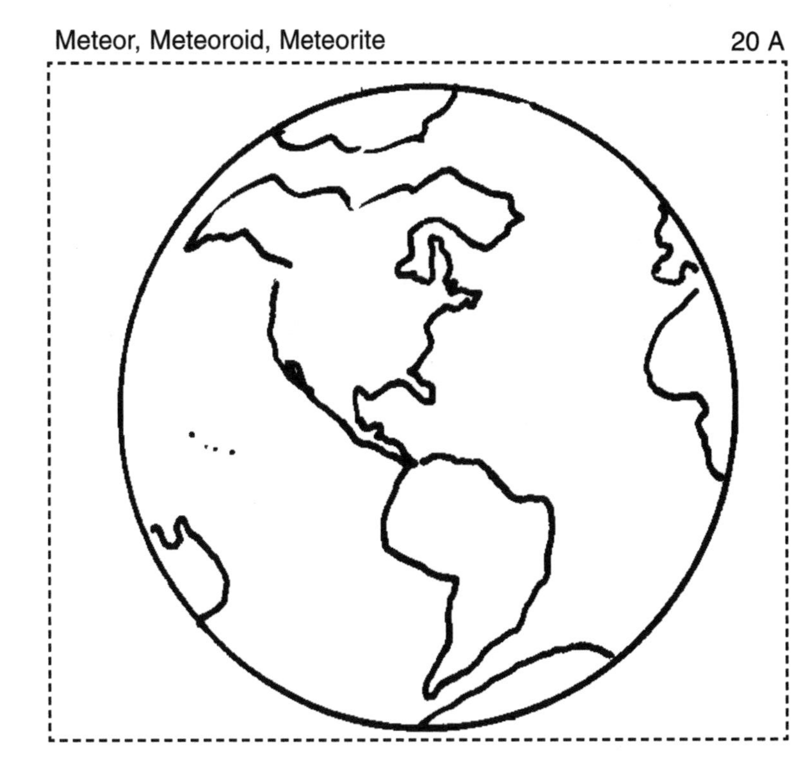

20 B-D

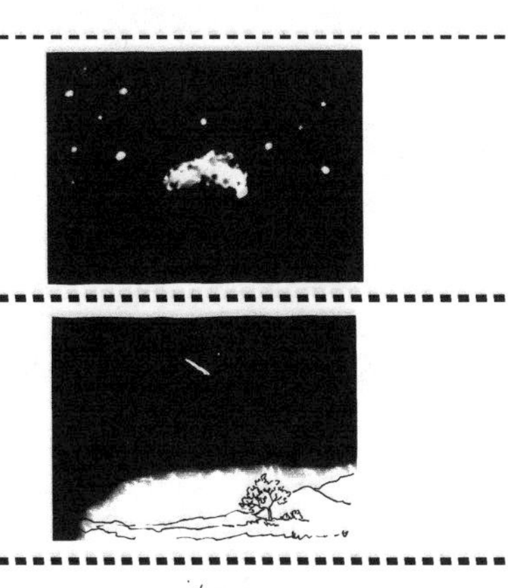

Timeline 20E

In 1894, Admiral Robert Peary discovered the Ahnighito meteorite in Greenland.

Timeline 21 A-F

A Russian scientist Konstatin Tsiolkovsky (1857-1935) first developed theories that led to the multi-stage rocket.

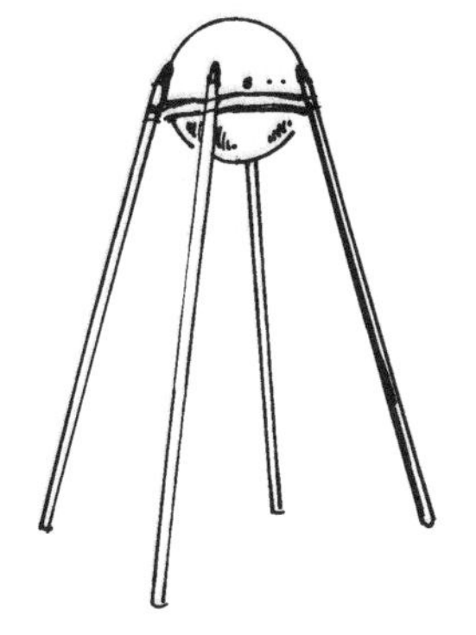

In October 1957, the USSR launched *Sputnik 1.*

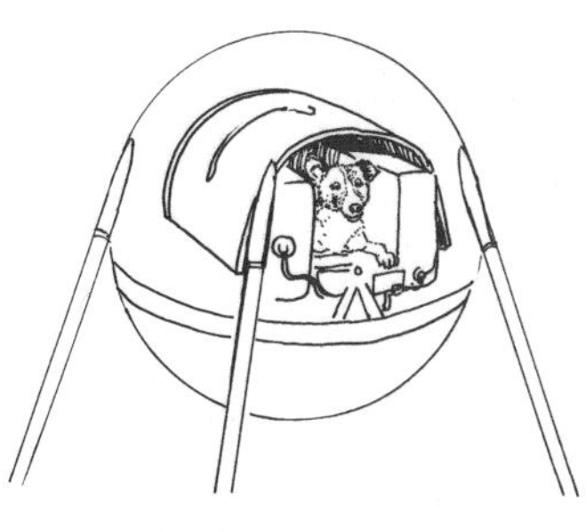

In November 1957, the USSR launched *Sputnik 2* with the first living animal aboard, a dog named Laika.

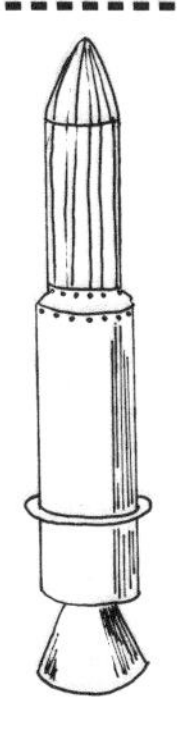

In January 1958, the U.S.A. launched their first satellite, *Explorer 1.*

In January 1961, the U.S.A. sent Ham, a chimpanzee in a *Mercury* spacecraft. Ham returned safely.

In April 1961, Yuri Gagarin of the USSR became the first man to orbit Earth in the *Vostok 1.*

Timeline | Freedom 7 | 21 G-L

May 1961, Alan Shepard became the first American in space.

In February 1962, John Glenn became the first American to orbit Earth in *Friendship 7.*

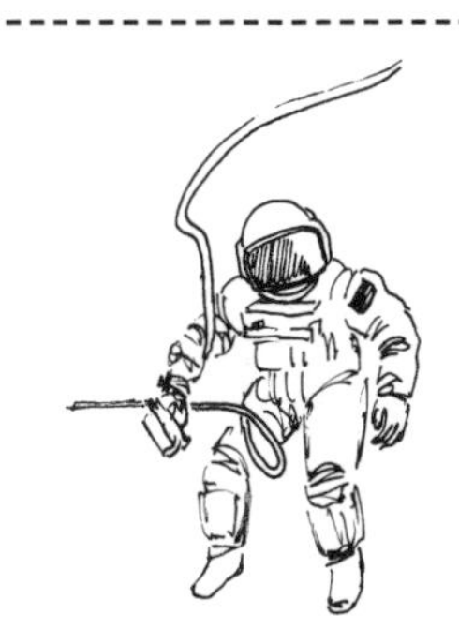

In March 1965, Alexiei Leonov of the USSR became the first person to make a space walk from *Voskhod 2.*

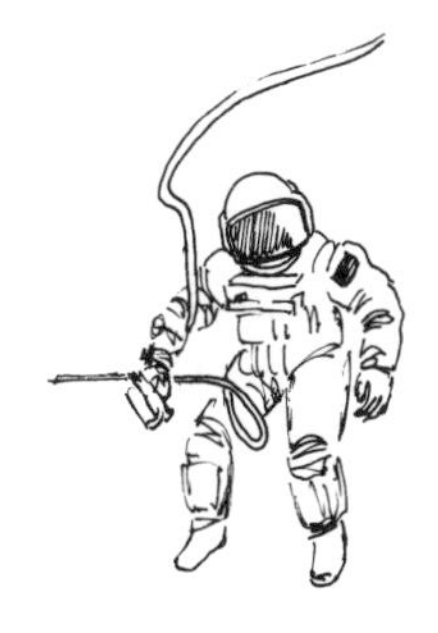

In June 1965, Edward H. White became the first American to make a space walk from *Gemini 4.*

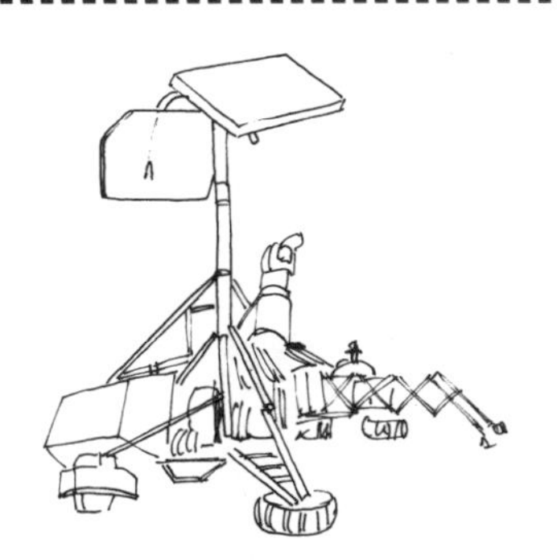

In February 1966, the USSR soft-landed the unmanned *Luna 9* on the Moon.

In July 1969, American Neil Armstrong became the first man to walk on the Moon.

Balloon Rocket | Lab 21-1

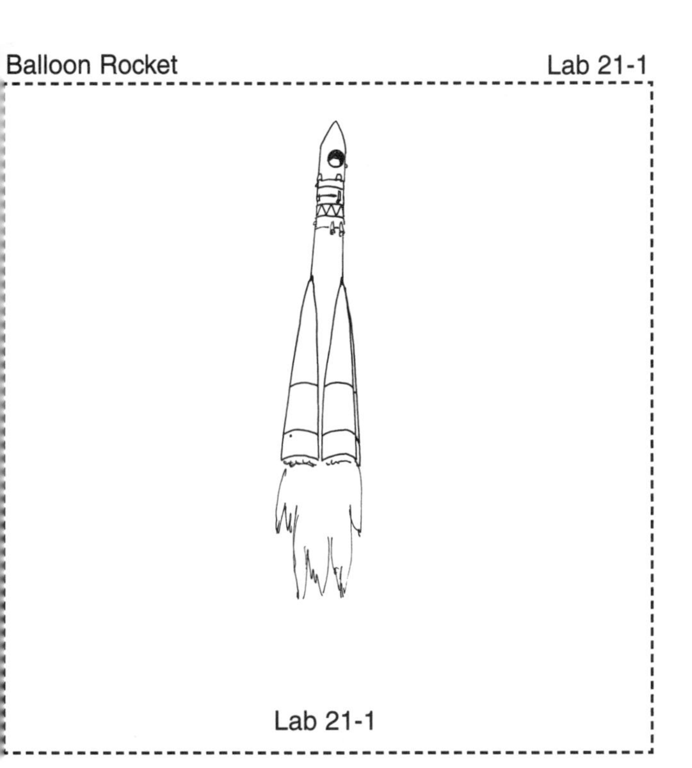

Lab 21-1

Robotic Arm | Lab 22-1

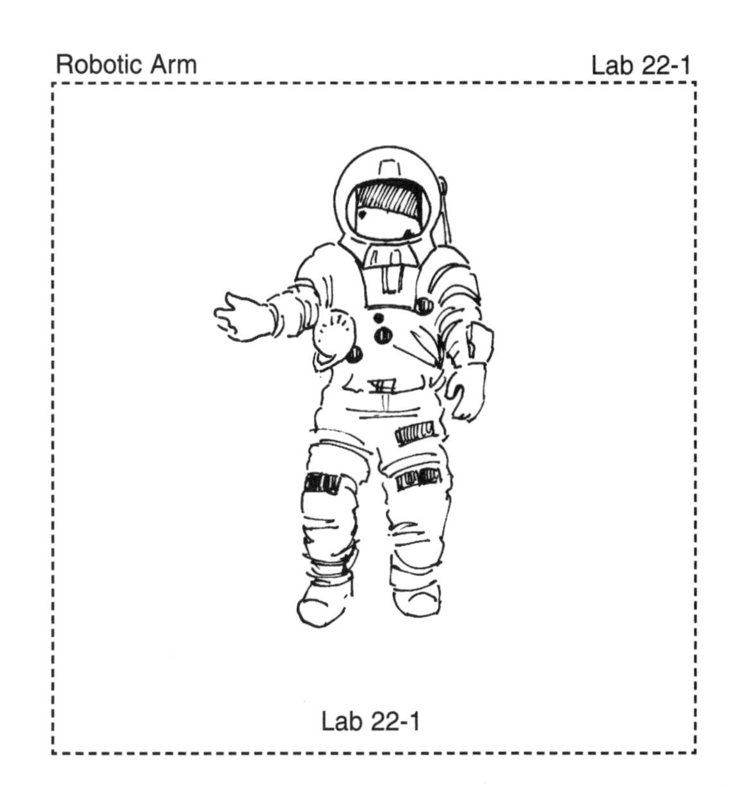

Lab 22-1

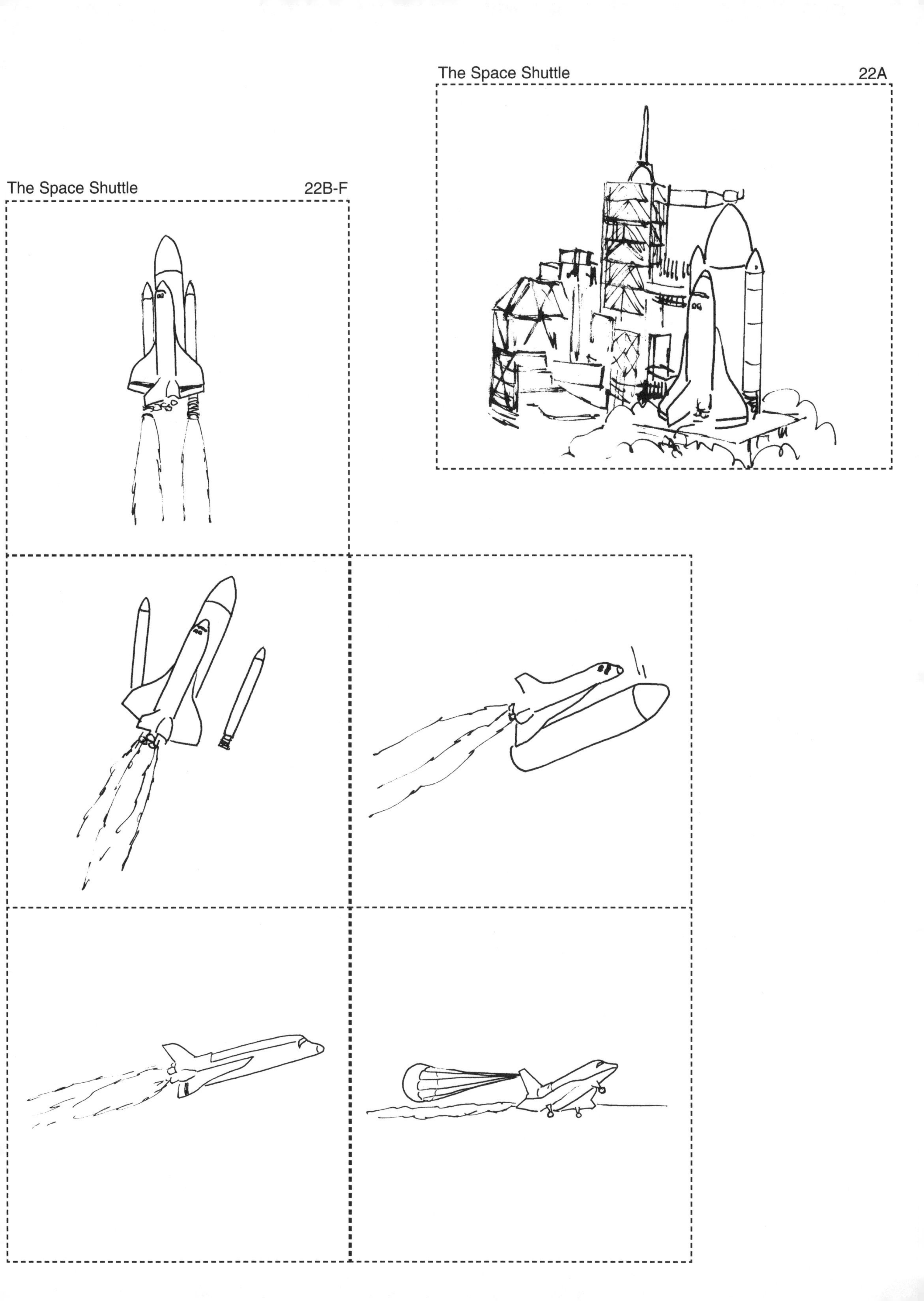
The Space Shuttle
22A
The Space Shuttle
22B-F

Timeline 22G

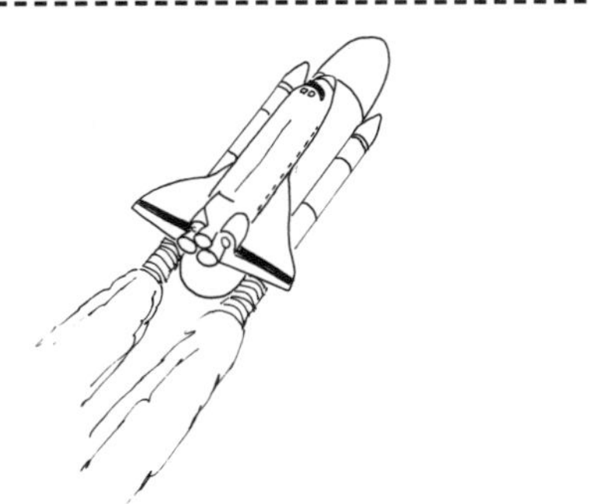

In April 1981, John Young and Robert Crippen boarded the first American space shuttle, *Columbia.*

Timeline 23B

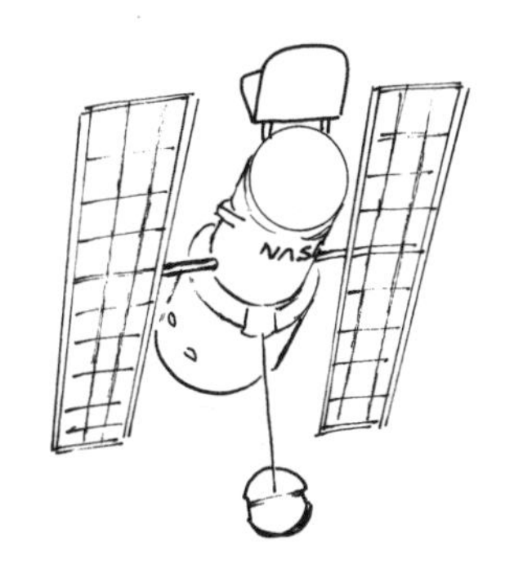

April 1990, the Hubble Space Telescope was launched from a space shuttle.

Send and Receive Messages 23A

Z												Z											
Y												Y											
X												X											
W												W											
V												V											
U												U											
T												T											
S												S											
R												R											
Q												Q											
P												P											
O												O											
N												N											
M												M											
L												L											
K												K											
J												J											
I												I											
H												H											
G												G											
F												F											
E												E											
D												D											
C												C											
B												B											
A												A											
	1	2	3	4	5	6	7	8	9	10	11		1	2	3	4	5	6	7	8	9	10	11

Working in Space Lab 24-1

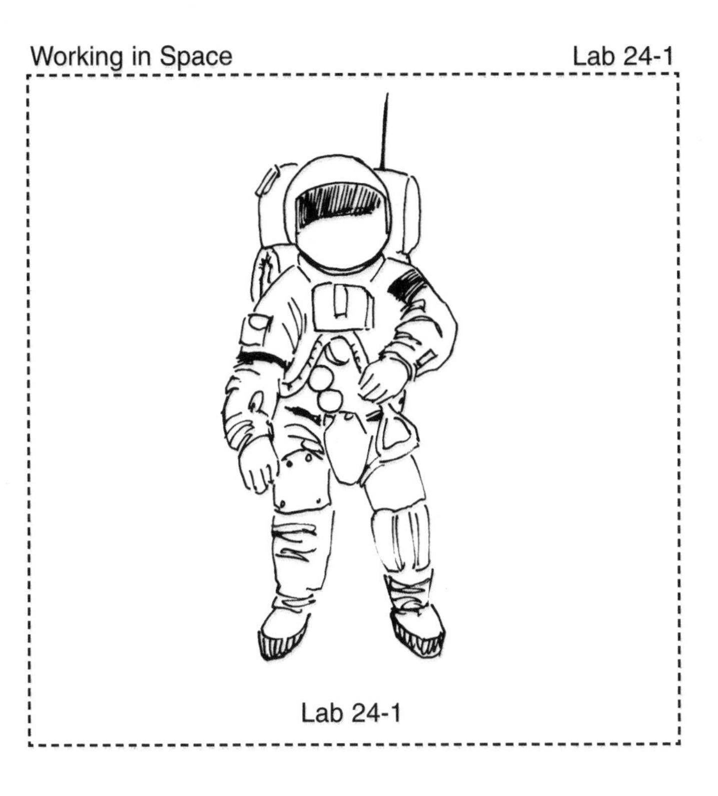

Lab 24-1

Timeline 24A

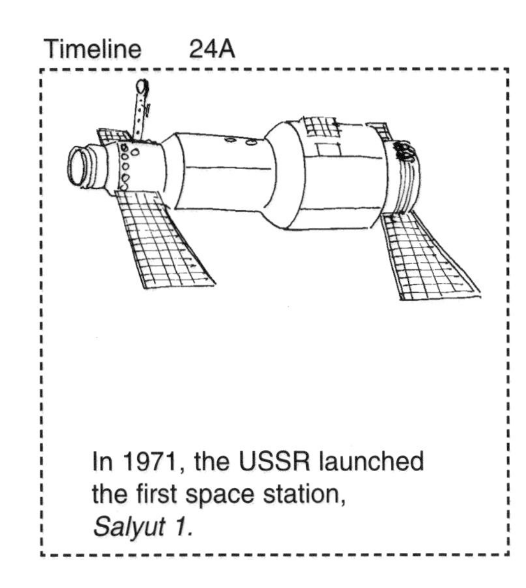

In 1971, the USSR launched the first space station, *Salyut 1.*

Timeline 24B

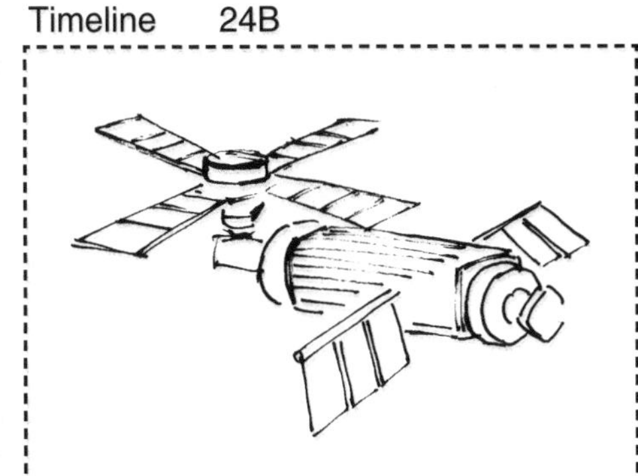

In 1973, the first American space station, *Skylab* was launched.

Timeline 24C

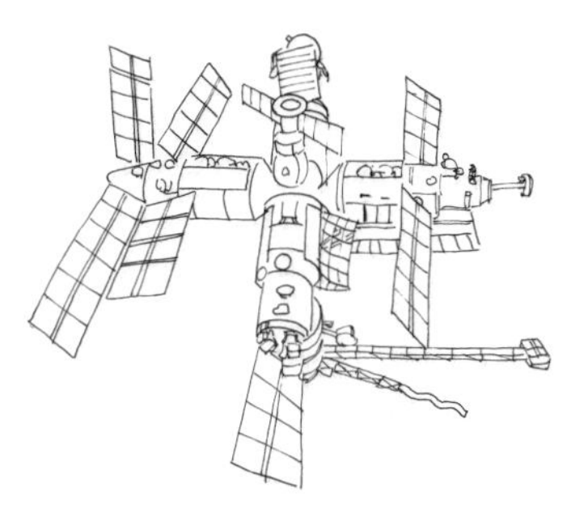

In 1986, the Soviet space station, *Mir,* was launched. Sections were added to it for many years.

Timeline 24D

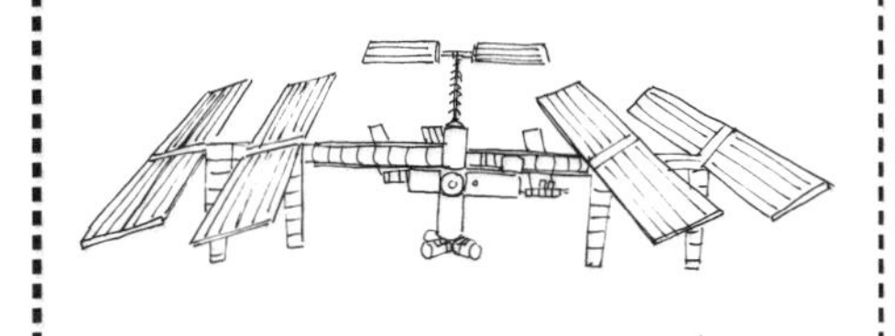

Currently the International Space Station (ISS) is underway. This is a joint project with the USA, USSR, Europe, Japan, and other countries.